HAYMON verlag

Geoffrey Ball

No More Laughing at the Deaf Boy

*A Technological Adventure between
Silicon Valley and the Alps*

Edition:

4   3   2   1

2014 2013 2012 2011

© 2011

HAYMON verlag

Innsbruck-Wien

www.haymonverlag.at

ISBN 978-3-85218-714-3

Graphical presentation of cover and text:
hœretzeder, grafische gestaltung, Scheffau/Tirol
Pictures: Archives Geoffrey Ball

Printed on eco-friendly chlorine- and acid-free paper.

"He usually never writes enough stuff down.
He thinks if he knows it, then that's good enough ...
not for the rest of us."

Dr. Richard L. Goode, Stanford School of Medicine,
Professor Emeritus Otolaryngology,
Head and Neck Surgery

"Great invention requires a great story. Our lives are deter-
mined by the stories we live and the stories we create. Sometimes
we choose our paths; sometimes they are chosen for us. How we
act and react are what comes to define who we are, how we
see the world and what we contribute. Where our path begins
sets the stage for where we end up. My path started in the city of
Sunnyvale, California, the heart of Silicon Valley."

Geoffrey Ball, Axams, Austria

This book is dedicated to all those who still suffer from hearing loss, to my loving wife and sons; to my parents; to my mentor, Dr. Richard Goode; and to Ingeborg Hochmair, who saved my inventions.

Arriving in Sunnyvale

"There is a road, no simple highway,
between the dawn and the dark of night.
And if you go, no one may follow.
That path is for your steps alone."

Jerry Garcia

I will never forget the first time I saw Serra Park. The year was 1969, and I was five years old. My father was at the wheel of our purple 1961 Mercedes Benz 190 sedan, which we had just recently driven all the way across the United States from Massachusetts. He was really proud of his Mercedes even though it was purple. But it had great seats and plenty of room for me and my two-year-old brother to fight for the first five states of our cross-country journey. After that my mother moved to the back seat to maintain a bit of peace as we crawled across the lower forty-eight.

We had plenty of time to enjoy our ride as my father's philosophy of driving is truly binary. In his opinion, the car is either "on" and travelling at 54 miles per hour, or it is "off." This remains true regardless of whether he is on a wide open highway or circling side streets looking for parking. He always drives 54 miles per hour. So when the "We're here!" announcement finally came, it brought with it a great sense of relief.

We went and looked at our new home at 1526 Kingsgate in Sunnyvale, California. Sunnyvale was in the center of what would later come to be known as Silicon Valley. In keeping with our family's peculiar color taste (or complete lack thereof), the house we had chosen was bright pink, though I was later to learn that the correct name was salmon. Fine, but it was pink to everyone else. I can only imagine what the neighbors thought of our purple car parked in the driveway of our bright pink house. After we finished chatting with the former occupant of our new house and checking out the great swing set in the backyard, we drove around the block. "Guys! Here is the park!" Dad announced.

I peered out the window as we drove up and parked the car. There before me was Serra Park. My five-year-old eyes had never ever seen such utter beauty. The sun was setting over the Santa Cruz Mountains to the west, and the beautiful California dusk sky provided a breathtaking backdrop for the setting. The park staff had turned on the tall walkway lights that lined the paths running in and out of both ends of the park. The play structures were gleaming with white fresh paint. The miniature play town and steamship-design climbing structures stood proudly, hosting a small army of children who were gleefully hanging from them and running around. There seemed to be hundreds of newly planted redwood and sequoia trees that stood five to eight feet tall, with stake sticks holding them up. The cement pebbled walkways were freshly laid and provided a maze of possibilities. The man-made lake, fed by the bubbling man-made creek, was in tip-top condition, and the fountains were pumping rooster tails of spray. The new bridges across the gentle rapids capped off the whole affair perfectly. The sand box had mounds of fresh clean sand.

I had never seen such a place. I had never even imagined that such a place existed! Lowell, Massachusetts, had nothing like this, and for a kid from that grey, bleak city, it was truly a Eureka! moment. It was a five-year-old's Eldorado. It was paradise! It was Sunnyvale.

I am from Sunnyvale, California, and damn proud of it!

Kingsgate Drive

A stream begins
Beneath a stone
Water flows
The path well known
Over and over
Again and again
To repeat the path
Never to end

The best street in the whole world to grow up on was Kingsgate Drive, located on Sunnyvale's south side near Serra Park and Serra Elementary School. Like many other people, I recall my childhood home with great affection – and with good reason. In 1969, Sunnyvale had approximately 50,000 residents living mostly in single-story suburban style homes intermingled with vast tracts of apricot, pear and cherry orchards and a few acres of flowers. The main boulevards were Sunnyvale Saratoga Road to the east, Homestead Road to the south, Fremont Road to the north, and the finished portion of Highway 85 to the west. Serra Park, with its fine man-made creek and amazing steamship play boat complete with steering wheel, was a short walk away, and Serra Elementary school was adjacent to the park.

From 1969 through the 1970's Sunnyvale was in its hey-day. Moffet Field Naval Air Station, originally built as an airstrip for dirigibles, had been the genesis of a key research and development hub for NASA, Lockheed Space and Missiles, Northrop, and many others. The development of the transistor eliminated the need for vacuum tubes, and the defense industry was in its prime, driven by the close proximity of Onizuka Air Force Base, the "Blue Cube," and the cold war-era thirst for high technology and cutting edge electronics. Hewlett Packard was arguably the dominant player in the Valley's booming electronics industry. These were the days before the area was known as Silicon Valley. Sunnyvale was already a mecca for electronics engineers, and any engineer worth his salt, such as my father, was dying to land a position in the Valley. The power of the electronics industry drew top engineers from around the globe, so the Ball family became good friends with people like the Camenzinds (from Switzerland), the Siggs (also from Switzerland), and their friends the Heinemanns (from Germany). The Valley was attracting the best and the brightest from all across the globe, and our community was a truly multicultural one.

The impact of Stanford University on the development of Silicon Valley cannot be overstated. Stanford was a hubbub of activity, and many Saturdays found my father and me walking around the campus, looking at all the activity both inside and outside the labs This was back in the days before security was all that it could be, so it was no problem to stroll around and see students and researchers working on their projects. My father and I would spend hours upon hours in the Stanford libraries and at the bookstore, where my father found and read the latest integrated circuit and electronics publications. Stanford was truly alive then, and the place was electric with energy. In the early 70's, it was really quite the sight to see. I was mesmerized by all those long-haired hippie students making the incredibly magical devices and inventions on display, many of which were glimpses into the future.

The demand for a highly educated workforce exceeded the levels that Stanford and nearby San Jose State University could supply. The exploding electronics industry and their supporting fields and services desperately needed new employees in order to grow. De Anza and Foothill junior colleges became key factors in training and educating new workers for the fields of electronics engineering, manufacturing, mechanics and computer technology. Again, in the early 1970's these institutions were places where innovation was in the air. "De Anza days," when the entire campus was thrown open to the public for the weekend, allowed students to showcase their latest achievements. We never missed these epic technology demonstration events, which comprised everything from arts and crafts to the forerunners of modern digital computer games, including a computer connected to a black and white display screen that would play endless rounds of tic-tac-toe and never lose. Other devices on display, including a working seismograph that recorded the shocks of the San Andreas Fault earthquakes, were a source of fascination to most of us. I think we were more interested in understanding earthquakes than we were afraid of them, since anyone who lives in Sunnyvale for more than a year or two is sure to feel at least a couple of good rollers.

Kingsgate was swarming with the sons and daughters of the techies who turned Silicon Valley into what it is today. The families of Kingsgate were a wide cross-section of the Valley at the time. We had several neighbors who worked in the defense and aerospace industries, electronics, real estate, or law, as well as a grocer and a lawn-sprinkler installer. And most of them had lots of children. The Banker family two doors down from us had four daughters; the Stevensons next door to them had three, and the Schenones beside them had four daughters and a son, so just those four families on Kingsgate had 15 kids, counting me and my brothers. Kingsgate was a very small street linking Dallas to Lewiston, yet in 1970, from end to end, there were 47 school-age children in 22 homes. There was no shortage of playmates – or of potential babysitters. My favorite was Erin O'Conner, who took me under her wing and helped me out all the way through high school by giving me advice and pointers along the way.

When the moving van carrying my family's belongings pulled into the big driveway of 1526, it was the greatest arrival I could have imagined. It seemed like everyone on the entire street came out to watch. We had only had a small two-bedroom apartment in Massachusetts, so could not have taken the movers too long to unload and carry all of our possessions into 1526, yet somehow they made a day of it anyway. By the time they were done, I had met Matt Schenone, who by day's end would be my new "first best friend."

The very first week we lived in the salmon-colored house smack in the middle of Kingsgate, my brother and I realized that although our house may have been pink and may have had a purple car in the driveway, it had one thing going for it: It was a magnet for all the kids on the street. There were several reasons for this, the first being that we had the widest and flattest cement driveway – perfect for roller skating, bike turnarounds and dodge ball. The Schenones also had a large driveway, but theirs was blocked by an old Dodge that Mr. Schenone was always going to fix up some day but never did (he had it towed away years later).The fact that they had converted their garage into an extra room for the two older girls meant there was no garage door suitable for "wall ball." If our home had a redeeming factor, it had to be the backyard, which was small but had everything else going for it.

The previous owner of 1526 had somehow acquired from the Sunnyvale Parks and Recreation department the old jungle gym (a.k.a. monkey bars) and swing set that had been in Serra Park before it got new playground equipment. Having proved too large for the previous owner to move, both this huge climbing structure and the swings were in our new backyard. Unlike store-bought play park equipment, this was real heavy duty gear. Our predecessors had also left behind a small outdoor goldfish pond chock full of fish and lily pads. To top it off, there was a large crabapple tree in our yard that turned out to be the favorite climbing tree in the neighborhood. A kid could climb way up into the branches and then toss "crabapple bombs" on moving roller skating targets on the driveway below. Every morning when my brother and I woke up, we would be inundated by a horde of kids coming over to play. We skipped the awkward new kid phase and immediately became the "rock stars" of Kingsgate because we lived in such a great house, even if it was pink or salmon or whatever. It was the best.

Matt Schenone soon had me running his football games. He would always yell out, "Quarterback! Called it first!" (he always called it first), but I was always quite happy to be his wide receiver and sometimes running back, even though I had no clue what those terms really meant. Soon Matt and I had progressed to a level where we could take on the big kids up the street. Joe Walker and Kent Bates, who were both older than we were and two grades ahead of us, would team up against Matt and me. We always got trounced soundly as we could not really do much to "Big Joe," who was twice our size and could throw the ball much better than we could. Kent was not as much of a football talent as Joe was, but he was faster than we were. Joe also knew all the strange and baffling rules of American football, and since Matt and I were younger, it was no use to protest against Joe's rulings. If I snapped the ball back to Matt and somehow got open and caught Matt's pass and ran it in for what we thought was a touchdown, Joe would invariably come back with a penalty call such as, "Ruling! Ruling! Receiver interference on the defender past the ten yard line. Five yard penalty. Lose a down!" In the 273 matches that we played against Joe and Kent, Matt and I had a record of one win and 272 losses. They were nice enough to let us win one game on Matt's birthday.

Matt lived three doors down from us on Kingsgate. He had four older sisters, and his father was a real estate agent. Tony Schenone and his co-worker Mrs. O'Conner, who also lived on Kingsgate four doors down from 1526, had sold much of the real estate in the southern Sunnyvale area. Mrs. and Mr. O'Conner had three children, and their youngest, Erin, turned out to be the best and most beautiful babysitter my brothers and I would ever have. Matt loved his sisters and parents most of all, and after that it was football and basketball. Every night when Tony got home from work, he and Matt could be seen tossing baseballs and footballs back and forth.

Matt and I were best friends (and I was his best wide receiver) for years. We were quite a pair. Later, when I was around 10 or 11, Matt somehow changed. He would get angry with me, and we started fighting. It got worse and worse until we finally started avoiding each other at home and at school. I made new friends, and Matt found new wide receivers in Pat Selami and Mark Marino, who lived a few streets away. I later found out that during all this time, Matt's mother, who had rarely been seen on Kingsgate, had been suffering from scleroderma, a horrible affliction for which there is no cure. She passed away around that time. I hope that I allowed Matt to vent some of his anger and frustration, and if it helped him to take it out on me, I'm glad. Matt was my first best friend ever; the first to meet me and welcome me to Sunnyvale. He went on to have a great career running the public relations group at Valley Health Center. Matt also died of scleroderma in 2003, and I miss him terribly.

The wide sidewalks lining all the streets in Sunnyvale were terrific for bikes and skateboarding, and all the paved driveways were excellent places for bike chases and endless games of follow the leader. And with 47 kids living in such close proximity on Kingsgate, there were more than enough willing participants. The streets of Sunnyvale are also very wide by suburban standards and well lit with large green streetlights, making after-hours games of hide and seek and kick the can a terrific way to end the day before the mothers of Kingsgate began to call us home from the front porches.

One of the criticisms of Sunnyvale is that it is too organized and too plain: Everywhere you look, there is a sidewalk, and every twenty feet there is a tree placed by the city arborist. The city streets tend to have a monotonous military organized look that contrasts with the comparatively more cutesy look and feel of the streets of Los Altos, located just on the other side of Highway 85. Newcomers to the Valley are often surprised to find that as they drive along El Camino Boulevard they can easily pass from the City of Mountain View, through Sunnyvale, into Santa Clara, and then on to San Jose without even noticing where one city stops and the next begins. Drivers have wasted many hours looking for an electronics company located in North Sunnyvale, all the while driving into and out of Santa Clara since all the streets and corporate parks have a frustrating sameness. The lack of discernable landmarks only adds to the feeling.

What Sunnyvale lacked in cuteness and ease of getting around, though, it more than made up for in the quality of life of its residents. Almost everyone could walk to excellent parks, grocery stores, work, and schools; for others, those things were just a short drive away. For a planned community, the city got more right than not. In the 1970's the schools were well-funded and full of the children of workers in the electronics, defense and aerospace industries. Serra Elementary School had two classes of twenty kids for each grade, K-6, for a total of nearly 300 children. As Matt and I walked with his sisters to our first day of kindergarten, both sides of the streets had a line of kids stretching down the sidewalks. Crossing guards were out in force with stop signs provided by the Safety Patrol force to stop the occasional car that approached the school. The bigger kids raced by on their bikes. Unlike today, almost all the kids walked or rode their bikes to school. Hardly anybody's parents drove them to school unless it was raining, and the few kids who did arrive by car quickly rushed away in shame. We have sacrificed independence by joining the army of SUV's dropping our children off at elementary school.

My first years of elementary school at Serra were happy times for me. The staff of three janitors kept the place and immaculate inside and out. The squeaky clean desks still smelled faintly of ammonia every morning, and all the linoleum floors had been buffed to a shine so bright they reflected the recessed lighting. Not a leaf hit the ground without being banished into a garbage can in short order. The large windows and the panels were clean and usually open due to the fact that Silicon Valley has such a mild climate, so mild that many often complain that there are no seasons. The kids were also generally immaculate, thanks to the many stay-at-home moms, and the clothes that we all wore were bought for us at the nearby Sears Roebuck and Mervyns.

My kindergarten teacher, Mrs. Whitely, was supported by an army of willing mothers of students. They were a well-established group in the elementary schools, and it was not uncommon to have two or three volunteer moms in class serving as "helpers" on any given day. There was a feeling of safety and security, and everyone generally helped out, including the older kids looking after the younger ones.

As much as I liked Serra Elementary School, the City of Sunnyvale Public Library was even better. The library was also a favorite haunt of my father's, so once a week, on Friday evenings or Saturday mornings, we would hop into the purple Mercedes and ride north up to the library, located just off of El Camino Boulevard, next to City Hall. While my father went to peruse the latest stacks of electronics magazines and books located to the right of the entrance, my brothers and I would tear off to the left to the Children's Library. We all had our own library cards with "full privileges." Those cards were a great source of pride for us and allowed us to check out up to nine books at a time for up to two weeks – for free!

Diagnosis

Silence makes no sound,
Yet much is there,
Easily found
With attention and care.

One of my earliest memories is of when I was a toddler running through my aunt's house to see the giant grandfather clock each time it went through its hourly song before striking the hours. It was loud, really loud. And then one day, after a long bout of sickness and high fevers, I can distinctly recall staring at the clock and waiting for it to start to clang. But it never did. I could see it moving as it went through its motions but couldn't hear it at all. I can remember trying to ask Aunt Marilyn to "fix it" or "make it louder," to no avail. I could not have understood what this meant to me at the time. But looking back, I absolutely can recall that that clock, which at one time had and had sounded so great and been so loud that I could hear it from the other end of the house had now fallen completely silent.

Now my mother swears that she had known about my deafness well before I understood that I had a hearing problem. The first time I can recall failing a hearing test was at Serra School in 1969, in the California Hearing Associates mobile hearing test van that was parked out in the front parking lot. During the day, each class of kids would pile in, and each student would take one of the seats and put on a set of headphones. After a few minutes of holding up our hands when we heard a tone, everyone would pile out – except for me. I had to stay and be tested and re-tested and tested again by grim-faced adults who whispered amongst themselves (though they did not really need to whisper as I could not hear them anyway). Today I know this means that at one time I could hear, and then one day at a very young age, I could not. My hearing loss may have been severe as defined by the hearing science world, but the diagnosis of it and the effect it had on my life would be profound.

It was really something when all the kids left the hearing test and my mother was called to come down to the school. At first

I was not sure what to think, but then I found out that there was something really wrong with me. That day a feeling of dread sank in, and I have carried the memory with me ever since. I failed the hearing test again at age six, and then at age seven and again at eight. After that, the good folks who operated the California Hearing Associates test service began to recognize me and figured out that re-testing me with the other kids was pointless as I was being tested so much anyway. I was a bit disappointed as I had always thought that one day it might get better; that one day I would pass that test and that I would be let go with the other "normal" kids. But it never happened.

My hearing loss probably started during my infancy. I had had more than my share of childhood illnesses that often kept me in bed with high fevers, swollen glands, and chronic recurring ear infections and necessitated lots of trips to the doctor. What definitively caused my hearing loss I will never know. I have also had allergic reactions to some of the antibiotic class drugs. Today the ear doctors (otologists) generally agree that my hearing loss was most likely caused by a high fever or by an ototoxic reaction to antibiotics, or both, with the smart money being on an ototoxic reaction to a shot of Gentomyocin. But what caused my hearing loss does not really matter. It would not have changed the result.

"This boy has severe hearing loss! Severe hearing loss, Mrs. Ball! He is going to need lots and lots of help, Mrs. Ball! Lots of it!" shouted the audiologist.

By the age of 11 I had become somewhat used to being "re-diagnosed" with severe hearing loss from time to time, but this audiologist was particularly zealous. Each time my father changed jobs or our health plan changed, a new audiologist would inevitably "discover" my hearing loss again. By the time I was tested by this latest irrationally exuberant audiologist, I was already somewhat of a pro at being diagnosed with hearing loss. Unlike the first times I learned that something was "seriously wrong" with me, I did not cry; I did not have one of those huge lumps in my throat; I did not feel like my life was forever changed and I was going to have to go to a special school or something. This time I got mad.

"Well we know that! You know! We know I cannot hear. What is wrong with you? It really is not cool to act all excited about this!" I exclaimed. I was irritated. The way she was acting was ridiculous.

The audiologist, who was young, just stared at me, stunned. Behind her, my mother was looking at me with a big frown on her face. I thought to myself, *Oh great. I'm in trouble again.* But on the way home in the purple Mercedes, Mom explained that she was not mad at me at all; it was the exuberant one that had got her ire.

"Geoff," Mom said, "sometimes people are going to do stupid things and act stupid about your hearing loss. It is not your fault."

"Mom," I replied, "I don't want to go back to that girl. She does not understand it."

"Fine. We will see what we can do." And with that, Mom took me back to school.

I hated my deafness. It terrified me. From what I could surmise, the doctors were trying to rule out some really serious bad things that could be wrong with me. Though I did not know what the terms 'acoustic neuroma' or 'tumor' meant, I knew that they were not good. What if it got worse and I lost the remaining hearing that I had?

Being diagnosed with hearing loss was horrible, and the whole terrible process made me feel worse. Even today, just remembering it gives me a sinking feeling in the stomach and a serious case of the chilly willies, and of course I can still recall the deep uncertainty and dread. It is the feeling of having lost something precious that you can never get back no matter how hard you tried not to lose it or how desperately you want it to back. It seemed hopeless, dire and cursed. In the first weeks after my diagnosis, I spent hours upon hours in soundproof rooms being tested for hearing and speech. No matter how hard I tried to do better, the results were always the same. *Dang it! Failed another test!* After a few months, the hearing tests stopped and life returned to normal for a while, but the sick feeling in my stomach remained.

Perhaps one of the reasons I hated my hearing loss so much was the undeserved stigma that it has. It is common for people with hearing loss to be labeled with the dated term "deaf and dumb." I am not sure where this crazy saying originated, but it most likely comes from the fact that many mentally or otherwise developmentally challenged people are also hard of hearing. It may also stem from the fact that those of us with hearing loss often answer the wrong question with the right answer, which can make us seem "dumb" when in fact we may be quite smart. Not hearing well also means that we cannot hear how loud our own voices are, so we can often come across to others as obnoxious or loud. We find ourselves in many embarrassing and confusing situations with no good social protocol to follow. It is one tough nut.

One of the many social conundrums for the hearing impaired is the fact that if we cannot hear what a person said or is saying, and we move closer so that we can hear them better, they begin to speak more softly. It happens every time, and it's maddening! Or when someone learns of our hearing loss, they start to speak much too loudly, sometimes shouting and often using lower-level, basic vocabulary. Sometimes they throw in wild hand gestures for good measure. "GEOFFREY!!! I! WANT YOU! YOU! TO READ THIS! TO READ THIS SENTENCE! TO THE CLASS! TO THE CLAAAASS, THE CLAAAASSSS!" The teacher waves her hands and points excitedly at the passage, while all your classmates stare at you with bemused expressions. Oh, you just want to die. At such moments I would often freeze up, a shocked and embarrassed, while my mind raced to find the right words, the right thing to say, all the while literally dumfounded by the idiocy of it all.

Such acts are not limited solely to the act of speaking to the hearing impaired. Upon learning that I had hearing loss, one teacher that I had immediately moved me to the very front of the class and took to writing on the black board in absolutely huge letters in red chalk. Whenever I was in the room, out came the red chalk and the writing increased to two to three times its normal size. Again, if you're deaf, you're dumb, so of course I would also benefit from much larger letters in red. I just sat there feeling inconsolably demoralized.

Of course there were many times when I just wanted to scream, "I can see fine! What are you doing? Don't make me sit at the front! Don't make big letters for me! The rest of the kids will think I am an idiot!" So I just sat there squirming in my chair each day, thoroughly humiliated, feeling naked and exposed and embarrassed beyond words by the best of intentions with the worst kind of thinking behind it all.

I am sure that the reality was not that bad and that what the other kids actually thought was probably nothing like what my imaginative young brain made it out to be. But at the time, I wanted to disappear. I did not want anyone to know I was different, especially my classmates. I probably had a lot of mixed-up feelings that had no basis in fact, so I just hung on the best I could. It was tough at times. After my hearing loss was diagnosed, researchers and graduate students from nearby university programs and other hearing research institutions began to visit me. I became a study case for speech pathologists and hearing researchers. They would often sit there and watch me, take notes or give me something to read or an exercise to do. Sometimes they would ask me to read a passage out loud. They would give me new words and then have me try to sound them out. With the help of my mother, who always read books to me and my brothers every night, I had somehow taught myself to read before I started school, and for some reason the way that I read and learned to speak and understand new words was what fascinated them most. I can remember a lot of questions from the researchers regarding how I read, how I learned to do it, what this word was in relation to another word, and so on.

Looking back, it seems to me that they were spellbound by the fact that I never learned to sound out words from the beginning to the end, as was usually the case, and that I read by recognizing the patterns of words and of entire sentences. I will never know exactly what it was about my reading, vocalization and hearing that was so intriguing to them. I can recall one young graduate student who had spent a lot of time with me explaining, "We are studying you because you are very interesting to us. You do not do these things like the others, and we want to know how you do it so maybe we can understand it better and help you and others."

At the time, the last thing I wanted to be was different. In my creative little brain, I was sure that they were looking for a reason to take me out of Serra School and send me to the school for the deaf. I did not want to be "interesting" to researchers. I may not be able to recall what they found so interesting about me, but what I do recall is that out of all the concepts that the many special education experts and speech therapists worked on with me, there was only one that I found interesting: lipreading.

I got a lot of extra help developing my ability to read lips at school. I was not the only child at Serra Elementary who was given extra attention and extra time for special needs. There were actually several of us. Even though we were told we were "special," I think all of us had figured out that in some way we were in fact "not normal." I had more speech help than any of the other kids at first. As my speaking ability for some reason or other improved rapidly despite my severe degree of hearing loss, I was given more and more time to practice my lipreading. To those of you without hearing loss, reading lips may seem almost like voodoo, but it was the right choice for me. I practiced the techniques for hours with speech coaches. They had me practice lipreading in noisy, confusing situations. They gave me endless exercises to practice reading lips when I could only see only part of their mouths, or sometimes just their cheeks. Over and over, again and again. This was much more fun than spending hours and hours on vowel and consonant production. "O" "OOOOhh." "O." "Now, Geoffrey!" "S." "Sssss." "S". I can remember it like it was yesterday But I thought lipreading was cool, and I thrived on it. When I started showing up for my hearing tests, the audiologists were astonished by how good I had become at it. At first they thought my hearing had improved; then they thought something was wrong with their test equipment. They soon learned that hiding their mouths when they read off the words for speech testing was not enough, so they faced in the other direction during testing. I became so good at lipreading that most people had no idea that I could hear so poorly. I can recall one of my hearing testers telling my mom, "Mrs. Ball, Geoffrey here, well, he is the best little lipreader I have ever seen!"

The California school system was flush with funding for special needs kids at the time. In elementary school, I received more than my fair share of extra help whether I wanted it or not. Soon I was meeting with a speech therapist three days a week to develop my speech patterns and pronunciation. I received extensive lipreading training. I became a world champion lipreader. I was really, really good at it. When the other children had foreign language course work, I was sent to get more speech and extra help with English. (At the time the belief was that learning a foreign language could be detrimental to learning proficient English skills – a belief no longer held by hearing professionals). I did well enough with all of this that early attempts to teach me to learn how to use sign language were scrapped. I was put in special classes, often with truly deaf kids, but more often with other special needs kids. Some of these efforts helped; some probably did not. Some of the special needs teachers were great; some were not. A few of them really "got it" (and, more importantly got *me*), and what they did for me truly helped. My speech is quite good today, and my pronunciation is clear. No one is perfect, though, and my wife says I still say "stupid things" all the time, but at least she can understand what I say!

It was not long after I was diagnosed with hearing loss that I was fitted with my first hearing aid. It was a huge clunky device with a large, unsightly ear mould. At the time, audiologists in the United States did not believe in hearing aids as a viable treatment, and their oversight body (the American Academy of Audiology) therefore did not allow them to dispense acoustic devices. My hearing aids were fitted by a man operating out of his home, which was squashed in between an auto muffler repair center on one side and a vacuum cleaner sales and service shop on the other, down on First Street in San Jose. The place was tacky. It had shiny light reflectors on the acoustic ceiling. The office was dank and cramped, and it had an awful smell, likely due to the three barking Pekinese dogs that had the run of the place. The man's wife, who helped run the front office area, had a beehive hairdo that was so high it almost hit the doorways when she passed through. My ear doctor at the time, Mansfield Smith, had a real health care office that was obviously designed for treating people and helping them to get well. This was not that place. This was nothing like it. The dichotomy for me as a young child was obvious: How on earth could I go from a bona-fide health care facility to such a place? *This*, I thought, *cannot be good.*

The first time they put the hearing aid on me, I felt like a mutant alien – like I had just landed on a different planet that was full of electronic humming and squealing, screeching inaudibility. They showed me how to put the earpiece in my ear canal, how to put the larger piece behind my ear, and how to use the wheel to adjust the volume. I told them I did not like it, so the man put it back in a test machine and looked at the readout.

"It's OK. You just need to get used to it," he told me.

"But it hurts and it sounds bad!" I said.

"You just need to give it some time," he repeated.

I put the device on, went outside, and was almost bowled over as the sounds of the traffic on First Street roared into my brain. Everything was so loud! When my mom took out her car keys, the "ching-a-ching" sound felt like it was pounding on my head.

"I hate it," I told her.

"They said you will get used to them, so just keep trying them," Mom replied. But I knew from the start that this was not for me.

"Can't the doctors do surgery to fix my ears?" I asked.

"No, your hearing type cannot be helped by surgery. That is what the doctors said."

"Nothing?"

"No," she said.

Now the good thing about getting fitted with hearing aids was that I got to skip the morning session of school on Monday. But the really bad thing was that the teacher had taken it upon herself to tell the entire class where I was and what was happening to me. Thus, all my classmates knew about my hearing loss and that I would be coming back that afternoon with a hearing aid. Good idea? No, it was not!

When I got back and walked into the classroom wanting nothing more than to sit down and disappear, every single kid came over and said, "Let me see it! I want to see it!" "You told them! You told everyone!" I accused the teacher. And when she looked at me, I knew she had – it was obvious. I was now surrounded by the whole class. One kid even tried to take the device off. Others spun my volume wheel. The hearing aid man had told me not to touch the wheel for at least a week until I got used to it.

Oh God, I felt lower than low. It seemed to me that my life was ending. That day I heard the sing-song taunt for the first time: "Deaf Geoff! Geoff is deaf! Geoff can't hear because he's deaf!' It was a bad day. A really, truly bad day. I wanted to move to Austria.

Minutes turned to hours, and when school was finally over for the day, I ran all the way home, locked the door, and buried my head in my pillow, convinced that I was the newest mutant at Serra School and determined not to come out ever again. But when I laid my head down, my hearing aid started squealing like a banshee. I could not turn it off and I could not take it off, so I just sat on the bed, convinced that my life was over and that this hearing aid thing was not going to work. And that I was going to have to go to a school for the deaf.

Early Entrepreneurship

Silence comes and silence is
The quiet place
True thinking lives

So there I was, living in Sunnyvale. I had great friends, a pink house, a purple Mercedes that would take me to a great library once a week, and clothes from Mervyn's department store. I couldn't really hear anything, but I could read lips like nobody's business and had unlimited access to books. I tried my hearing aid but found I did better without it and eventually seldom wore it. All it ever really did was give me headaches anyway. As long as I kept working hard and performing in mainstream schools, it was unlikely I would be sent to the school for the deaf. I was getting more extra help at school than anyone could ever possibly need. Thank God for Sunnyvale.

In the early 1970's there were far worse places for a kid diagnosed with hearing loss to grow up than in Silicon Valley, California. Many of the local physicians that treated me in these early days, including Dr. Mansfield Smith and Dr. Rodney Perkins, were, in fact, in the top tier of practicing otologists at the time. I hated going to all the audiology centers for testing, but I always liked seeing Dr. Smith and Dr. Perkins. They gave me and my mother hope. They always had something positive to say. These men truly were my anchors and helped me cope with my hearing loss. They helped me keep it together and be the best I could be. I have no idea where I would be today without them and their positive influence. I know that may sound like a tired cliché, but I absolutely mean it.

I did not know it then, but books were my saving grace. Television in the early 70's was largely devoid of real educational programs for kids, and as a hearing-impaired child, I could not really hear the words anyway. Although I was already becoming a champion lipreader, I had learned that it is impossible to read the lips of Bugs Bunny or any of the Sesame Street Muppets. Television by that time had already become a big problem for me. When it was loud enough for me to hear, nobody else could stand to be in the room. I mean that literally: It was so loud it hurt their ears. So I had a choice: I could sit in front of the TV and make up words in my head, or I could read. So I read, and I read.

I read every book they had in the children's library for my age group, and when I had finished them all, I read them again. Then I moved up to the next level of books. The Sunnyvale Library helped me tremendously as a youngster, and it would later play a key role in my future. The Sunnyvale Public Library was also a patent library where you could look up all patents issued in the United States for the latest inventions, so it was a place where I would spend a lot of time as a young man.

To the average person, hearing loss is off the radar screen. Most people are surprised to learn how widespread the hearing loss problem truly is. Sensory-neural hearing loss (a.k.a. nerve deafness) affects 11 % of the population. Many of these people could benefit from hearing aids, but the vast majority rejects them for whatever reason. The strong social stigma attached to wearing a hearing aid would leave many feeling "deaf and dumb," though this is an outdated social response. Modern devices can help most patients if they give them enough of chance by wearing them long enough to get used to them, and most patients with mild to moderate hearing loss do very well with acoustic amplification. But they do have to learn to put up with the inconvenience, the issues with ear wax, the feedback that can occur, and the discomfort. Many who try hearing aids give up or only rarely use them. The often-repeated comment that it "just does not sound natural" is a common reason for device rejection. Hearing loss affects people of all ages but is most prevalent among seniors. As we live longer, hearing loss rates will increase.

Approximately one percent of the population is also affected by mixed or conductive hearing loss. Patients with this type of hearing loss can often benefit from surgery to repair the function of the eardrum or to repair or replace one or all of the three tiny bones that transmit sound to the inner ear. However, many of these patients receive only temporary or inferior results, either from attempts to use amplification or from attempts to surgically restore hearing function. Hearing loss is a medical anomaly. Sensory-neural hearing loss is the single largest chronic condition that remains untreated in a majority of sufferers. It affects approximately 30 million people in the United States today, and 80 % of them do nothing about it. It is a true healthcare oddity.

There are many reasons for this. A predominant one is that many or most hearing loss sufferers do not or cannot realize how much they are missing. That is why the single largest group of referrers of the hearing impaired to hearing health care providers are spouses or partners who, in a nutshell, get sick and tired of repeating themselves. Sometimes they have finally heard "What?" once too often, so they essentially push, drag or carry their loved ones to the clinic to see what remedies are available. There is a little hearing industry joke that goes: "Who sells the most hearing aids in the industry today? Wives."

Many people do not fully appreciate the simple act of hearing. Since we do not have to think in order to hear or even *try* to hear, most of us take this seemingly passive sensory input for granted. We do not need to think about hearing; it just happens. Beyond learning that three tiny bones of the ear (the ossicles) are the smallest bones in the human body, most people know little about the true miracle of aural functions and the biomechanical wonders that occur during the act of hearing. In fact, if you asked a person the question, "If you had to give up either your sight or your hearing, which would you give up?" the answer would almost always be "hearing." I believe that is the wrong answer.

Humans are truly visual creatures, and what we see seems so important that we cannot imagine living without it. Most of us would definitely choose to keep our sight. What we don't realize is that if you can hear, you can still communicate with your friends and family, listen to music, and have discussions. Without hearing, you lose ability to effectively communicate. Once people are made aware of the ramifications of hearing loss, they realize how important hearing truly is to their psycho-social well-being and participation in daily life, and they generally change their minds. Hearing loss causes social isolation.

With a total loss of hearing, there is a marked decrease in the ability to even speak well, and over time your ability to speak will become severely impaired as you will not be able to produce clear intelligible speech or monitor your volume or intonation. I have personally witnessed how patients that present with sudden onset of hearing loss lose their ability to control their speech at an alarming rate. With total hearing loss, you lose the ability to control your voice.

Hearing health care professionals know that it is absolutely imperative to get the hearing-impaired child the earliest and best intervention possible. If the auditory processing pathways are not stimulated early and well, they may not develop well or at all. Without appropriate auditory stimulation, the child's ability to understand and follow the spoken word will be impaired. And if the ability to follow speech correctly is impaired, it will have lasting effects on the child's ability to understand the written word. His or her reading levels can fall well below those of their peers, and poor reading leads to poor writing skills development. Early intervention with the best treatment available is crucial for the development of key communication skills. One might be tempted to think that the deaf would always be terrific at reading and writing as this would be something they could really focus on that does not require auditory input. In fact, the opposite is often true. The fact is that hearing-impaired students frequently have reading and writing abilities that are well below those of the average person with the same educational level.

To add insult to injury, learning to use sign language as a primary means of communicative (in place of speaking a mother tongue) seems to make it harder for many hearing impaired to learn to read and write as effectively as they could. This is due to the way sign language operates. Sign language relies on a different format than the spoken word, and effective signing depends heavily on speed and short cut use for effective communication. In my view, children should be mainstreamed on the spoken word format whenever possible. There are now few adolescent or pediatric hearing impairments that cannot be helped, with good results, by hearing technology, so sign language will probably become even rarer than it is now. It still offers the only effective means of communication for some – not just the hearing impaired, but also those with impaired vocal ability and other developmental challenges. It is tough for me to be in a position where I have to admit that on the one hand it is a good thing that technology has greatly reduced the need for sign language, but on the other hand it is not a good thing as the pool of people who sign is shrinking. In today's world, most people rarely see sign language users. Think about it. When was the last time you saw someone using sign language? If you can recall, it was most likely on TV or at large public speaking event. Based on the progress we have made, I think the days of sign language translations for media broadcasts will soon be largely a thing of the past.

The good news today is that for the hearing impaired there are certainly more options for hearing treatment than existed when I was growing up in Sunnyvale. Cochlear implants, once just a dream, have been pioneered and developed into robust treatments that are a godsend for so many. Today, newborns are screened for hearing in most if not all developed countries, so we can catch hearing loss sooner and get the kids the help they need. Many implantable solutions are now available, and many new systems are being deployed in new and exciting ways, offering unprecedented benefits in truly challenging cases. Hearing aids have much better packaging, and smaller, more discrete devices are available for moderate hearing loss. Digital signal processing has also made them much better than they were in the past. Yet the stigma of hearing loss stubbornly remains, and most people do nothing.

As surprising as it sounds, there are many positive things about being hearing impaired. A big upside for me was the development of a true love of creative expression through drawing and painting. I think I may have gotten more than my share of illustrative skill from the many drawing and art courses that my mother signed me up for at the Sunnyvale Community Center. I took two years of courses taught by a man named Mr. Kirov until something happened to him and his son took over teaching the courses. Mr. Kirov taught fine drawing with charcoals and inks as well as cartooning. Three times a week, I would spend two hours in class drawing on my Strathmore 44 pad with pens and ink and charcoals under Mr. Kirov's watchful eye. I believe that learning to illustrate and paint well at a young age helps to develop higher order three dimensional conceptual thinking and imagination. I have been drawing ever since, and this is now the medium of choice for me when I start down the path toward a new invention. My art ability, coupled with later formal mechanical illustration, design and architectural courses, has been a key asset for me.

Silicon Valley

The first known inhabitants of Silicon Valley area were the Ohlone Indians, who settled in the area around 3000 B.C. and stayed until the mid 1700's. No one can be certain, but it seems that these early settlers imbued the heavy clay soils deposited on the floor of Silicon Valley with a ridiculous amount of hope, optimism and entrepreneurial spirit.

Plenty has been written about what sets entrepreneurs apart. Many suggest that those who are attracted to and bitten by the "start-up" bug are highly motivated and creative people who are more eager to take risks. A lot of ink has been used trying to quantify the personality and psycho-social aspects of the makings of true entrepreneurs. If we had all this information, I think it would be possible to identify those likely to become the next generation's innovators. But we can never have such detailed information, and we can never quantify the luck, timing, motivational and countless other factors that set entrepreneurs apart. Some of us do it for the simple fact that this is what we know. It is what we grew up around, and to not be "starting up" something new, to not be working on the next "new thing" in our field would seem abnormal to us. If we are not working on the cutting edge or on the next new thing, we are not working.

Silicon Valley is legendary for innovation. Since California was invaded in the 1800's by adventurers rushing to the foothills of the Sierras in search of gold, pioneering the next 'new thing' has seemed natural to us. True innovation takes a certain amount of overconfidence, like the passion that motivated the 49ers to endure the foothills' freezing winters and searing one-hundred-degree-plus summers as they sifted through endless sludge panning for gold and looking for few payday nuggets. I also think that it takes a bit of craziness to truly follow your dreams and to keep at it even when all is lost.

Luck has a lot to do with success: too much, really. Never underestimate the role of luck and of its evil sister, bad luck. Those who have met with great success in the Valley, those who now have mansions up in the hills overlooking the Valley and San Francisco Bay, would prefer to take comfort in the conviction that their hard work, perseverance and smartness were the primary reasons they were successful. There is no doubt that most of them earned their success it. Many worked at it for years, but they more often than not had a good deal of luck on their side. Lady luck blesses the miner who sticks his shovel into the hillside and pulls out a huge nugget worth tens of thousands of dollars while a miner working perhaps even harder a scant ten yards further upstream walks away with nothing. The Stanford Business School does not teach its students how to be in the right place at the right time. The truly successful simply seem to have a knack for timing things just right and having the right new product, the right new business and the right people around them to make it all work.

On hot days, Matt Schenone, his sister "Janine the Bean" and I ran a lemonade stand out in front of 1526. The many times we actually managed to get the stand set up and stocked with sweet syrupy lemonade (from a can, made up and iced), our business model was to sit around in the hot sun and argue for hours about what the name of the stand should be and what to do with all the profits. Janine always got to be the boss because she was the oldest. On a typical day, we would sell three glasses at 25 cents each: one to my father, one to Mr. Schenone, and one to Mr. Kozina, who lived directly across the street. The corporate upheavals, mass walkouts and labor issues that we endured as a team and thrust upon Janine should have qualified her to be a CEO by age 11. As bad as it was, we must have learned something: mostly, I think, that our location was too quiet and that we needed to move the operation to a place with more foot traffic. I wanted to put everything on a cart and set up our stand in front of the 7-Eleven on Homestead Road, but our parents shot that idea down. We also learned that warm lemonade from a can tastes pretty bad, even when it is 101 degrees outside.

I worked at my first real Silicon Valley startup at age 11. The company, InterDesign, it was the dream child of Hans Camenzind and my father, James V. Ball. Together, Hans and my father were a formidable team and arguably some of the best integrated circuit[1] engineers in the field at the time, and they decided to set up their own IC business. Hans and my father had met back in Massachusetts, and they had had moved their young families to Silicon Valley at the same time. Mr. Camenzind was originally from Switzerland, and since both the Ball and Camenzind families were new transplants to the Valley, we began celebrating Thanksgiving with other local transplant families in Big Basin State Park, a tradition that continues to this day.

The original InterDesign company headquarters was in a small group of offices located just off Murphy Street in downtown Sunnyvale, right next door to the Tao Tao Chinese restaurant, which is still there today. They quickly outgrew that space (and were probably getting fat from eating all that epic Chinese food) and moved to one of the new business parks in eastern Sunnyvale, on the border with Santa Clara. After they relocated, things quickly moved into higher gear for InterDesign.

My first job with the company was to help my father build all the lab benches for the outfit. We headed down to Orchard Supply hardware, bought the biggest radial arm saw we could find, and began ripping these huge 12 × 2 boards into the base supports for the benches. For two days, 1526 Kingsgate was an engineering lab bench production facility. My job was to help carry the wood to the saw, stack all the pieces up, and put all the excess in a pile. Then we loaded all the materials on the roof racks of the purple Mercedes and hauled it to the new facility for assembly. It took us four trips.

The first time we walked into InterDesign with a load of freshly cut lab bench parts, there stood Hans and Pia Camenzind, with their four kids running around the new facility. You could just see

---

1   In electronics, an integrated circuit (also known as IC, microcircuit, microchip, silicon chip, or chip) is a miniaturized electronic circuit (consisting mainly of semiconductor devices, as well as passive components) that has been manufactured in the surface of a thin substrate of semiconductor material. Integrated circuits can be found in almost all electronic equipment in use today and have revolutionized the world of electronics. Computers, cellular phones, and other digital appliances, now inextricable parts of the structure of modern societies, were made possible by the low cost of the production of integrated circuits. (Source: Wikipedia)

the pride in Mr. Camenzind's eyes. He was truly happy, truly "on." He and my father had started down the path toward developing the next new thing in integrated circuits. There was electricity in the air – literally.

The new InterDesign building was a single story "tip up" with approximately 30,000 square feet. In the front were the main administrative offices, which Pia was setting up. The executive offices for Hans and my father and the engineering staff were off a corridor down the right. There was a small board meeting room to the left and a cafeteria that already had soda (Tab and Fresca in addition to Classic Coke) and candy machines in it. In the back of the building there was a warehouse area adjacent to a large manufacturing area, and the engineering and test labs were accessed via a common corridor.

Dad and I set about assembling all thirty-odd lab benches. It didn't take us long, and when they were set up, they completely transformed the large empty spaces into a company. By the end of the weekend, InterDesign's new headquarters had come alive. It became standard practice for me to accompany my father down to InterDesign headquarters most Saturdays or Sundays as he always worked at least one day on the weekend. Hans and my father set to work staffing the operation and within weeks had hired 20 engineers and technicians.

One of my first official tasks was to pull all the weeds surrounding the site and clean up the parking lots. This was not an easy thing to do. The hills surrounding the Valley and the Santa Cruz Mountains had been extensively logged to build San Francisco and San Jose in the early 1800's and again after the fires that followed the 1906 San Francisco earthquake. The Valley had since been used for agriculture, and the same thick clay soil that was ideal for fruit trees had now allowed an abundance of huge, deep-rooted weeds to flourish all across the InterDesign lot. But now the Valley was now proving to be more fertile for the emerging high tech industry than for apricot, pear, almond and cherry orchards, which were being uprooted at an amazing pace. The soil left behind was thick, hard clay, and when it was dry, it was as hard as a rock, and pick axes would bounce off it.

The early settlers saw the advantage of this thick clay and used it to make adobe. If you put Silicon Valley earth into square wooden forms, mix in a bit of straw or reeds, and let it dry for a few hours in the sun, you have adobe bricks. Stack them into four walls, throw up a couple cross beams and a thatched roof, and you have your own adobe hut. Get help from a bunch of your friends or from the local Indian population, stack the bricks up even higher, and you have a mission like the ones that dot the El Camino Real of California, where the early Spanish settlers built churches to spread Spanish rule and the Catholic faith among the natives. Long story short, there are few Native American Indians left in the region today (in fact, I cannot recall ever meeting one in Sunnyvale) but the ground, I assure you, is still hard as a rock. As beneficial as clay soil was for building missions and huts, pulling weeds out of it was nearly impossible. It took me two hours to do each side of the building, and by the time I returned the next weekend, my efforts had already been negated by new growth. The only good thing about pulling weeds, besides the 50 cents an hour I earned, was that I would occasionally scare off one of the last remaining Silicon Valley jackrabbits. Fortunately, I was soon to be promoted.

As InterDesign grew and began ramping up for the production of its first chips, the engineering group had a growing need for breadboard wiring. Today, ready-made breadboard wiring kits can be purchased, but in the 1970's, someone had to strip out all the wires for the breadboards and production fixtures.

This was before the days of advanced electronic computer-based simulation circuit design tools were available, so circuits had to be designed and then built and tested with discreet components before any photo layout could be attempted. It was all hands on. Even the photo layouts, a key component in the IC that defined the actual circuit, were all done by hand. I can still recall often finding my father in his den at 1526 working late into the night at a black backlit light table, using exacto blades and tiny scissors to cut out his circuit layouts by hand.

I was promoted to the job of "head wire stripper." My father and I went down to the local flea market at De Anza College and found a handheld wire stripper that could strip any gauge wire and had an automatic return. It was my first real piece of technical equipment, the first purchase of what would eventually become a history of millions of dollars in capital equipment outlays for me. The original wire stripper my dad bought for me is still up in my lab, and I still use it.

Using the wire stripper, I removed the ends of colored electronic wiring cut from spools into lengths of between one and six inches and put them into boxes marked short, medium and long. Along with my promotion came a 100 % pay raise – to one dollar an hour, a princely sum for me at the time. Pia had set up the official company accounts, and I got my first pay check at age 11. I did not know it then, but ever since that time, I have always had a place to call work and a job, often two or more jobs at the same time.

After a few weekends, I had stripped so many wires that my right hand was callused and blistered, and the boxes were overflowing with wires. I was making them faster than the engineering and technical staff could use them during the week, while I was at school. That's why I got my second promotion.

This time my father promoted me to "manufacturing technician" but with no increase in pay, much to my surprise. By this time InterDesign had an automatic IC (integrated circuit) test machine. I would place the IC's one at a time into these long plastic cartridges; then my father or one of the other technicians would help me load them on to the machine because I was not tall enough to do it myself. I would put a box at one end where the machine would accept the units that "passed test" and a second box where the machine would spit out the chips that "failed test."

The automatic test system was not perfect and had a habit of rejecting good units. So after the IC test had finished working through all the cartridges of IC's, I would take all the units that were in the "failed test" box, take them to one of the lab benches, and put them on a manual test fixture. I would carefully load the IC's into an eight-slot socket, lock them in position, and then read the voltage values on an assortment of scopes and volt meters. My father had written down the acceptance criteria: what values each unit needed to be to "pass" and which levels would be a "fail". I put the IC's that passed the manual test into a box labeled "accepted."

Manually testing IC's was a tedious, boring and difficult task. Stripping wires had been pretty boring too, but it seemed like a lot more fun than manual IC testing. One good thing about working in the test lab at InterDesign was that I was usually alone and rarely needed to talk to anyone. I worked primarily on the weekends and holidays, so most of the daily employees were not around, and my hearing loss was never a problem. In fact, it helped me concentrate. Sometimes Mr. Camenzind would come over, count up the units in the boxes that passed test, do some calculations, shake his head, and then go and complain to my father. Sometimes almost none of the IC's passed. When Mr. Camenzind saw a large number of units in the "fail" boxes, his complaints increased proportionally. I quickly learned that it was best to remove and replace the failed IC boxes as fast as I could in case he walked by the IC test lab.

InterDesign's startup phase was a critical time. If and when the parts they were making kept failing at high rates, they could not keep up with their orders and had to spend much more on their production costs. Eventually, the company solved these and other issues and became a successful startup.

InterDesign bought a Volkswagen van that Mr. Camenzind buzzed around the Valley in and used as the family van on weekends. The InterDesign van made many, many trips to our annual Big Basin Thanksgiving feasts and other extended family get-togethers. In addition to his engineering and design roles, my father had also begun working with customers to improve designs and identify new applications and niches for InterDesign's products. Most of the chips they built were custom-designed for larger customers. He got a company car, and in keeping with our family's long color-challenged theme, chose a bright metallic green Plymouth sedan with a white vinyl top, a matching metallic green interior, and white-wall tires.

It was not long before Hans Sigg, also from Switzerland, joined InterDesign, adding one more clan to our extended family and one fine engineer to the company. InterDesign went on to become a highly successful business. In 1998 it was sold to Plessey, which was then later acquired by Mitel. My father went back to work for

National Semiconductor, and Hans was able to start his own consulting business and continue his work on new projects.

InterDesign was a success, and working there at such a young age and seeing it grow and prosper and survive challenging times, I definitely caught the startup bug. The opportunity I had to be a part of it – albeit a microscopic part – has no doubt stayed with me to this day. It also gave me a great deal of pride and a sense that despite my own personal challenges and shortcomings, I would find a place in the world and get good jobs.

Looking back, I think that one of the key building blocks in my character, one that would eventually help me as an entrepreneur, was the game of football, called soccer in the United States. It was an unusual and virtually unknown sport in the U.S. in the early 1970's, and in the Valley, soccer was played primarily by European and Central and South American émigrés.

I was introduced to soccer by a Kingsgate neighborhood kid named Steven Duncan, whose family had just relocated to Sunnyvale from England. We signed up for an American Youth Soccer Association team, and soon we were practicing almost every evening and playing games on Saturday mornings. I had found my sport. Being hearing impaired did not seem to be a disadvantage on the soccer field. In American football, being able to hear the plays called in the huddle was a key thing I had not been able to do. My limited ability often resulted in me running the wrong routes and the wrong plays, taking balls in the face, and generally looking like an idiot. Soccer had no scripted plays. It was always changing: defense, then offense, and then back again. Unlike baseball, it was not boring for me thanks to its super fast pace of constant action. Hearing what the refs said was not so important, since they always used hand signals, very loud whistles and flags. But the best thing about soccer was that I was really good at it, and it taught me one thing about myself: I was fast.

Being fast and moving toward the ball, getting there first, knowing when to pass, and working with your teammates to time the ball were important. Knowing where your man would be, knowing where the ball would go and getting to it first, and anticipating your opponents' moves were all keys to success.

The first year I played I did not really know what I was doing. And since most of the coaches and players spoke little English, Steven was not much better. But by the second year I had it figured out. I scored three goals in first game, and I led the league in goals and assists at the end of the season. No matter how loud the sidelines yelled, clapped and screamed, I was alone in my silent world, focusing on the game.

We won every game that season except one away game at Pippen Park in North Sunnyvale. At that time, North Sunnyvale had a growing population of Central and South Americans, and every single boy on the other team spoke Spanish or Portuguese. I did not score three goals that day, that's for sure. In fact, what we learned was that as much as we loved to play soccer, the rest of the world was a lot, lot better at it than we were. They put three tiny little players in the front center with two wingers and played the halfbacks up, which basically put seven players on offense. Our poor goal keeper did the best he could to keep up. At half time, the coach moved me to a new position called "sweeper," which would essentially be my position for the next 15 years and which meant that he wanted me on the ball no matter where it was on the field. We didn't really stand a chance that day, and our poor team, the Pirates, lost to the Northern Sunnyvale Santos.

Playing soccer most weekends built up my legs and my lungs. Soon every time we did a "giant lap" in gym class at Serra, I finished first. Sometimes I would come in so far ahead that I had the water fountain to myself for quite a long time.

An important lesson I learned from soccer was that the more we practiced, the better we got. The few losses my teams had were usually because practices had been canceled that week that rather than because we were outplayed. Practice was the key to success, except when we played teams with truly superior talent like the Santos. I also learned that there is nothing like doing something, doing it well, and being one of the best in or on the field. Once you are really good, it seems easier to get better, and I was able to spend my time working on tough moves. I learned to kick and pass almost as well with my left foot as with my dominant right. I learned that a team that had great talent but a poor coach, poor morale and shoddy teamwork would often lose to opponents with far less talent who played together as a team.

Teamwork and timing were what mattered. I learned that in addition to the true advantage of being fast, there is a certain beauty in passing the ball to your teammates. I can remember one play like it was yesterday: I was out in right center, dribbling the ball up towards goal. I made it around the fullback and had a great shot on goal, but Steve was behind the keeper on the left side of the net and had a truly wide open shot. So rather than take my pretty good shot and get the goal for myself, I flipped the ball off to Steve, who punched it in for a score. Sharing Steve's glory was just as good as getting it myself.

I got my first job as a paperboy at the age of 11, delivering Sunnyvale's *Valley Journal*. In 1975 readers had a remarkable choice of newspapers from which to get their daily news fix. There was the *San Jose Mercury News*, which had both morning and evening delivery; there was the *Sunnyvale Scribe,* which was delivered twice a week; there was the daily edition of the *San Francisco Chronicle*; and for some reason that few of us paperboys understood, daily afternoon delivery of the *Palo Alto Times*. By the time I started delivering, the *Valley Journal* was feeling the pain of putting out a daily paper and had already cut back to three times a week rather than daily. So each Monday, Wednesday and Friday morning, I would get up at 5:30 a.m., fold my 122 newspapers, put them in my handlebar bags, and peddle out on my route.

The first day I loaded my bike with the newspapers, it was so heavy in the front that the bike flipped over and landed on top of me before I even got started. Once I righted the whole thing, I made it to the bottom of our driveway, but when I went to turn right, the bags got caught the front wheel and jammed it. The sudden stop catapulted me end over end out onto the street, where I landed on my head and wound up on the sidewalk in the shape of a pretzel. I found myself facing the front end Mr. Kozina's Pontiac Catalina, which promptly stopped. Mr. Kozina helped me up, and, sure enough, sent me on my way, bloodied, bruised and late. This was a lot harder than my InterDesign work.

My route covered the entire area between Dalles, Cascade, Hollenbeck and Mary Avenues, plus every street and cul-de-sac in between. The *Valley Journal's* policy was to deliver a paper to every single house unless they had specifically called in requesting no delivery. Three mornings a week, it took me an hour and a half to deliver all my papers before racing off to school. Crashes were frequent because when all the papers were loaded, they weighed more than I did and made the front of the bike heavy and hard to control. At the end of each month I would visit all the homes and collect 75 cents from each of my customers for all my effort. The company also paid me two cents extra for each paper I delivered and a little more if there were advertising inserts. In a good month, I could make a total of $90 with tips, a small fortune for a 12 year old. During the Christmas holidays I could make an extra 15 or 20 dollars in tips. I found out customers tipped even better if I wore a Santa cap during the holiday season. It was a good job, and I served the *Valley Journal* well, but it was hard work.

Delivering all those papers three times a week was good exercise, and I always tried to get up on time, but it was tough, really tough getting out at 5:30 each day. I do not know how my parents put up with it all. I wondered often how the "real" paperboys like my friend Mitch Kirk did it. They delivered the *San Jose Mercury* every single day including Saturdays and the dreaded three-pound Sunday morning edition. The *San Jose Mercury* newspaper boys also had to deliver the daily evening edition, which meant that most days they covered to their routes twice a day. On top of that, they had to make all the collections and still find time to go to school and do homework. It was really tough on them, and it left them with bad attitudes even though they made more than twice as much as we lowly *Valley Journal* delivery guys did.

Because I kept getting flipped over my handlebars from my newspapers, I saved up and bought a new newspaper bike at the Bicycle Tree, which was located down next to Farrell's Ice Cream Parlour on Fremont. It was a bright metallic yellow (carrying on the Ball family color-challenged tradition for at least another generation) with a black seat and black lettering that said "Challenger

BMX." Sure it looked like a bumble bee, but it was something I earned with my own hard work. It was also an investment in my paper delivery business, not to mention a great reduction in my morning face plant rate.

Now, for some unknown reason – maybe because he was jealous or just so overworked from delivering papers all the time – Mitchie stole my bike. In the weird way that local junior grapevine works, all the kids in the neighborhood knew he had stolen it, even Mitchie's brother and Bob Chapman, a kid on the next street. I knew Mitchie did it, and Mitchie knew that I knew. I mean, I had put the papers outside the house with my bags next to my Challenger BMX at 5:30 a.m. and gone back in the house to use the bathroom and to have a quick breakfast. When I came out, my bike was gone. Gone! At 5:30 in the morning! Being the great detective that I am, I quickly figured out that the only other person up that early in this neighborhood was ... Wait for it ... another paperboy, and that could mean only Mitchie. I grabbed my dad's bike, raced over to Mitchie's house, and found him riding out on to his driveway. When he saw me, his face turned red with pure guilt. "Mitchie, did you take my bike?" I hollered. "Nah!" Mitchie answered, and sped away as fast as he could. I chased after him but soon realized I was out of time as I had to deliver all my papers before school. Mitchie dug in: He denied my accusations, and his friends, brothers and fellow *Mercury News* paperboys closed ranks around him. And even though we all knew he took it, there was no concrete proof since there were no eyewitnesses.

And here is the lesson I learned: Mitchie was a nice kid who probably just did not like me or was just doing something kids do. Maybe he was getting back at me because my soccer team had trounced his or something. I'll never know. But what I do know is that stealing that bike has haunted Mitchie and affected him a lot more than it affected me. I had to carry the stigma of being hearing impaired, but he gave himself his own stigma by being a thief, and he has carried it with him to this day. I know that he has gotten teased about it (I heard this from a mutual friend of his brother's) for the last thirty-plus years, and he probably will for the next thirty. I know that it probably has done him a lot more harm than good. Sometimes when you do something stupid, it sticks with you for far longer than you might imagine. Up until that time, everyone thought Mitchie was one of the cool guys and a great skateboarder. After that, he was looked upon with suspicion and doubt by the collective world of Sunnyvale kids. So if anyone reading this knows Mitchie, I think you should suggest that he go buy 15 or 20 bikes to donate to the Toys for Tots program.

Mitchie may have stolen my bike because he was mad that I had a big part in trouncing his team on the field, but I think a better reason would have been because he was jealous over Kristi Michels. Kristi lived over on Cascade Drive, two blocks away from 1526. Kristi was the best first girlfriend ever. And at the age of 12, over joint hot fudge sundaes at Farrell's Ice Cream Parlour that I paid for with my earnings from my paper route, we made it official. We were "going together."

In addition to being the cutest girl around, Kristi was also the first girl to go out for hardball baseball in the Sunnyvale Serra Little League. Prior to Kristi, only boys were allowed to play, but Kristi broke the "no girls" barrier. Kristi and I were both pitchers, and we were probably one of, if not *the* first boyfriend and girlfriend to ever pitch against each other on opposing teams in an official league anywhere. Kristi was also better than a lot of the guys. In fact, to be honest, I think she played baseball better than I did. I was a better pitcher, but Kristi got more hits; I was a better base runner and stole more bases, but Kristi was a much better fielder. All that did not really matter much to me because I secretly thought that compared to soccer, baseball was a truly boring game anyway. Kristi soon started playing soccer as well.

Unlike most girls, Kristi had a super-loud booming voice with a wide smile and wonderfully easy-to-read lips. She was also one of the few people that knew how bad my hearing loss was, but fortunately it did not bother her; in fact, she just thought it was fine. Kristi was a great support figure for me at the right time because now that I was at Cupertino Junior High School, I was getting teased a lot more than before, not just because of my hearing loss, but also because of my last name.

A certain type of young man took a disproportionate amount of pleasure in teasing me about my last name, Ball. In those days, ball was quite the nasty word in the wrong context. I had learned early in life not to tolerate teasing about my hearing loss; that if I turned and walked away, the teasing would only get worse. Teasing me about my hearing loss was off limits, and if you did it, I got in your face and pummeled away. Eventually word got around that it was not a good idea to tease me, and even kids twice my size learned to leave me alone. My reasoning at the time was that even if I did get beat up, my opponent would not go home pain free.

Over time I had built up a bit more experience in schoolyard skirmishes than most, and things got better. I do not want to make myself look like a bully waiting for a fight; I was not. In my situation I learned that if I ran or turned the other check, it would only prolong and escalate the problem. It was better for everyone to stop it as soon as possible. And Kristi really stuck up for me with the other kids. We used to ride our bikes all over Sunnyvale, go bowling at Sunnyvale Lanes, play miniature golf at the El Camino Real Golf Land, and do what all young kids did. She was my first best kiss.

But when I started getting involved with the YMCA, things with Kristi came to an end. The Northwest YMCA that served our branch was actually in Cupertino, California, and it ran all sorts of programs for kids and families. In the summers I was always, and I mean always, at Y camp someplace. There were camps all across the state that we would travel to, and this meant that I was on the road a lot.

In fact, I have a history of breaking away to try something new. The first "big break" for me came when I had the chance to leave Serra Elementary. When I was in the 5th grade, they gave all the students a test for aptitude and ability. Unlike most standardized tests, this was a new one that tested for problem solving ability as well as aptitude, and I apparently did extremely well for once. Because my score was high, I was given the chance to move from Serra Elementary to Grant Elementary School in Los Altos, where they had a new advanced Extended Learning Program. When I went and met the teacher, Mrs. Seacrest, I thought she seemed good, and so I agreed to go even though this would mean a really long bike ride each morning. It also meant that I would be leaving all my friends and classmates at Serra, but I figured it would be neat to start over.

School started in September, and that year in northern California had an Indian summer. It was very hot, so I wore shorts to school. Now this may seem like nothing, but at that time, no self-respecting boy would ever dream of wearing anything other than full length blue jeans to school. By the second week of school, several other boys followed my lead and started wearing them as well rather than swelter all day. Mrs. Seacrest had noted that I was not wearing my hearing aids and was electing to rely entirely on lipreading instead.

"Why won't you wear your hearing aids?" Mrs. Seacrest asked me.

"They just make everything way too loud and confusing, and they give me headaches. My hearing aids suck ... and all the other kids think I am stupid when I wear them," I replied. "All they do is make everything so loud that my head hurts. It's more confusing."

Although my hearing aids made everything louder, they did not make anything clearer. Mrs. Seacrest sent me home with a note to my mother asking her to explain what was going on. My mother made me read the note that she wrote back to Mrs. Seacrest:

Dear Mrs. Seacrest,

Last week my son wore shorts to school. He said to me, "I know the other kids will probably laugh at me, but I am wearing them, and that's it." Now several of the boys are wearing shorts. My son has always found his own way. He has his own drummer.

My son has had his hearing tested over and over now and he has tried using his hearing aids but says they do not help him. He has been to the world's best hearing experts. He is an advanced lipreader and he has managed to do well enough and keep up with the other kids. Many have said that he would eventually fall behind the others, and they cannot believe now how well he has done so far. Though they thought that at

some point he would need to go to a special school for the hear-
ing impaired and deaf, this is no longer the case. Now
he has moved to an advanced program and he will find
"his own way" to make this work as well.

Yours truly,
Diane Ball

That was my mom, all right. I think mothers never get enough credit. My mom certainly put up with more of her fair share with me: All those endless trips to the doctors' offices, to the hearing aid shops, and to the audiology and speech testing centers could not have been fun. But I think the best thing she did was read to me and my brothers (loudly, for me) every night. That may have made all the difference.

Working hard, not doing stupid stuff to harm your name and honor, being fast, and showing up on time ... Simple stuff, but it works.

The Garage

"To invent, you need a good imagination and a pile of junk."

Thomas A. Edison

The garages of Silicon Valley have such a legendary reputation that they almost seem to have risen to the level of mythology. But it is not a myth, it is a fact. Hewlett and Packard made their first transistors in a garage in Palo Alto, and many other companies also got their start in garages. In Silicon Valley, garages are not for cars.

The garages in Silicon Valley are such a hotbed for developments for two reasons. The first is that due to the mild weather, you can actually park your car outside without worrying about the car being freezing cold and ice-encrusted each morning. So leaving cars outside is really not a problem. For garage work in winter, a simple space heater can warm the place up. A second reason is that most of the garages are quite large and can accommodate two full-size cars, a washer and dryer, and a small workshop area. Remove the cars, and you generally have at least 300 square feet of space. In our world, this meant you had plenty of room for a good-sized research and development lab.

My father's garage at 1526, though not famous, was a bit of a local legend even by Silicon Valley standards. There was not a tool, a screw or fixture in existence that could not be found in my father's garage. Whenever something broke or was missing a part, my brother Chris used to say, "Let's go ask Dad. He's sure to have a tool stuck away somewhere that he has been saving for this situation." It was true. My father was and is still a garage sale junkie. He loves garage sales and second-hand equipment stores such as Haltek, and the stuff he bought was often amazing to us but junk to my mother. She just could not understand the beauty and value of a precision Swiss-made lathe or a woodworker's or carpenter's bench acquired for only a few dollars. In all fairness to Mom, I guess a lot of it was junk, but it was at least really cheap.

Unless you were my mother, you could appreciate Dad's knack for seeing gold in what others would see as garbage. In a bunch of old terminal equipment, my dad would see rechargeable batteries and switches he could pull off and re-use. In a bunch of old wire, my father saw a solution to being able to improve TV reception. In short order, our garage was transformed into a lab that was fully equipped with an electronics work bench, oscilloscopes, meters, heavy machine tools, precision Swiss machine tools, test leads, fixtures, equipment boxes, hardware, connectors, vacuum molds, coil winders, and countless boxes full of parts. Somehow he found space for a little work bench for me and my brothers that was fully equipped with a saw, power mill, sander, and tools.

I can honestly say there was never, ever a car in the garage at 1526. Our old Mercedes was purple anyway, so protecting it from the sun was not going to make it look any better. It never saw the inside of our garage, not one single time. I probably learned more about electronics, physics, manufacturing and how stuff works in the garage than anywhere else.

The offspring of all of the engineering types in Sunnyvale had free range to design, build and test their own projects. If a kid wanted a new cool toy or water balloon launcher, rocket or whatever, the surest and fastest way to get it was usually to go out into the garage and build it. In the next neighborhood, Frank Fellenz (one of my future engineers) was out in his garage building explosive potato guns and tennis ball launchers and all sorts of projectile-hurling devices that would alert the authorities today. But back in the 1970's in Silicon Valley, with all the open orchards, there was still enough space for mayhem. In the days before Toys R Us, if you wanted something really cool, you built it. And so we did.

Gas-powered airplanes were a favorite of kids like Frank and me. If we blew up the planes (which had an uncanny ability to scorch fingertips before flying off on their own) we could strip out the engines and rebuild them.

One of my first major inventions came about when I took the gas engines off the airplanes and remounted them on a simple dual axle car that I built so that they would be propelled forward. The problem was that the steering was off, so the cars drove in a curve rather than straight ahead. One day, the car's front wheels blew off, leaving only the back wheels. The thing took off in a perfectly straight line with the front end sliding along the ground like a ski. Perfection! We ran home and started making new versions of this epic "drag sled" design with only back wheels and a simple ski for the front. They were amazing! Soon other kids were building them, and we went to Serra Park to race these super fast, dangerous, gasoline-powered land dragsters. Why nobody lost a finger or an eye I will never know.

When the Estes company began selling model rockets out of the local hobby store (including solid fuel engines that also exploded), we were able to fire projectiles into the flight path of the P3 aviators that flew in and out of nearby Moffet Field. Frank was a true master of this, as was Greg Kremer, who lived across the street from 1526. My rocketry career lasted for about a year – until I discovered it was more fun to mount the rocket engines on drag sleds and watch them race across the ground before exploding.

Launching water balloons was also considered a higher art. My father's garage was extremely well equipped with surgical tubing and large bales of elastic rubber. Solving the issues of propelling water balloons to the next neighborhood street, targeting, and preventing launch eruptions was no trivial task, I assure you. We regarded such work as hobbies. In the 1970's it was not considered cool to play with toys if you were a boy over the age of eight. Having hobbies was the ticket, and the more hobbies a boy had, the more his peers revered him.

My list of hobbies, which was more typical than not, included HO gauge slot car racing, model rocketry, robotics engineering, electronics, mini gasoline engines (yes, it is a hobby), model railways, and model building, not counting the other weird things I did including painting and botany, which I rarely admitted to even though I had built a full-sized green house out back. Trips to the toy store were generally replaced by trips to the hobby store. The first was the Hobby Shop, located on the corner of Fremont and Mary Avenue. It was a bit expensive, but they had a decent stock of supplies and plenty of balsa wood, model kits and neat parts. Each year, young boys like Frank and me would enter the Hobby Shop model building contest, competing for the prize for the best model (judged on best paint and best design in one of four age groups. The next was Kiddie World, which was located near the Sunnyvale Public Library on El Camino Real. They also sold toys, but one side of the entire store was chock full of model building supplies, track, and radio control airplanes. The Engine House was the last and perhaps strangest of the three. It was located on a lot was clearly out of place in the neighborhood, a residential street near Serra Park. The store itself was in what used to be the main house for one of the orchards, a spooky building that some of us thought might be haunted. The owners had a huge warehouse full of old primarily model train equipment, but they also had loads of parts and accessories, including a large assortment of outdated and older parts so we could keep our inventions running.

Our garages were full of parts, and our minds were full of ideas. As a result, the sons and daughters of Silicon Valley were getting quite an education doing their own research and design in the garages. I was soldering and putting my first circuits together by age 10, and I built my first robot when I was about 11. My brother Chris was eight when he built his first robot. If something broke, we fixed it. Sometimes even if it was not broken, I took the thing apart to see what made it work.

We never ran down to the store to replace a model car or plane unless we had exhausted every option to fix it ourselves or to re-work it into something else. My younger brother was on the losing side of these R & D endeavors and seemed to have a knack for getting hurt. He once burned his hand really badly on one of the rocket engines when we were trying to use it to fly a plane, and he was often covered in Band-Aids after trying to start gas-powered propeller shafts. Nothing really serious ever happened, thank goodness, but we will never know why.

Besides the formal contests that the hobby shops had, there was another real and recognized ongoing contest going on. It was not all about who could go to the store and buy the next cool thing. I never owned the most popular toy of the time, which was the Evil Knievel stunt cycle; in fact, I never even saw any of the neighborhood kids with one. Very few of us had such things and believed them to be useless except as what guys like Frank called "good cannon fodder," meaning that they would look cool only if they were blown up. Frank was the master of procuring illegal Chinese-made firecrackers and M-80's in his neighborhood. Kingsgate had no such master, so getting real explosives was tough for us. Anyone who had a few packs of Atomic Firecrackers or a legendary M-80 explosive lying around was held in highest regard. Tony Dennis, who lived on Mary Avenue, always seemed to have a few, but we never could figure out how to get them ourselves.

Greg Kremer lived across the street from 1526. He was three years older than I was, and if memory serves me correctly, his father was an aerospace engineer for Lockheed. Greg was a legend in the hobby world. He had built over 200 model airplanes, and virtually every single commercial and military aircraft model that could be purchased lined the walls of his room. His finished models were engineering masterpieces with ultra smooth finishes that he achieved through airbrushing, the use of toxic model "dope," advanced layering, sanding, and amazing hand painting that he did himself. They were breathtakingly beautiful. He also made rockets that flew higher than anyone else's. He and his father had produced a huge HO slot car track that was permanently mounted on two sheets of plywood that were suspended from the garage ceiling and could be lowered with a neat pulley system. It was his crowning achievement. It was epic beyond belief. I was sold.

With the help of my father, I built my own HO slot car track, though was not as big as Greg's. Since there was not enough space in the garage, we built it in the room my brother and I shared. We added paper mache tunnels and landscaping that we had spray painted; we also put in model trees and buildings. Once the track was finished, we started racing the cars. Those HO slot car tracks were great fun, and since the cars did not stick to the track, we could have epic wipeouts and slide around the corners until the cars broke down. They did that all the time, so we were forever fixing them.

HO cars were powered by a low-voltage AC power supply that worked with a potentiometer to control speed. The parts of these cars consisted of electronic contacts, also called brushes. The brushes typically had super small micro springs, and the contacts drove a motor that consisted of an armature, small gauge wire coils, two or more magnets, a drive shaft, an underhousing, a body, and micro small machine parts. We became experts at fixing these devices and could completely rebuild one in an hour or less. My brothers and I learned more about electronics, electromagnetics, assembly and engineering from working on our home projects than we would have thought possible. In fact, if anyone had told us how much we were learning from all our "hobbies," they would not have been as interesting and fun as they were.

When skateboarding hit California in the mid 70's, it was really a ground shift in the world of kiddom. Skateboards had been around for years, but the development of polyurethane wheels meant that we could now speed down sidewalks and streets without the fear of going flying off the board when the wheels got stuck. The sport originated in Dog Town in southern California, where they had started to skate in the swimming pools left empty by a seven-year drought, and the craze spread like wildfire to the rest of the state. The sidewalks of Sunnyvale were perfect for skateboarding, and the curbs were perfect for jumps. But the skateboards supplied by early manufacturers were, except for the wheels, still made of solid molded plastic and pretty terrible. They were too small and much too slippery. In the garages of California, hundreds if not thousands of little skateboard shops sprang to life. I found that I could put my woodworking skills to good use making our own skateboards out of multi-bound hardwoods and bent plywood. We could add kickbacks and wheel wells, add grip tape to the decks, and make the boards wider, longer, stiffer or more flexible. And we did.

My first attempt at starting a company was "Dalles Surfer," named after the street that crossed Kingsgate, which for some reason the City of Sunnyvale had paved with an extremely smooth type of asphalt that was perfect for skateboarding. In the garage at 1526, I made all sorts of boards: long ones, short ones, swallow tail designs, and one with a very long nose that was great for slalom. Due to extraordinary failures in marketing, the only skateboard I ever sold was my mother, who paid $5 for the best board I had and then gave it to my younger brother, Chris. This was too bad, because he would not let me ride it after that. Other than that I never sold a single deck, and to be honest, other guys made much better boards than I did. When my brother Chris started making boards as well, it was not a good sign. The competition was everywhere.

With skateboard production becoming too crowded a field, I decided to move on. One night, while watching the news, I figured out that Gerald Ford had coined the term "WIN" (Whip Inflation Now) as a call to the nation. At the time, inflation was wreaking havoc on the economy, and the idea was to beat it.

Now what the average person in the Valley was supposed to do to influence a macro-economic indicator such as inflation was lost on me, but I saw a business opportunity. I ran out to the garage, flipped on the saws and started creating handmade circles with the cut-out letters "WIN". I spray-painted them silver and gold and attached a rawhide cord so they could be worn around the neck. In about two hours, I had a dozen of these discs in three sizes. Before the paint was dry, I was out selling them door to door to the unfortunate inhabitants of Kingsgate. I figured that if I got out there first, I would have a head start on the competition. I can only imagine what my potential customers thought when they found me at their front doors, hocking gaudy silver and gold trinkets that carried a questionable political slogan for a questionable national call to action as part of a questionable presidential policy. I did not sell any WIN necklaces. This time not even my own mother was buying.

I would spend hours out in the garage, tinkering with this and fixing that. One time I took apart my father's precious HP-35 calculator, which had cost $600 at the electronics counter at PayLess, a drug store with a baffling array of tech products. One day, when my father was at work, I unscrewed the housing screws for the bottom and was amazed.

Before the introduction in 1972 of the modern hand held calculator, you could identify any competent engineer by his slide rule, usually worn in a leather holster. I can recall hours of watching my father do calculations over and over on his slide rule each night as he worked on a new circuit. The HP-35 changed everything. I was at its unveiling at the PayLess Drug over on Homestead Road. There must have been a hundred engineers crowded into the electronics department awaiting the first shipment of calculators. It was like the Beatles were coming. When the first boxes came in and were unloaded off the trolley and onto the counter, there was an eerie silence. The boxes were opened, and as the first units were lifted out, the crowd shifted forward, everyone standing on tiptoe as the greatest device they had ever seen came into view. Oohs and ahhs filled the air. For a calculator! With a list price of $600! In 1974! This was beyond what most engineers could afford to spend at the time, but the first device was sold within a minute, then another and another. Some engineers were accompanied by their CEO's and CFO's. The devices sold as fast as they could be unpacked and sold out within two hours. My father and I waited in line so that he could take it for a "test drive." He must have been impressed, because we had one the next week.

So when I took a screwdriver to the back of it, I was a bit nervous. The components inside were some I had never seen before. It had a complete PC board layout with discrete electronic components, the pads had been screen formed with some process I could only imagine, and the number of chips packed into this thing was impressive. How could you fit all those chips into such a small space? How could you run a display driver off such a small board? I was freaked out about taking my father's calculator apart and quickly put it back together. I must have done a good job, because he never said anything about it.

I spent a lot of time out in the garage lab trying new things: figuring out what parts could go together, how many light bulbs you could solder together and make work with a D battery, how to put simple component boxes together, or how to fix something that was already broken. My father was quite the inventor himself. He always had at least ten projects going at any one time. He built everything from furniture for the house to electronic test fixtures for use at work. He built solar panels to heat his hot tub, which we hoisted on to the roof. He almost always had a small manufacturing line for something.

My brothers Chris and Michael and I were not allowed to touch anything on Dad's work bench, and he hid all the best tools or stored them out of reach. He could rebuild and rework just about anything, but there were countless projects that he started, worked on far too long, and often didn't finish. When he did complete a project, though (and there were many), he did a good job. His problem was that he was a true tinkerer by nature and that he moved through projects noting the many discoveries he made along the way. I did not inherit the tinkering gene from my father. Out in the garage, I learned to form a 3-D picture in my head of what I needed or wanted. At first, whenever I started a project I would get frustrated because what I had in my head was not what I wound up with in the end. Eventually I was able to make and create almost exactly what was in my head.

I generally have one or two big ideas or projects on my mind at a time and then a host of smaller ones. My father, on the other hand, usually had the twenty or so big projects that he was working on simultaneously in his head and then probably another 80 more in the back of his mind to work on in the future. For me, finishing a project is the goal. For my father, the process and the new ideas he discovered along the way were just as rewarding. If my father finished a project and in the course of doing so had not come up with five or six spinoff project ideas and a host of discoveries, he was not satisfied. I tend to finish projects in a more linear and direct fashion one at a time, then reflect and move on to the next.

Today my own garage is clean and spiffy, and all my tools are organized so that I can find them. At work I have an advanced lab where I can do anything I need, so I have never felt the need to bring the lab home. My father's garage is still largely the same as it was back in the days on 1526. It has now moved to the new house on Chemowa Court, which is right around the corner from Kingsgate and closer to the park. Our garage was not the Silicon Valley garage where Steve Jobs and Steve Wozniak built the first computers that would become Apple, nor was it where the first transistors were first assembled, but it was my dad's garage, and to me it was the best. Years later I would take a team of my engineers and sales force to Stanford University to attend a conference, and after that to see the garage.

I told them, "You know, this garage is not the most famous garage in the Valley, but it is where the invention came to life."

And my father said, "That's right! In fact I still have a couple of the first units saved up here in this box!"

And sure enough, he dumped the parts on the bench and there they were. He still had them after so many years! Like my brother Chris said, if you need it, you're sure to find it in my father's garage.

Music Classes

Come face the music
Come taste the wine
Hear them preach
Then everything is fine

Mrs. Sigg was quite an accomplished musician, as was her husband, Hans. She was a gifted cellist, but I believe she could play just about any instrument. She gave recorder classes at her house, and since she was a good friend of the family, I was dispatched to take weekly music lessons at her home. Usually there were two or three of us. She taught us how to hold the instruments, how to use our breathing, and the proper body position: "upright and slightly forward." I loved the way Mrs. Sigg pronounced my name "Gwooophrey") with a heavy Swiss accent and a twinkle in her eye. I learned that I could feel the vibrations for the bass through the floor, so keeping time was a rather simple trick. The problems I had all through my struggles with music were that I had no ability to hear the subtleties of tone, I could never tune an instrument, and I could really never tell how loudly or softly I was playing. Music was something that I did, but badly.

Mrs. Sigg knew I was hearing impaired, and she spoke to me loudly and always made good eye contact. She was not shy, so she would often yell instructions in my ears. Somehow my hearing was just good enough that I could hear the tones or feel the vibrations from the instrument through my teeth. I enjoyed the music lessons, and unlike a lot of kids, I actually practiced enough that I did get a bit better, though I would never be able to master any instrument due to my hearing. One of the other girls in Mrs. Sigg's class and I even performed in the Christmas play for our entire congregation at St. Luke's Lutheran Church. The tune was "Silent Night," and we played the first intro lines as a duet until we were joined by the organ blasting out the verses.

Later I played saxophone in the school band, and because the fingering was the same as the wooden flute, it was fairly easy for me to learn. I played sax right up through high school and was even in the Homestead High School Marching Band, the "Fastest Band in the West." I think my only saving grace musically was that, being hearing impaired, I had developed a really good concept of keeping time and rhythm because I could feel the beat through the floor. Whenever Mrs. Sigg gently tapped her foot on the floor, I could feel the vibrations. Other than timing, I was pretty bad, but perhaps people were more willing to put up with me. "Hey, that deaf kid is playing something," I heard (lipread) a person across the room say one time. I suspect that maybe my mother and Mrs. Sigg had conspired a bit on the music matter. Having me play music was another argument for keeping me out of deaf school. One good thing about music class is that there is generally little speaking. Another is that music teachers are typically incredibly loud and animated people who shout across the room at their charges. This was a huge break for me because I had grown accustomed to teachers in all my other classes positioning me at a desk or a chair at the front of the room because they had been told to stand more or less in front of me and talk louder. In most cases this meant that they shouted in my direction all the time while standing only a couple of feet away. I appreciated the effort and suspected that I was probably the cause of many strained voices, but they didn't realize how much more important it was for me to see their lips than for them to shout all day. Whenever they turned to write on the board, it was impossible for me to follow no matter how loudly they spoke. Sitting at the front and sometimes in my own row was incredibly embarrassing. I often imagined the other kids smirking and laughing and making fun of me in the rows behind me, which did happen, but far less than I imagined. I often gave a perfectly good answer to an entirely different question than the one that had been asked. Whenever the teacher called on me, I would freeze, terrified that I had heard it wrong yet again and that the class would burst out laughing. I often wanted to disappear. What was great about music class was that the teacher rarely called out a question and demanded an answer. As bad as sitting in front was, it was not nearly as embarrassing as the times when the class first learned that I had hearing aids. On bad days, when I answered too many of the wrong questions with my version of the perfect answer, I found that if I practiced ahead of time, kept focused and followed along, I was usually good to go.

Somehow my parents signed me up for the children's choir at St. Luke's Lutheran Church. Being in choir and being in music helped me become aware of the world of sound, and at the same time I became very aware that I was missing a lot more than I realized. My family attended St. Luke's Lutheran Church from the time we arrived in Sunnyvale until the great schism of the Lutheran Church forced us to leave and go to a new branch of the Lutheran Church over in Los Altos. If you ever want to become cynical about organized religion, I strongly suggest reading about the schism that occurred in the Missouri Synod of the Lutheran Church in the 1970's. Talk about blowing something completely out of proportion! The whole matter is what I call stinking thinking: petty, vindictive, political, and filled with delusions of self-importance, grandiosity and aggrandizement – in other words, all the things that Christianity is generally not supposed to be about.

At St. Luke's we were bombarded each Sunday with the super singing cast of the Pastor Mitchell family. Daughter Claudia would blast away on the church organ, with son Paul jamming along on his synthesizer. From the front of the sanctuary, Pastor's bellowing tenor voice would fill the air. Add a youth choir, an adult choir, a bell choir, and assorted other church instrumentalists, and it was nothing short of a weekly church music extravaganza. It was like going to a live Sonny and Cher concert, only at church. When the Mitchell family really got going, Sunday service could last up to two hours.

All during junior high school, too much of my young adult life was spent at church. For two years, I had to go to confirmation classes each Monday and Wednesday. I had choir on Tuesdays, and there was also Sunday school, which I hated: the same old stories over and over. We also had to attend the regular weekly church services. A lot of the church lyrics and literature seemed forced and lacked clarity, but I had no choice. I don't think Pastor Mitchell ever took much notice of me until after my confirmation, when I went to his office and said,

"Pastor Mitchell, last week I was confirmed as an adult member of the church, and that means I'm entitled to participate in church as an adult, right?"

"Yes, that is right," he said. "You are now an adult in God's eyes."

"So as an adult member of this church, I want to do the Gospel reading like the other adult members."

He looked at me, stunned. The reading of the Gospel was an honor and traditionally the domain of the senior members of the church. My motivation for asking to do it was not so much the honor as the idea that anything different could only help make those incredibly long services less boring. A few weeks later I was assigned a robe to wear as I walked alongside Pastor Mitchell in the processional to the front of the church and sat in the pew off to the right (which was ironically almost identical to my seating position in class at elementary school). At the key moment in the service, Pastor gave me the look, and I climbed up to the pulpit and belted out the reading to a stunned group of parishioners. In fact I could not even see over the pulpit, so none of the parishioners could really see me. It was my first real public speaking event, and it did make the church service go by faster. I had been doing the readings for about a year when other parents started making their kids do them as well. I learned you have to be confident to be a good speaker and belt it out clearly. I liked public speaking.

Being a hearing-impaired/deaf person and being shy at the same time is really almost mutually exclusive. It takes a lot of gumption and pro-action for a hearing-impaired person to be successful in the hearing world. If you are too shy to ask someone to say something again, or to speak a lot louder, you are in a tough spot. I learned that if I began speaking first, I had a much better chance of controlling the conversation. If I could keep the conversation on track, then I had a much better chance of following it. If the conversation took a sharp turn – say we were talking about something that happened at the pool, and then suddenly the topic changed to what we did at camp last summer – I would not be able to make the switch with everyone else and would get lost. The more I talked, the more I understood. I also learned to end sentences with a question and then listen for and lipread the answer. It is a lot easier to listen and read lips for an answer to a question, especially if it is a yes or no question. Predicting what others will say next has always been the key to good lipreading. By talking and stopping at certain points, I learned what people were likely to say and when they were likely to say it. I also figured out what they were least likely to say. When they said something totally unexpected, I was usually lost. So, to cut a long story short, today I talk too much. Ask anyone.

At St. Luke's Lutheran Church, Pastor Mitchell had actually taken a strong personal interest in carrying the Lutheran teachings to the deaf community. He hired a deaf assistant minister and started a deaf congregation, and soon there were classes in sign language for non-deaf members. A teletype machine was installed at the church, and before long we had five or ten new deaf members, most of whom drove in from out of the area to attend our incredibly long and boring church services, which were now accessible to them thanks to a sign language interpreter. The interpreter stood off to the left side of the pulpit, signing everything for the deaf, including the music. I can remember all the church girls running around signing "I love you" or "Jesus is Lord" and practicing all the hand signs for individual letters. Sign language was in vogue at St. Luke's. But here is the thing: The assistant deaf pastor, who was profoundly deaf, could read lips really, really well, yet he had also learned to speak at a very decent level. Sign language frightened me. I did not want to learn it because I thought if I did, then I might have to start using it. They started to teach it to me one time, but after learning a few signs, I quickly decided it was not for me and that I would not do it.

Dr. Mansfield Smith had been totally against me learning sign language. Dr. Smith once told my mother, "Mrs. Ball, if you let them teach Geoffrey here sign language, he is only going to able to communicate with other people who can sign, and that is an incredibly small group. Besides, he just does not need to go down that road." Not only was he right in his thinking; he was in fact more right than he could have known at the time.

When I was thirteen years old I had a problem. The results of one of the endless hearing tests I had taken, or perhaps something one of the docs had noted during an exam, did not check out. To rule out the more serious problems, I was scheduled for more extensive testing. In addition to all the usual audiometric testing, I had electrodes affixed all over my head and was told to sit still for a few hours. I was literally mounted to a backboard and strapped securely into place and scanned. Once that was all over, I got to do it all again three months later. Eventually I figured it out.

"Mom," I said, "they're looking for cancer, aren't they? Something bad."

"They're just making sure," my mom answered.

"Did they find any yet?"

"No. So far, so good."

"Well, let me know if that changes."

A few months later, after one of the docs at the clinic had called my mom, I asked her if I was going to get cancer. I was not sure what that was, but I knew that it was really bad news for me if I had it. She said, "No, it looks like everything is fine." So I rode my bike to Serra Park and pedaled to the top of the high hill near the artificial pond, where I stopped and looked around. It was the best feeling ever. I told myself then that this was as happy as a kid could be: to be in Serra Park, and to be alive, and to not have cancer. I climbed almost to the top of my favorite redwood tree. I was on top of the world and about as high up in Sunnyvale as I could get.

Later on I would perform in the bell choir at St. Luke's Lutheran. After only a few weeks in the choir, I was moved to the most advanced set of bells even though there were others with more experience. The great thing about playing bells was that it was all about rhythm and timing. They were easy to play because I didn't have to tune the bells or worry about volume level or breathing. I just had to keep time and when the notes came along, ring the right bell: bing, bong, or ding. That was it. Each month we would travel to hospitals, shopping malls, senior residences and of course other churches to perform. We even played in a two-day performance at Stanford University during the Christmas season, which was when bell choirs were in high demand, and we were on the Channel 7 news on Christmas Eve. I think at least seven people saw us. After our show at Stanford, I had to walk my bell case a long way across the campus from the performance area to the parking lot. It was one of those sunny, crisp December days, and I decided then and there that it would be a great thing to be a Stanford man.

The ability to appreciate music must have helped my appreciation for the importance of better amplification for the hearing impaired. Today I can play the guitar, saxophone, recorder and harmonica without embarrassing myself too much, as well as several other instruments which I play badly. Worst of all, according to my wife, is my singing, which she says I just should never ever do.

On Becoming a Lifeguard

Return of the tide
The ebb and the neap
Longest echo
Silently sweet

I can't recall when I decided that I wanted to be a lifeguard, but it was certainly when I was quite young. I remember that when someone asked me, "Geoffrey, what do you want to be when you grow up?" I would say, "A lifeguard". I started swimming young and never stopped. You do not need to hear well in the pool.

When I went to the pools and beaches, I would see the lifeguards and surmise that this seemed like a pretty neat job. You are responsible for saving lives, you get to swim all the time, and you are the boss of the beach. You get paid for being out on the beach, near the water, and outdoors, plus you get to wear red shorts and sunglasses. What could be better?

At the age of 14, I earned my Red Cross advanced lifesaving certification, which had required spending four full late winter weekends freezing my unmentionables off in an icy pool at the YMCA camp near La Honda in the Santa Cruz Mountains. The pool heater was not working that year, and the water was so cold that when you jumped in, your brain started screaming, "Get the heck out!" After twenty or thirty minutes in the water, I could not feel anything below my neck. I was the youngest person in the certification course, and I found out later that I was one of if not *the* youngest certified lifeguard in the state of California. To me, this was the greatest, and I felt a true sense of accomplishment. What made it possible was that I was a really strong swimmer, but also that I had an advantage. Everyone has a hard time following instructions and hearing in a swimming pool, so instructors bellowed out commands and used animated hand signals that were hard to follow. But unlike the others, I could read the instructors' lips and was used to nonverbal language. So for four cold weekends in a pool out in the middle of nowhere, I actually think my hearing impairment worked to my advantage, and I was certified.

The best reward for passing lifeguard certification was that I moved to the top of the list for the best assignments as a camp counselor in the YMCA summer camping program. The only problem was that when I was wearing hearing aids, I needed to be able to take them off quickly before jumping into the water. My solution was to wear a hat. When a swimmer was struggling and needed assistance, I would take off my cap, strip off my hearing aids, put them in the hat, and drop the hat on the ground with the aids safely tucked inside. I could do this in a flash without taking my eyes off the swimmer.

With my lifeguarding and camp counseling and other work with the YMCA, I was more involved with the Y than I ever was in extracurricular activities at Homestead High School, "Home of the Mustangs." Located at the cross-section of Homestead and Mary Avenues, the campus was a sprawling network of the State of California's finest cinder block construction, with a giant California Black Oak tree in the front.

Erin O'Conner, my former babysitter, took me to my first day of high school – my freshman year. Despite her best efforts to prevent it, I was met by a posse of the older boys led by Joe Walker, who promptly picked me up and stuffed me butt end first into a garbage can. "Welcome to Homestead High School! Fresh! Freshman!" they shouted.

Looking back, I was always picked on, ribbed and hassled by groups of older guys. I got much more of their attention than all my friends combined. At the time I thought this was due to my being different, but now I think that it was a good thing. Joe and the other older guys singled me out and gave me more grief than my peers because they knew I could handle it. Getting picked on by the older guys was nothing new to me, and it was not limited to high school. It followed me everywhere: to the Y and even to the church youth group. I must have been a fun target because I could take it and be a good sport about it. I knew, though, that if it ever went too far, I could always give back as good as I got. I was a target who earned high regard, and those guys actually did me a big favor. After a few more trash can stuffs, everyone in my class knew who I was! I guess I have Joe to thank for that.

The other great thing about Homestead High School was the HOH or "Hard of Hearing" program for the Cupertino Unified High School District. This meant that all the kids who were deaf or who had severe hearing losses like mine – about ten of us – were in a special class for one hour a day. The first time I walked into the classroom, I was amazed to meet other kids with hearing loss, half of them deaf and the other half hearing impaired like me. Up to that point I had only really ever met one other hearing-impaired kid, a guy named Jeff who played on one of my soccer teams. We probably would have been a good for each other and should have become good friends, but Jeff lived way out near Ortega Park.

The director of the HOH program was Mr. Harvey Day. The goal of Mr. Day's hearing-impaired group was to give us a chance to get the extra help we needed, to focus on issue areas and make them better in our other classes, and to boost our abilities in reading, writing and speaking. Special counselors for extra speech coaching and more acute issues were also brought in when needed.

Of everyone in the class, a beautiful girl named Sharon and I were having the best success dealing with our hearing loss. Sharon was quickly adopted into the clique of cool girls at Homestead and was so gorgeous that any guy would have been more than willing to overlook her lack of hearing. Unlike me, however, Sharon had a strong speech impediment: She rolled off her consonants and basically did not use the letters *t* and *s* at all. She actually sounded quite cute. And she was disarmingly nice to everyone.

The most animated of the group was "Disco Charlie," who had decided that it was very cool to dress and walk around campus like Jon Travolta. He was wrong, as the fad of disco had already come and gone. But this did not stop Charlie from strutting around campus in all black: tight black pants, a black shirt, a black leather vest, and black boots with four-inch heels. He was in his own world, but he was quite happy to be different.

No matter how we all tried to cope, though, we hated being hearing impaired. Most of us grew our hair really long to hide our hearing aids (on days when we chose to wear them), and we all practiced our lipreading and worked hard to improve our speech. Mr. Day met with our teachers regularly and made sure we sat in the front rows of our classes. Yikes! Front row again through four years of high school!

Mr. Day, my mother and I met after the first day of school to discuss my classes. My mother was alarmed because I had somehow been signed up for metal shop, auto shop, wood shop, and electronics, as well as drafting, level II. Apparently there had been a disconnect, and my guidance counselor had determined that since I was listed on the administrative forms as being deaf, I should have a schedule that was heavy on shop classes so that I could be schooled for a career in the industrial arts. In other words, she thought that I should start training for a career fixing cars, working in the steel mills, or doing other heavy industrial type work. This in fact was not totally unreasonable thinking. Many of my fellow HOH students became carpet layers, morticians, car mechanics, etc. - all professions where hearing is not so important.

With my mother jumping up and down and Mr. Day working with the administration, all my shop classes were soon removed from my course schedule, and I found myself in harder, more mainstream courses including biology, physics, English, and mathematics. I did keep drafting and electronics, thank goodness. Mr. McCollum, a fantastic electronics instructor, would become a Silicon Valley legend himself. Steve Wozniak was one of Mr. McCollum's stellar students and an aide in his electronics class. I also seem to recall seeing Steve Jobs stroll through the Homestead High electronics lab from time to time but cannot be sure because I also saw him at the computer store and at Haltek electronics. It is hard to believe now that seeing these guys around was no big deal, but who could have known at the time?

All the HOH students were exempted from the foreign languages requirement at Homestead High. The school thought that since they were working so hard to teach us how to learn to hear and speak English, there was no point in having us learn a foreign language as well. Some of the experts also thought that it might be detrimental to all our efforts to become better at English. I can see why they thought this: Why risk all the development that had gone into our English training by experimenting with alternative languages?

However, today I know of a young woman with cochlear implant who can speak three languages well. Ironically, my lack of early exposure to foreign languages has made understanding and speaking German incredibly tough for me now that I live in Austria. Had I been exposed to and encouraged to develop alternatives to English at a younger age, it might have increased my chances of developing proper German skills later in life. Now, after six years of living in Austria, I still speak embarrassingly poor German. I will most likely have to have special one-on-one training to really make any significant improvement.

Mr. Day had me do the standard course work in his program and work with speech specialists and other counselors as needed, and when I was having trouble with a subject or a teacher, he would arrange extra help for me, sometimes with a tutor, but usually with older students. Mr. Day also began giving me advanced writing and reading assignments almost immediately. He would assign me a book to read, and when I was finished with it I would have to write a book report or compare and contrast it to another author's work. Then we would discuss it together, and I would get a grade.

The first books Mr. Day chose were simpler reads, and I ripped through them in a week. At first, he was pretty astonished at how quickly I finished the reading assignments.

"Did you really read all this so fast?" he asked.

"Sure did, Mr. Day."

"But how?"

"I just like it, that's all." I was not sure why he was asking.

I read all the time because I got a lot more out of books than movies or TV. When I went to the movies with friends, I could not hear and follow the film. The movie theaters rarely had the volume up anywhere near loud enough for me. At home, my father had wired a set of headphones that I could use with the TV, and that was better. He had also rigged up a speaker I could place next to my head so that my brothers could also hear. But I preferred to read.

Starting in my freshman year, I read all the Tolkien novels, a lot of Twain (still my favorite), and Shakespeare, whom I appreciated but who quite honestly gave me a headache. Mr. Day kept a list of all the books I read during high school: at least three or four books a month, depending on the length and the difficulty. By the time I graduated, Mr. Day's list showed a grand total of 187 books (my goal had been to finish 200 by graduation). The other kids hated Steinbeck, but I read all his major works and essays. I read Mailer, Orwell, Conrad, Jung, Kesey, and Dickens. I read the biographies of Rommel, Churchill, Jefferson, and Lincoln. I read *The Art of War* and essays on political philosophy and argument. I read screenplays, scripts and even a few manifestos. Mr. Day also had me read management books such as Peters' *A Passion for Excellence*; books about Edison, Newton, Galileo, and Einstein; and Kidder's fantastic *Soul of a New Machine*. I read a book all about hydroelectric power generation, water systems, sewage treatment plants, and the electrification of Southern California. I read about the agricultural history of the San Joaquin Valley, a true snoozer. Thanks to Mr. Day, I have a voracious appetite for reading that continues to this day.

Making me read and write about these books was probably the single best thing that could have happened to me, and Mr. Day had to bend a few rules to keep me centered on his novel approach. As he explained it to the school principal, "I assign him books, and he reads and reads and reads. What could be better?"

I attended Homestead High from 1978 to1981. The hippie phase that had blessed Silicon Valley with a significant influx of counter-culture made itself evident in numerous arts and craft fairs, a belief that hair (including the guys') could never be too long, and some views that seemed mistakenly optimistic to me: that there was truly no such thing as a car or bus that was too broken down and no such thing as adopting too many stray dogs. For years, any time Mom loaded my brothers and me into the purple Mercedes, we would see a line of hippie vans and Volkswagens on Highway 17 and crowds of them at the Cats restaurant in Los Gatos, hitching rides to Santa Cruz. I thought the hippies were cool. They were always saying things to me like, "Peace!" or (my favorite) "Peace, little man!" Way cool! I was the "little man," I could dig it. They were certainly laid-back people, and the recreational drugs that they used to "turn on" kept them generally mellow, at least until the disco era came along, and cocaine and speed became the drugs of choice. Then things got not so nice. And when the Hells Angels motorcycle gang took control of the drug trade, it got even worse.

The City of Sunnyvale Police Department was suddenly coming to class to speak to us and give us stern warnings. The message was crystal clear: If we were out at a park, especially in the Stevens Creek Dam areas, or anywhere else for that matter, and if the Hells Angels or any of the motorcycle clubs showed up, we were to run away. That was the message: Run! All of us were pretty well aware that those guys were bad news. And since we could not tell who the real baddies were, we ran away from all of them. After the Angels' involvement in the tragedy at the Altamont rock concert, we really did not need to be told twice. Every time one or two of these guys showed up, we immediately vacated the premises. Now in all fairness, not all the people that dressed up and acted like Hells Angels were in fact bad guys. But if you felt compelled to dress up, ride a chopper and cruise around acting like or at least looking like a drug dealer, we gave you the benefit of the doubt and took off. The good thing was that we were OK as long as we stayed within the city limits. It was only when we went off to explore the foothills or the areas up near Stevens Creek Dam that we ran into bikers.

As someone who was raised in California where a lot of the biker fad originated, I am simply amazed by how main stream this fad now is. I see people following the current trend of looking like a Hells Angel, complete with tattoos and a chopper, and I just don't get it. If you had told me back then that some day in the future, hundreds of good people would dress up in all-black outfits nearly identical to those the drug dealers wore in my youth, I wouldn't have believed you. I am always astonished when I see people riding around on motorcycles and looking the same as the people and motorcycles I spent a good of my youth running from. On some level I understand the "thunder in the mountains" concept, but on another, I really don't. Nonetheless, I am sure I am not the only kid who grew up on the West Coast and now looks at the modern Harley Davidson crowd with a bit of disbelief.

In addition to my involvement with the YMCA and lifeguarding, I also got very involved in other sports such as kayaking, surfing, skiing, swimming, windsurfing and soccer. As for organized clubs, I was in the Speech and Debate Club, the California State Model Legislature, and Youth and Government. On top of this I was working. Whether it was as a maintenance man at the Y, a temporary technician, a punch card operator, a Christmas tree lot salesperson, a copy/errand boy, or a lifeguard, I was always doing something. In my junior and senior years I took courses at De Anza College and spent half my official high school course time there.

One of the best jobs I had during high school was when I was hired by the Sunnyvale branch of Farrell's Ice Cream Parlour and Restaurant. I was fifteen and a half years old and had just received my work permit. I started out as a busboy/dishwasher working right after school, and within two months I had been promoted twice: first to host, then to waiter.

Audiologists had begun to dispense and sell hearing aids in 1980, and I had just gotten my new hearing aids with directional microphones, which worked better for me. I had little cards printed up that said something like, "I will be your waiter today. I have very bad hearing, so if you could look at me when you place your orders, that would be a super help. Thanks!" I got much better tips using those cards.

For most of the population of Sunnyvale, Farrell's was the place to go. Located in the old Alpha Beta supermarket shopping center at the corner of Fremont and Mary Avenues, it was a hubbub of activity. Farrell's sold ice cream sundaes, burgers and fries by the boatload and was, as the song says, "fabulous fun." Their staff was famous for hosting birthday parties, and I can assure you it would be a rare thing to find a family in Sunnyvale that did not make regular visits to the place.

But Farrell's unfortunately was nearing the end of its run. The Chuck E. Cheese Pizza Time Theatre chain had just started up, and they quickly targeted the kid birthday market. Instead of just ice cream and burgers and a big drum roll, Chuck E. Cheese offered you pizza while a mechanical rat sang pre-recorded songs. I was sure that Chuck E. Cheese was just a fad, but for the next year or two new ones popped up almost as fast as Starbucks coffee shops would in the future. Farrell's down home shouting and singing and player piano couldn't compete with Chuck E. Cheese's combination of pizza and video games, and the business started sinking fast.

The Farrell's franchise was bought by various holding companies, and each one tried to update its image. Farrell's sold pure decadence: epic high-fat burgers and fries followed by high-fat ice cream with hot fudge and other high-calorie toppings. Suddenly a new owner would put in a salad bar, and the next would offer new coffee drinks. When they made us start pushing frozen pizza, we all knew that Farrell's was in deep trouble. The final nail in the coffin was when it was purchased by Pepsi Co., and the franchise soon died out. Today a few Farrell's have survived in far-off places like Eugene, Oregon, or Hawaii. Ironically, there are not many Chuck E. Cheese restaurants left either. If Farrell's had just been able to hunker down for a spell and stick to its core business of delivering the best high-quality, saturated-fat-based products you ever tasted (Oh the Hot Fudge Nutty Nutty!), they could have survived. When Farrell's closed its doors, Sunnyvale lost an important part of itself.

The Sunnyvale Town Center, a mega mall built right on top of where downtown Sunnyvale used to be, opened in 1980. One of the more questionable calls the city elders ever made was to essentially demolish the old W.T. Grant building and almost all of the original downtown Sunnyvale and build a huge mall right next to the quaint Town and Country Village shopping center. The intent was to compete with the other local malls, but they got it wrong. By eradicating the old district, they robbed the downtown of its soul. They put a huge, ugly, two-story parking deck, directly in front of the mall, and the approach from the other side streets was not much better. It was literally possible to drive right past the new Sunnyvale Town Center and completely miss it. They anchored the mall with a Montgomery Ward's, a Macy's, and a J.C. Penny's, but virtually all the other malls in the area had better versions of these. Only two years later, the Sunnyvale Town Center was in trouble; in fact, it had never once rented all its retail space. The only reason anyone went to the downtown mall was to go to the terrible dank and dusty movie theaters. In the final analysis, they had erased downtown Sunnyvale to put up a subpar strip mall which was never the success they had envisioned. Amazingly, all this happened at the same time that the Old Mill shopping mall in Mountain View was closing for the same reasons that would eventually shutter the new Sunnyvale mall.

One of my best buddies from my high school days was Greg White. Greg and I had had met at day camp way back in 1973, but we did not become good friends until years later. Greg was one of the most interesting people I would ever meet. His parents were big Stanford University alumni and very successful. They had an awesome house up on top of Arboretum Drive in Los Altos, with the largest S-shaped driveway around and amazing views of the entire Valley. Greg and I were both well-read and fancied ourselves budding intellectuals, discussing our latest reads late into the evenings. We would drive Greg's old Vista Cruiser station wagon up into the Santa Cruz Mountains and to the all the state and county parks to go hiking and hang out and continue our discussions of the writings of our heroes, including Conrad, Updike, Steinbeck, Mailer, Orwell, Jung and so many others. We would also go over to UC Berkley to get pizza at Blondie's and to find the latest Berkeley student publications, newspapers and the occasional communist manifesto. We were both camp leaders and both crazy about the wilderness and skiing.

Our backpacking trips were many and memorable. One time we hiked the entire Skyline to the Sea Trail, which starts at the top of the Santa Cruz Mountains and ends at the Pacific Ocean. We had made reservations to stay the night in the Big Basin Redwoods campground. When we checked in at the ranger station, the ranger was upset because we were both only 16 years old, and he made us call our parents, who finally convinced him that it was OK. Then he made us camp next to the ranger area, which was infested with raccoons who stole all our food during the night. The next night we shared our campfire with a bunch of what we thought were hippie intellectuals. Looking back, they were probably really just hippie bums. Our dream was to hike all through Alaska – in the winter. I have no idea why.

Greg and I became truly great friends. I am sure my parents thought Greg was a less-than-ideal influence on me, and I am sure Greg's parents felt the same about me. But do teenagers' parents ever really like their kids' friends? At that time, most of our friends were "New Wavers," and the photos from that time show Greg and me looking more like surfer hippies than anything else. We had definitely been influenced by our backpacking and outdoor activities. I think being hearing impaired led me to appreciate the wilderness at a much deeper level because I was very visually oriented and because there were no crowded social situations and loud rooms full of confusing background noise out on the trail.

Sunnyvale High School was closed in 1981. The "baby bust" generation was now of high school age, and there were just not enough students to keep all the local high schools open. Mr. Day's special education course for the hearing impaired was moved to Monta Vista High in Cupertino. Since by this time I was doing quite well in my classes, I was given the choice to stay at Homestead for my senior year and graduate with my classmates or go to a new school and stay in the HOH program. I chose to move because the thought of attending a new school appealed to me. The class I would miss most was Mr. McCollum's electronics class. For me, the decision to change high schools was not a question of opting for a better place; it was more about finding out what it would be like somewhere else.

I fit in pretty well at Monta Vista. I joined the speech and debate team because I felt improving my speaking would help my chances in the California Model Legislature. I was also the cartoonist for the school paper.

I had one social breakthrough at Monta Vista, though, that ranks above all others. The prettiest and most popular girl in school was named Kelli Nichols. She was on the drill team and most guys' dream girl. She was also a certified member of the in crowd at school, a group my friends and I never belonged to. Three days before the Winter Prom, I saw Kelli's friend in journalism class. When I asked her who was taking Kelli to the prom, she told me Kelli didn't have a date.

"She is going to go with me!" I announced to my friends.

They all said, "With you? No way, dude. Like no way!"

"She has to," I replied. There's not enough time left."

I walked across the quad to where Kelli was standing with the in crowd and said, "You don't have a date to the prom yet, and I wasn't planning on going, but I would like to go with you. We have just enough time if we skip classes the rest of the day to go rent a tux for me and get a dress for you. What do you say?"

"Oh my God! Yes!"

She was so excited. I turned around and looked at my friends, whose mouths all were hanging open in disbelief.

Kelli and I had a great time at the prom, but we never really dated much after that, primarily because we were both too busy. I was into my first attempt at running a "real" business with a friend of mine named Gary Crawford, whom I had met through the YMCA. In art class I had started making silk screens, which I could use to make prints. I had made this one to print checkerboards down the sleeves of any shirt. This may sound kind of silly, but soon everyone at school wanted checkerboards on their sleeves, and then down the legs of their pants. So with visions of putting Ocean Pacific clothing out of business, Gary and I launched Casual Concepts Surf Designs. And before long we had so many orders coming in that we had no idea how to handle all of them.

Under the guise of looking for employment, we toured as many other silk screen printers in the area as we could. We studied their operations, their designs, and their machines, and we got hold of a bunch of their supplier information. When I got home, I put everything I had learned on paper.

I described what I had seen to my dad, and when he helped me design and build a four-screen rotational photographic screen print system based on the lazy Susan concept, we were off and running.

Gary and I had a falling out after losing our first big job order, and then, to make matters worse, the Crawfords' house in Cupertino sustained damage from a fire, and Gary's, mother refused to let us work there afterwards. Since Gary did not have access to a car, it was hard for him to get to Sunnyvale, which is where the new headquarters were. I was on my own. I got orders for the windsurfing championships from Frank Fellenz's boss at the Sunnyvale Board and Sail Center on the El Camino Real. I got orders from a lot of high school groups and even the local surf shops. Soon everyone around had checkerboard sleeves. I thought that this would be a great profession and for a while was sure I could beat out Ocean Pacific, the largest surf wear company around at the time.

Late one night shortly after I had graduated from high school, I was working on a large silk screen order. I was covered with paint and sick and tired of t-shirts. My father came out to me and said, "You know, Geoff, there is no doubt in my mind that you could spend a few more years on this t-shirt business and build it up and make a decent living out of it. Or how about this: We buy you a pick-up truck and you go off to college at the University of Oregon."

Whatever hesitation I had ever had about going to university disappeared then. I was more than likely to wind up being one of the many average printers in the Valley at the time, not the next Ocean Pacific. The writing was on the wall, and I figured that college was the better call. Just before I left for university, I made one last stop to see Dr. Perkins and to get my hearing aids tuned up by his audiology staff. I had read about the new hearing implants that were being worked on for profound hearing loss.

"When can I get a set of implants and get rid of these hearing aids once and for all?" I asked Dr. Perkins.

"We are working on something, but it is still a couple of years away," Perkins replied.

"If I can help with the research or if you need patients for research, please let me know".

Dr. Perkins laughed at what I said, but I was serious. He could not have imagined at the time just how serious.

University Days

*"I am always ready to learn although
I do not always like being taught."*

Winston Churchill

I had always thought that my lifeguarding experience would help
me fulfill my dream of being a military officer – preferably a Navy
frogman – someday. After all, when you are in the water, you cannot
hear anything anyway. Besides, I had already proven that I could
lifeguard and had not let my hearing get in the way. The first time
I talked to a local recruiter about enlisting in an ROTC program,
he was eager to sign me up – until he found out that I had a hearing loss, which automatically disqualified me from serving. Disappointed, I waited a few months and visited the recruiting office
again with the intention of applying for the Air Force. Same result.
I finally went back one last time, but the recruiter just laughed in
my face. "Look!" he hooted to his friends. "It's the deaf boy! I keep
telling him he can't sign up!" Still stinging from his ridicule, I managed to say, "Yeah, OK. Well, what about the Coast Guard? Maybe
that would be all right." I waited hopefully for an answer, but they
only roared with laughter. I walked out and never went back.

The strange thing about being hearing impaired was that my teachers and parents thought it was great as long as I was bringing home
B grades in high school. The audiologists had repeatedly told my
mother and me how remarkable it was that I had gotten by so far.
"Next year, he's really going to start having problems," they told her.
According to them, "next year" was always the point in time when
my hearing loss would start causing me real problems in school.
But luckily for me, "next year" never came, and I always managed
to do just fine in my classes.

I have always wondered what those people would have thought
had they been told that years later, I was accepted by a major Pac-
10 school like Oregon. The reason I wanted to go to the University of Oregon was that it had great programs in physiology, biomechanics and sports medicine. Sports rehabilitation and surgical

injury repair and rehab seemed like my dream career path at the time. Combining electronics and advanced systems engineering to create devices that improved biomechanical function was a very lofty goal and one that I felt at the time was well beyond me.

I also liked the idea of going to school in Oregon because it was close to skiing and some of the best kayaking rivers in the United States. The Hood River area was a windsurfing mecca for anyone with a board and a sail. I did get to do all these things, usually in the pouring Northwest rain.

Coming from California, I had no idea just how much in rained in the Pacific Northwest. I figured that if it rained twice as much as it California, then this would mean only four to six weeks of rain a year. I had no idea that it rains off and on there almost every single day and is usually grey and overcast. The bleak weather in the Pacific Northwest is unsettling and unending. I was shocked to find myself skiing in the rain, kayaking in the rain, running in the rain, and even playing tennis in the rain. Everyone did everything in the rain. When the sun did come out, which happened at least twice while I was there, it was like a national holiday. But despite the rain, or maybe because of it, I did well at university.

Almost immediately after I had unpacked my bags at Oregon, I met Dr. Don Van Rossen, who was the swim coach and ran all the aquatics programs for the university. He and his wife Virginia soon put me to work with them and with all the groups they were involved with, including Sports for Understanding (an international youth exchange program) and the National Swimming Pool Foundation. I became a Certified Pool Spa Operator (CPO) and then helped with CPO training programs for others. We also were on the organizing team for the Olympic Scientific Congress, a two-week conference of the world's experts in biomechanics, physiology testing, and sports medicine.

Dr. Van Rossen always had some kind of crazy challenge for me: everything from swimming ten laps of the pool underwater without taking a breath to challenging me to take 23 credits in a single term, both of which I did.

I did a project on the biomechanics of the breast stroke and tried to use a stroboscope to access motion for improvement. I had a very lucky break at Oregon as one of my best friends turned out to be none other than Randy Pryde, a physiology department graduate student who would grill me and push me on all the lab stuff. All my previous electronics work came in really handy because I was already familiar with all the equipment we used in the labs. I was soon doing advanced electrophysiology tests with neurostimulators, electrode arrays, force gauges, and everything I could imagine at the time. The electronics labs at Oregon were terrific, providing first-class scopes and signal generators and all the parts I needed to make text boxes as well as the equipment I needed for experiments. I learned so much. I did not know it at the time, but I was much better at all this than I thought. The university had surprisingly well-equipped physiology and biomechanics labs with really good state-of-the-art test and analysis equipment, electronics, and racks of equipment, most of it new or almost new. The computer science lab was also tip top, and I took a lot of computer programming courses. Back in those days, we did most of our programming on a DEC 99 machine, which was a far cry from even the most basic PC. The best time to run programs was during the late evenings and early morning hours, when the system demands were lowest. I quickly learned never to wait to run the final programs until during finals week; otherwise, due to the wait times, my project might not get done in time.

I was surprised by how successful I was at university. I was elected president of my dorm and was a founding member of Lambda Chi Alpha. I was in charge of the intramural sports program, and I held a leadership position in the Eugene Young Life program for high school students. I was always involved in a lot of extracurricular campus activities in addition to my formal studies. One of the factors that really contributed to my success was that I rarely went out. While most of our classmates were partying, my roommate, Hans Go, and I spent most Fridays and Saturday nights in our dorm room or at the library studying. Hans had a reputation in the dorms for studying all the time. I saw how well Hans did on his exams, so I studied hard too. My exam scores were never as high as Hans', though, and to this day I still think if I had been able to hear better during the lectures, it would have been a lot easier for me.

I rarely told anyone about my hearing problems. I still hated my hearing loss and was extraordinarily self-conscious about it. I did not even tell my closest friends unless absolutely necessary. I was still reading lips, and there is no doubt that I missed more than my share, especially when people were talking to me from behind. My hearing aids did not perform well: I would say they were lipreading aids at best. In loud environments they were worthless (all they did was make the noise louder) so I avoided such settings as much as possible. That was another reason to study with Hans rather than go to parties, where I could not hear anyone anyway. The only time my hearing loss was a serious issue at university was when I could not find my hearing aids one night before mid-term exams. I had to race down Interstate 5 all the way back to California to get my back-up pair, which I had left at home. When I got to Sunnydale, there a message on the answering machine from Van Rossen: "We found your hearing aids, you dope! You left them in the coaches' locker room! Get your ass back up here!"

Hans Go had gotten a job in the main administration building, and because he was handy with computers, he had access to the administration computers and the latest Macintosh. Hans worked from 5 p.m. until 10 p.m., after the regular daily university staff had left for the day. I accompanied him to see the new Mac. When he showed it to me I was impressed, first by how tiny the Mac was, but also by the interface, which was the first "real" PC interface I had ever seen. It blew DOS away.

We started playing around with it to see what it could do. We quickly found a program that allowed us to search all the directories on the main frame and to see all the links. Much to our amazement, within a few minutes we had found the files for all the students' grades. "Well we certainly can't just pull them up!" I said. "They must have some kind of password or security key that you need before you can make changes to the grades," Hans replied. But when we simply hit the return key, all the records were displayed. In short order we had pulled up my complete transcript with all my grades. So much for computer security.

"Surely we can't just change the grades from here," Hans said, but he was wrong. I had been given a grade that was a mistake. I had protested it, and the professor had agreed to change the grade, but he left the university without turning in the administrative change forms. So now I was pretty much stuck with a D when in fact I had earned a B+ in the course. This alone drove me crazy, but it also meant that I would have to repeat the class. The professor was now long gone and there was no way to change it. But now here we were looking at my official transcript, and just one click would fix it. I could correct the professor's mistake and change it myself to what it should actually be. Hans and I both knew that there was no way it could ever be traced, but we did not do it. We could have given ourselves all straight A's and nobody would have figured it out. Without knowing it and without even trying, Hans and I had accidentally hacked in to the mainframe computer with security so lax that it was really non-existent. But we chose to do nothing because we knew this would be a pure violation. We were both afraid to cross the line into cheating, even if it was to remedy a mistake. So we closed it up and never went "surfing" through the administrative files again.

I am sure the university has much better security today, but it would not surprise me if a suspiciously high number of computer science students graduated with straight A's back then.

By my senior year at university I was the director and head coach of the newly opened Downtown Athletic Club in Eugene, a new state-of-the-art-facility. I ran all the swimming, aquatics, guard, water polo, swim team and personal training programs and had a staff of four working under me. That year also marked the beginning of a sports medicine and injury rehabilitation program in cooperation with one of the local physicians.

Since the facility was new, they had little experience, and I had negotiated a deal (it is embarrassing to write this down even years later) where I would get 90 % of all the fees my programs brought in and the facility would get 10 %. This 90 % remained in place even when I hired my own staff to do the work. I was making what I considered a small fortune at the time plus taking a full university course load. The Athletic Club offered me a full-time position once I graduated for even more money than I was already making, but I had to turn them down. I had other plans.

I graduated after only three and half years, and graduation day was essentially the very last day I would ever be in Oregon. I left to take an internship in Colorado Springs working for the United States Olympic Committee, the most highly desired appointment that I could have gotten right out of school. When I applied, my counselors all but assured me that these internships were so elite that I would have little chance of getting in, but two of us from Oregon were accepted.

The first thing I did at the Olympics in Colorado was give myself a serious head injury, a major contusion. It happened when my date, one of the Olympic skaters, was teaching me to skate backwards – at least that is what I was told. I cannot recall any of it; in fact, I can't even recall the skater's name. I had suffered a major blow to the head that scrambled my brains pretty well, and it took me about four weeks to even remember my own phone number. To this day I have no memory of anything that happened in the week prior to the accident or for about four weeks after it. In fact, it wasn't until about six months later that all of my circuits were functioning perfectly again and the headaches stopped. Today I wear helmets today whenever there is a chance of anything happening. Having this happen so soon in my Olympic career was unfortunate, to say the least.

Working at the Olympics was a dream assignment. One of the interns was required to work on this expensive new machine that analyzed the oxygen uptake in athletes' blood, and I got to help her figure out how to work and calibrate this awesome device. I also helped another intern do a complicated statistical analysis of the javelin throwers. We had great computers for doing this, and we were able to isolate key elements that we thought were the secrets to why certain athletes' throwing techniques resulted in much longer throws. We focused on the foot plant and the inset angle, and we thought we found a key.

Being an intern also meant that I got to help out with sports events taking place on the Olympic campus. One time, one of the film crews (I think it was ESPN) was short a camera man for the Pan American Tae Kwon Do championships, and I got to fill in and operate the camera for the event. I helped organize one of the Sports Governing Bodies' International Congress conventions. Under the guidance of real experts in sports medicine, I also helped tape up athletes before events and after injuries. I was on my way! I was sure that after another year or two of experience I could land a good spot in a sports med program and would be on my way to becoming a real doctor. But it was not to be. There were significant funding issues, and I became more and more aware that if I stayed on, it would be for really low or no pay.

After six months at the Olympics, on a return trip to Sunnyvale, I saw an ad for a full time research scientist at Stanford University. This opportunity seemed too good to be true. It would fulfill my long-term desire to be a Stanford man one day. On a whim and with little hope, I applied. I was sure I would not be good enough. The resume that I sent to Stanford was the first real job application I ever put together, and also the last. Ironically, I have never had to put together application documents or send out my resume for a job since.

I was sure there would be many other applicants who were better than me, but Stanford called me for an interview.

The Goode Times

The alchemist toils
Night and day
Searching for gold
To find the way
For tin ears to turn
Poor sound to good
Welcome to the labs
Of Richard L. Goode

I will never forget my interview with Dr. Goode for the Stanford job. I wore my best suit (actually my only suit), and it was incredibly uncomfortable. Linda Massengil, Dr. Goode's secretary, was shouting into her phone and seemed distracted. When I told her who I was and that I was there to interview for the research position, she said, "Dr. Goode will be here in a minute."

I was in the Ear, Nose and Throat clinic of the Veterans Affairs Hospital, which was run by the Stanford physicians as a training hospital. They also had a tremendous research program that was supported by federal research grants. I waited for probably an hour. I could hear a loud, booming voice yelling into phones, then at a resident, and then to Linda. Harried younger and older docs rushed up and down the hallways and in and out of rooms. There was a long line of patients waiting for either an ENT exam or to see the ophthalmologists located across the hall. On my way to the interview, I had gotten lost in the vast VA complex of buildings and was relieved to find that my tardiness seemed to have gone unnoticed. My palms were wet, and I was sweating even though it was a cool spring day. I was terrified, and my legs were shaking. I had no idea why I was there. I was sure I was way out of my league.

Finally, Dr. Goode called me into his office. The first thing I saw was the silhouette of a giant figure against the sun streaming in through the dirty windows behind him. Dr. Goode was the biggest man I had ever seen – not because he was physically large, but because it seemed like he filled the entire room with his presence. His office was quite spacious, but every single surface was piled high with papers, instruments, and devices. Boxes full of test articles and books were stacked everywhere, and the only free space was right next to his phone. The walls were full of degrees, diplomas, certificates and awards. I had to move a stack of books off a chair in order to have a place to sit.

Without missing a beat he began, or rather, his words simply took off. "Now Geoff, lemme tell you what we have going on here. I am a professor of otolaryngology at Stanford, and we run labs here and at Stanford, and we are looking for a lab guy to run 'em. So we study primarily ... primarily we study hearing and the biomechanics of hearing and ..."

The phone rang, and Dr. Goode answered it. "Yep I'll be right there," he said, and abruptly left the room. I could hear him talking and yelling back in the clinic where the patients were.

Twenty minutes later he was back. "... and so we use a microscopic stroboscope system to measure the ears, see. And so now, so now ... and so now you're saying to yourself, what is that? But really it is just a way, a way of measuring microscopic vibrations of the ear. We have several visiting scholars that help us with this. We also work on implants. And now lemme see ... Oh and we have Brad, who is doing a research project right now on neurorepair. He is a real kickass and he can help show you around, see ... So we are looking for a guy that can help out ... and from your resume here ... now lemme see ... let's see now. Where did I put it? Linda. Linda! Can you find Geoff's resume here?"

"I have an extra copy right here, Dr. Goode," I blurted out, handing him a copy. And then my mouth started working out of pure fear.

"Dr. Goode, I worked with a lot of that equipment in the physiology labs at Oregon and, well I also know a lot about photography and I know anatomy and physiology pretty well, and this work is also really important to me because ... well because I have a severe hearing loss myself." Then, stunned by my own words, I abruptly stopped.

Dr. Goode's eyebrows shot up and he said, "Oh really?" Then we spent half an hour talking about my hearing loss and my work back at Oregon with Randy Pryde. This was a bit ironic: Here I was, talking about my deafness, the one topic that I was uncomfortable discussing and that I rarely discussed with anyone, during the interview for my dream job. But since Dr. Goode was an ear doc, how bad could it be?

"Who is your doctor?" Goode enquired.

"At the moment, it is Dr. Perkins at CEI."

"Oh really? Rod? Well that's interesting because we have this project to make a new ... to make a new a hearing implant."

"Yeah I know. I have been asking him about it for years now, but he always says it's not ready. I told him I could help with the research. It has something to do with a coil, but it's not ready and ..."

Dr. Goode interrupted me. "Now Geoff, Geoff, you're kidding. Lemme call Rod."

And he picked up the phone and called Dr. Perkins.

"Say Rod, Goode here, yeah, yeah, yeah. Hey I have a guy ... I have a guy here in my office that is a candidate for our research position up in the lab here. He seems like he's our guy, and he says he is a patient of yours and that he talked to you about doing some research ..." Dr. Goode and Rodney spoke for what seemed like an hour before he hung up. I sat there in silence. I was not sure what to think.

Finally Dr. Goode said, "Well now. So Rod says you have quite a hearing loss!"

"Yes," I said, "but I read lips pretty well and I really do not think it would be a problem working here. "

"No. I can tell it will not be a problem. Not here. So are you thinking of going back to school at some point?" he enquired.

"I was interested in going to graduate school and eventually going into either research in biomechanics or sports medicine at some point, but I have no definite plans."

"Well ... I think you're our guy. Yes, I think that you are our guy. You work here a couple of years. We'll get your hearing spiffed up with our new implants and then we can get you off to med school. Maybe here."

I was stunned. I thought to myself, *What? Am I getting this job? Did he just offer me the job? What? What?! This cannot be happening. I was sure I did not stand a chance. What the ...?* I felt like I was dreaming.

Dr. Goode and I then spent the next hour or two in his office. Dr. Goode's phone would ring, usually with questions from Stanford, and he would dispatch answers. Linda dropped a stack of papers for him to sign on his desk, and residents lined up in the hallway waiting to get the input they needed from Dr. Goode on their cases. It was chaotic, to say the least. Dr. Goode was holding three parallel conversations at once and sometimes also working the phone at the same time. He was talking about hearing loss, biomechanical motion, ferrite cores, coils, push-pull amplifiers, and medical procedures I had never heard of before. I felt like my brain was going to explode. I was in the presence of an extraordinary person. It was the first of many afternoons spent sitting there and listening to the genius of Richard L. Goode.

Linda called me the next morning, and I had to go back to the VA to fill out a stack of forms and walk them over to the appropriate offices for submission. Because I was working under a federal grant, it took a few weeks for all the paper work to be approved. Before I could start, I had to get a TB test, make sure all my shots were up to date, and attend the formal new employee training that was held once a month. Under the arcane rules of the federal system and based on the number of graduate credits that I had at the time, I started as "Researcher Level GS-7." This translated into quite a paltry salary compared to what I had been making at the Athletic Club. But I knew that the chance to work with Richard Goode and to learn from him was more than worth it. In fact it would be invaluable. After I started working, Linda figured out how to get me a significant pay raise. Because I could type, she re-submitted the forms to change my title to "Researcher Level GS-7/Typing". That 'slash typing' delineator translated into a 35 % increase in my salary. Thank goodness I had taken two years of typing class in junior high school!

You only meet someone as unique as Dr. Goode on a few occasions in a lifetime. He was and still is in a class of his own. I could not possibly do justice to his CV here. And at the risk of being incredibly brief, let's just say he is a walking marvel of achievement. He also has the rare ability to be cross functional in terms of fields. He has been able to combine technology and knowledge in one field and transfer it to another; then apply science and technology from the second field and take another look at a problem or subject from a fresh perspective. He is the former president of the American Academy of Otolaryngology and a tenured Stanford School of Medicine Professor of Ear Nose and Throat. He has published hundreds of research papers on hearing, biomechanics, neurorepair, facial plastic reconstruction, and he has several patents. He was and still is one of the most famous and pre-eminent experts in his field.

On my first day of work, I again had to find parking and then negotiate the incredible labyrinth of hallways, flyovers and stairs on my way up to the lab. When I couldn't find it, I had to go back down to the clinic and wait for Dr. Brad Simmons, who was the chief resident for research. I was humiliated at not being able to find the lab on my first day, but I cheered up once I saw Brad. "You know, this lab is a real pain in the ass to find!" he declared as we almost ran through the facility. "I swear I get lost each time I try to find it!"

We finally got to the Goode lab, the place that would be my home for the next eight years. It was chock full, with walls and walls of equipment, stacks of boxes, and electronic gear and bottles of chemicals lined up in cabinets. There were machines and vials everywhere, plus two huge desks, the oldest greenest chairs you will ever see, and a huge chalkboard. There were notes and Post-Its stuck all over the walls. It was the largest soundproof room I had ever seen, with huge acoustic foam cones, refrigerators, microscopes, strobes, cameras, isolation tables, and wire racking full of test tubes. There was also a large tissue dissection area. Why, this place was a palace! I had arrived.

On the one hand, I was extremely excited and in a state of disbelief. On the other, I was really afraid in a Forrest Gump sort of way. *What will they think when they find out how I so much do not deserve to be here?* I fretted.

"Hey, you know, I guess we should introduce you to Leonard Kelly in the morgue and then to Dr. Aritomo. After that we can run over to the university for lunch and then go to the medical library to get some journals I need to copy. Oh, and we need to go to the animal lab to check on the rabbits for the facial nerve repair study we are working on," Brad said. We did all those things and more.

As we walked around the main campus, Brad stopped to introduce me to Blair Simmons and his lab staff. Dr. Simmons was a living legend in the field of hearing at the time. His lab staff and Dr. Charlie Long had placed an array of electrodes on the exposed brain of a cat and were monitoring the output via a crude paginated digital display system. "We think we might be able to use this as an intra-operative analyzer," they explained. "We're just not sure yet how to correlate the output, but we can see the changes in intensity as we control the input levels."

Then we were off to the morgue, where I got to see my first real cadavers. I had worked in anatomy labs prior to that, but only with very old and completely over-dissected specimens. These were only hours old.

Leonard Kelly, the lab director, sized me up and said, "So you're Goode's new guy. Are you ready to suit up?"

"Really? I mean, well can I?"

"Gowns and gloves are over there. I have two rules: The first is to always use universal precautions. Always."

I began gowning and gloving up. "Mr. Kelly! Mr. Kelly!" I called out as he stomped off towards his office. "What?"

"Umm, sir ... You forgot to tell me the second rule."

"Oh, rule number two is to always use universal precautions. Oh, and learn. Always learn."

The chief resident in charge of the dissection began barking orders, and soon I was using a bone saw to remove the skull in order to retrieve the brain. *This place rocks!* I thought to myself.

On one of my first days, I was helped by one of the senior necropsy workers, a very old and very short Swedish woman. As she was instructing me on how to remove the brains from the skull, she said in her heavy Swedish accent, "Vvvery goot, Gweeephry! Gooot. Ant now dat tee bwaaainn hass been removed, you must place it on tee scale." At this point, the brain slipped out of my hands and almost got away from me and fell on the floor. "Gweephry! Gweephry! " she admonished. "You must never dwop tee brains on der floor!" It was one of the strangest things anyone would ever say to me, and coming from an elderly grandmother figure, who could not have been an inch over four feet four, it was surreal.

At the end of my first year in the lab, I was still amazed by my new work environment. The more I worked on increasingly scientific projects, the more I came to appreciate how important it all was. Doing good science required a host of cross-functional skill sets that must all come together in order for experiments to work well. The people, the equipment, the specimens, the experimental set-ups, and the supporting tasks all had to come together in order to get an experiment up and running. I cannot tell you the number of times that experiments did not get done because one minor component was not available, or worse, because it was just simply missing. We were constantly on the move, buzzing from here to there to copy a paper, find a journal, locate a couple of test leads or whatever, and then running back to the lab to set up the equipment. It was a whirlwind of activity, and once you were good at it, it was addictive.

Since most of our labs did not have windows to the outside (which we joked was to contain the inevitable explosions), we frequently lost track of time. I was master of this, especially when I was doing temporal bone studies in the soundproof room where it was so quiet. It was normal for me to roll out of the room and look up at the clock and see that it was one or two in the morning. Sometimes we had experiments going that required us to do continuous measurements every four hours. In those cases I slept in the lab as there was no point in going home. I missed many key social occasions and more than a few dates because I lost track of time in the lab.

From the outset, I was dedicated. Dr. Goode's primary goals were to develop a way to turn "tin ears into gold" via the perfect passive partial ossicular replacement prostheses, to perfect a middle ear implantable hearing system, and to understand everything about hearing through basic research. We had applied research, directed research and basic research projects all within our primary scope. We also had a lot of side projects, such as mandibular reconstruction, neurosurgery and repair, and projects in almost all ear, nose and throat areas. I did not know it at the time, but I was probably the only full-time researcher in a funded lab working on middle ear implants in the United States, if not the world.

A key part of my work at Stanford was to measure the biomechanical functions of human ears. Most of us learn in school that the eardrum vibrates in response to sound waves entering the ear. What we were interested in was how much the ear actually moves in response to a defined sound pressure input. In other words, it was common knowledge that the motion of the ear in response to sound is very small, but we wanted to measure and define exactly how small those vibrations truly are. We also wanted to find out how much the human ear vibrated in response to low-frequency, mid-range and high-frequency sounds.

To do this, the lab had an arsenal of incredibly expensive equipment. A single scientific probe microphone cost $15,000, not including the $12,000 pre-amp it required. In order to measure such small motions, the lab benches were floating tables isolated to remove ground vibration, and they cost $25,000. Since this was before the advent of digital sound measuring equipment, virtually everything we used was analog, and it was expensive, hard to use and limited.

Almost everything we did was hard. In order to get the ears each day, I would go down to the morgue, remove the skull cap of the cadaver, and drill out the temporal region that contained the middle and inner ear structures. I would then remove them with an industrial grade set of forceps, replace the skull cap, and sew up the incision. This may sound like ghoulish work, but doing so many autopsies provided me with invaluable experience and contributed greatly to my understanding of human anatomy and physiology. The work itself did not really a bother me at all; in fact, my interest in it was endless. Mr. Kelly was a quite a character and ran the morgue in a serious yet swashbuckling style. The morgue always had a great group of pre-meds and volunteer staff.

One day when I was in the morgue working on a skull, there was a new medical student who had just been assigned to conduct the autopsy. He was obviously more than a bit weirded out by the sights and smells that greeted him when he entered the morgue for the first time.

The student tentatively asked Mr. Kelly, "What ... ahh ... what was the cause of death?"

Mr. Kelly looked the student right in the eye and answered in a totally serious voice, "Shortness of breath ... doctor."

The student lowered his eyes and replied, "Oh. Yes. Yes, I see."

"Yep," Mr. Kelly said. "Happens more than you would think. Sometimes they get such serious shortness of breath that they stop breathing. We see it a lot here."

"Oh yes. Yes, I understand."

Not one of us said a word. We all put on our serious game faces and went about our work, but inside we were all laughing hysterically. Of course everyone who dies stops breathing, so every cause of death can be attributed to shortness of breath. Here was a student who had just completed medical school at one of the best universities in the world and had a brain filled with a vast amount of knowledge and medical training, yet he had just fallen for Mr. Kelly's "shortness of breath" diagnosis gag. In some strange way, gallows humor made the work more bearable.

After I got the ears out of the skulls, I dropped them in the premixed solution that would preserve the ears so as to eliminate any chance of contamination during dissection. Then I would take the ears to the lab and dissect them to gain access to the middle ear, usually by drilling a route called the posterior tymponmetry, until I could see the stapes footplate and the other ossicles. I used a stereo operating microscope to make sure I had not damaged any of the miniscule structures. I would then mount them and start measuring them. This was done by placing a tremendous speaker with a tube into the rear canal, sealing it with petroleum jelly, then putting targets on the structures we would measure. I would then make sure that all the equipment was set to the right levels. After checking the compressor circuit, I could start measuring at the lower frequency tones, then the middle frequencies, and then the high frequencies. When we used the video stroboscope we would usually start our measurements at 134dB SPL (decibels of sound), which is about as loud as a jack hammer. But in 1988, with all our analog motion, we could only measure motion accurately to the cellular level. We needed to get sub-cellular to really understand the structures, but it was the best we could do. Measuring one ear, including dissection, took all day, and we measured at least four ears a week. I worked primarily in tandem with visiting scholars from Ehime University in Japan. I liked working with the Japanese docs: They could barely speak English, so a lot of our work was done via pantomime, pointing and talking very slowly, which was perfect for me.

One of my key projects, the active middle ear implant, required a lot of creative thinking. In theory, such a device would use direct drive to mechanically drive the tiny structures of the middle and inner ear. Use of such mechanical energy to impart microvibrations to the ear requires a direct contact between the ear and a drive transducer; hence the term direct-drive. In theory, such a device could replace acoustic hearing aids and be permanently installed within the ear. But in 1988, no such device existed. The only one that had been used at all was one that had been studied in Japan by Dr. Suzuki and Dr. Yanigihara.

Because Dr. Yanigihara from Ehime University was a close colleague of Dr. Goode's, we found a patient that needed the Japanese implant and surgically implanted him with the device. Dr. Yanigihara flew over from Japan to assist, and although the surgery was a technical success, the device did not activate. We did all we could and even considered doing a revision surgery to adjust the implant, but the patient didn't return. We never did figure out what was went wrong, though Dr. Goode later learned that the patient had apparently been a serious drinker and had fallen off a wagon. About a hundred surgeries had been done with this device in Japan, but the results were mixed, and in time the piezo-electric elements of the transducer often failed. The project was eventually abandoned.

It was becoming more and more clear to me that if I ever wanted to have a hearing implant someday, I truly had a lot of work to do. I began to think we were not just a couple but many years away from a hearing implant that would treat my own loss. Dr. Goode believed that an electromagnetic transducer offered the best hope for an implanted hearing device. I spent months that turned into years trying to optimize the perfect coil magnet system based on Dr. Goode's pioneering design. They always worked, but the devices required too much power and were too large, too complicated, or had other features that made them unsuited for widespread use.

Dr. Goode no doubt appreciated my abilities with photography. As he was always in need of 35 mm slides for courses he was teaching, for lectures or for case files, I was often up in the photo lab using our 35 mm Nikon FE and shooting on the floodlight stand. I had all the special lenses and exposure times and everything worked out perfectly, and I could photograph anything from textbooks to skulls to specimens. Occasionally I went down in the clinic or the OR to shoot a case, and from time to time I even helped the ophthalmology photographers if they got overloaded with patients. It had been quite a hobby of mine before, and I was glad to be able to apply it to science now. Making presentations back then before the days of PowerPoint was quite a task. Helping Dr. Goode prepare all his lectures and attending a lot of them also gave me a unique insight into his view of all things otology, not to mention that it was really fun to do.

One day Dr. Goode called and asked me to head down to the Stanford Audiology Clinic, where he met me and showed me a large box containing a new piece of equipment that had just arrived. "This is the acoustic rhinometer! It is a new device that measures the airway in the nose and can detect septal deviations. We can measure the airway before surgery and then measure it after surgery to make sure it has been improved," he explained. The device was essentially a simple computer hooked up to a probe. It worked by measuring the cavity volume of the nose. To operate it, it first had to be calibrated using a set of defined calibration ports. Once it was ready, the physician would place the device in the subject's nose and run the test. The computer would display a graph that indicated whether the cavity was open, closed, or partially closed. "I need you," Dr. Goode said, "to set it up and calibrate the machine and get it working. Then we can try it on some patients this afternoon." I got right to work.

I unpacked the device, connected all the hardware, turned it on, and followed the calibration procedure. I managed to get it all ready in about 15 minutes. I went to find Dr. Goode, who was busy with a patient. I told him that the device was all set and that

I would wait until he was finished; then I went back and waited next to the machine. Minutes went by. After half an hour I was bored, so I looked at the probe of the acoustic rhinometer and thought to myself, *Well why not?* I took the probe and shoved it up my left nostril to the correct position as depicted in the user manual. I ran the test, and the graph indicated that my nostril and airway were clear. I printed it out. When I placed the probe in my right nostril and ran the test, the graph displayed a blocked airway. I ran it again, with the same result: blocked. I tried it on the left side again, and that one was clear. Then back to the right, which the machine said was blocked. Dr. Goode finally returned.

"How is it going?" he enquired.

"I think there is a problem. The machine keeps saying that my left nostril is fine, but that I have an obstructed cavity on the right," I replied with concern.

"Really? Well then let's check it out!"

"What?"

"Come with me. Let's take a peek!"

Dr. Goode led me back to the clinic, where he sat me in a chair and eased it all the way back. All of a sudden, my boss was shoving instruments into my nose and directing light sources up my nostrils. What on earth had I gotten myself into? A couple of residents ambled into the room, interested in the spectacle.

Dr. Goode explained what was going on to them, shouting, "Yes! Yes indeed! Your left is fine, but you have a septal deviation blocking the right. You are completely obstructed on the right, just like the machine said! Oh, I love this!" Goode was overcome with the delight of diagnosis with a new piece of equipment.

"What?" I asked.

"You've got a deviated septum, babe! You're going to have to get that fixed!" Goode exclaimed.

I was stunned. A few minutes earlier in the day I had been harmlessly calibrating a machine, and the next thing I knew my boss was climbing on top of me, shoving instruments in my nose, and diagnosing and taking photos of my poor deviated septum. I am sure I had been walking around with it for a long time, but I had never noticed it, and it never bothered me one bit. But now that I had been made aware of the fact that I could not breathe on my right side, it began bothering me almost immediately. For the rest of the day, I kept focusing on my nose. I felt short of breath in a Leonard Kelly sort of way. Really: I felt like I was seriously oxygen starved. Dr. Goode had identified my problem, and now I was being psychosomatic. I had trouble getting to sleep just thinking about my poor nose and wondering if I would have a bizarre sleep apnea event and die during the night. The next day was even worse, and by the weekend I just could not take it anymore. The very next week, I had surgery to correct my deviated septum – all because of the damn acoustic rhinometer machine! The surprisingly part was that after my nose had healed and I no longer had a septal deviation, it was much better, and I felt like I could really breathe for the first time in years. That's the kind of thing that happened when you worked for Dr. Goode.

Besides doing work on ears, I was involved with other projects at the lab including neurorepair, surgical lasers, reconstructive surgery, dental implants, and mandibular reconstruction, to name a few. There were innumerable projects I could get involved in if I was willing to surrender everything to research, and I was picked up for a host of side projects. The physicians and MD PhD's who had procured research funding through grants and endowments almost always had huge clinical and surgical duties in addition to running their research programs. This meant that many of the research programs had to be run by remote control. As much as research meant to them, a sick patient who was in serious trouble trumped lab time. They would show up in their labs, turn on the equipment and just get started when their beepers would go off, and they had to return the hospital wards or the clinic.

Many were also good at getting funding, but they often did not get enough to pay for full-time professional lab staff (this was especially true of younger researchers), so they would try use graduate students. One issue with grad students is that they had other time commitments: classes to attend, exams to take, and what not. A second issue is that graduate students were often full of theoretical knowledge but typically had little if any hands-on technical experience. Many of them could wax away for hours on all the theory, but they couldn't take a research proposal, assemble all the equipment, get the specimens and test articles together, and make the project come to life. Since they were graduate students, they all too often lacked the time and connections they needed to help them negotiate the bureaucratic maze and get the supplies and materials they needed. They did not have the time to learn all the tricks of the trade. Seasoned researchers could solve this by tapping into the talents of PhD students for research work, but many young aspiring researchers could only dream of such help. If they were lucky, they could get a couple of really good research assistants to step it up to a higher level, but they were a rare find.

Sadly, the outcome of not being able to find and hire talented staff was projects being shut down or a researcher losing lab privileges. I have had the unfortunate experience of seeing far too many research labs closed down and cleaned out over the years.

I quickly gained a reputation for being able to make it happen in lab. Setting up equipment, getting it calibrated, and working out the bugs was in my DNA. Having grown up in Silicon Valley and having spent hours trolling through all the second-hand lab supply shops, I knew the best places to go to get almost anything. I knew where Haltek was and I knew what they had. So whenever some piece of equipment went down and we needed a new part, I usually knew where I could get a back-up unit or a new part, often on the same day. I would pick up perfectly good used equipment for pennies (I still do, only now I use eBay). Soon I found myself working extra hours on ophthalmology research, skin flap re-vascularisation, facial nerve repair, tympanic membrane replacement, collagen struts for nerve and vascular repair magnetic implants, and dental implants, all in addition to my standard lab work. I never took extra pay for this extra work. "Will work for pizza!" I used to joke.

Along the way I got really good with computers. These were still the early days of computing, and it was not standard practice to get automated systems to take data at a specified time and rate within a specific range, and then to dump this data into usable (and saved) files. Almost nothing was PC-based, and tests, few of which were truly automated, required constant attention and hordes of time. In fact, many data sets were still dumped on to X-Y plotters or strip chart recorders. The data would then have to be "ticked off" and manually entered into usable form. It was tough, time-consuming work that was subject to error. Even those of us who were good at it dreaded the monotony of it. Whenever we tried to have administrative secretaries help us out, they would invariably get it wrong through no fault of their own. Many tests had to be done at standard hours over the course of many hours and sometimes days. It was a common thing to see a car zip into the driveway and circle around to the back of some lab, where the researcher dashed in run one test or cycle another and then ran back out ten minutes later. I did not know it at the time, but the small digital control boxes that I had built in my digital electronics class lab back at Oregon were early forerunners of scientific device drivers. I was soon able to leverage my work from my days at the University of Oregon, combining my software programming to make little devices that would take data and store it in ASCII files or, in some cases, directly in to automated plotting programs. I then took it a step further and wrote software that would take the data, parse and format it, and do the required calculations. The data could then be rapidly run off into usable output and stored electronically.

One of the surgical doctors at the VA had a project to link all the intensive care units' computers together, and soon I was helping him. These were pre-internet days. I set up what was called a "node" that allowed us to link the Stanford labs with the VA labs and offices via modems and CompuServe or via a modem link.

At the same time I was just barely succeeding in trying to connect computers, a friend and I started a new sideline. Dan Stein, one of my lab buddies, was working in research for Stanford Anesthesiology. He and I had started brewing beer at his home in Palo Alto, and we thought we were getting pretty good at it. We made some really dark stout beer we called "Rasta Brau" and a few other lighter ales. I put up a zymurgy (a.k.a. beer brewing) computer dial-up number that was basically a few simple text pages that people could look at. We could not really call it a website because there was no web at the time, and the word "website" did not exist. I cannot recall what we actually did call it. I guess they were just pages. Essentially, if someone with a modem had my modem number, they could call my

PC from their PC and look at the pages that I had posted. I put up a few notices at the local beer brewing outpost, and somehow my "site" got looked at quite a bit, but I had no way of knowing that. My site, like most at the time, was essentially a simple black and white display. Many sites were simply basic ASCII characters, and most of the pages were pretty boring. We put some simple pictures on the page, but when people complained that it slowed it down too much, we took them off. It was hard to find any good information on AOL or any modems anywhere, but we had books that listed places you could modem into for good information. For most part it was slow and cumbersome and seldom worth the effort. In those days, going to the library was a much better idea.

One day one of the physicians told me about two guys he knew who were starting a computer project. One of the docs I was working with on our computer project said, "You should go talk to them. They know all about your work here, and you need to see what they are doing." I was initially surprised, because I felt that my computer work was really pretty weak. But I managed to track these guys down, and I met them in a couple of offices in the Town and Country Village shopping center across the street from Stanford. Both Stanford electronic engineering students, they were talking about these "lists" and said they knew that my computer was one of the more popular on the "web."

"On the what?" I asked.

"We call it the 'web'," they said. They went on to tell me all about how they were making these lists of computer sites and how this was going to change the world. "You should think about working on it with us," they said. I figured out that I had seen these guys before, behind the engineering building at Stanford when I went to try to get help with the electronics parts of the projects we were working on. I think Bob White might also have mentioned them to me, but I was obviously not all ears.

I was not really sure what to think. To be honest, I left there not even sure what it was that they were working on. At the time they just seemed like a couple of graduate students looking for some help on their project. They both seemed really tired and really out of it, as if they had stayed up way, way too late every night for the last week or two. These guys were clearly on a different plane than the rest of us and had ostensibly gotten to a point where they had lost touch with reality. It was really strange.

I did not understand what the two were talking about or how on earth they could envision a business opportunity in making "lists" of interesting online computer nodes through what they called the "web." The impression I got was that even they had a really hard time describing what they were up to. What's more, to be completely honest, their idea of keeping computer search lists seemed really dumb at the time. Why would anyone ever want to pay for lists and categories for good web nodes? Today it's almost impossible to recall or imagine a time before the internet, but back then the idea of making lists of phone modem call-in numbers and earning money with them was nothing short of ridiculous.

I told them I was really short of time at the moment but that I would keep them in mind. There were a lot researchers looking for help (preferably free) with their projects at Stanford, so this was nothing new, and at the time I thought nothing of it. It did not strike me as being a particularly "hot" or exciting project. A couple of years later I heard that these guys had kept working on their project and eventually founded a small company they named "Yahoo." I sure hope it turned out OK for them!

This was just the kind of experience one could have when hanging around and working near Stanford University.[2]

I finished my graduate work for my master's degree in 1999. My focus had been in computer science; in other words, I was interested in how to apply computational power to solve complex prob-

---

2   This story may strike you as incredible, but it really is not. I was around Stanford at the time and would often hang out around the engineering and computer programs at the same time the Yahoo founders were there. I clearly recall Jerry Yang but not David Philo. Yahoo's home page describes fledgling company being located in one of the temporary buildings behind the engineering school. I remember those buildings well, and I might have met Jerry there. The disconnect for me is that I can distinctly recall meeting Jerry and someone else who was definitely not David Philo at some rented offices on the second floor in the Towne and Country shopping center, across the street from Stanford. The Yahoo site makes no mention of such offices. Again, I am not being dodgy, but the entire meeting only took maybe 15 minutes, and at the time I thought nothing of it; nor, I am sure, did the two founders. The point is that I can clearly remember Jerry talking about and showing me his lists and concept. Long story short: I missed a great chance because I did not "get it," and that is a fact.

lems. I was eager to take the many existing sets of data, plug in assumptions and/or potential inputs, and model what the outcomes would be via different statistical modeling techniques. I was also interested in getting the vast amounts of data into digital form so that we could take full advantage of past work. I was fascinated with probabilistic and deterministic statistics and using computer power to attempt to project possible future outcomes. I wrote several software programs and leveraged existing database software to try to refine these models. When I took a course on linear programming, I was ecstatic.

Linear programming in itself is an exercise in trying to maximize desired outcomes while trying to minimize other factors, all within a set of defined constraints. For simple problems it is a straightforward exercise, but it quickly becomes very tricky once the problem goes beyond two dimensions. Sometimes the answers generated by linear programming are incredibly non-obvious. The key component I learned from linear programming and compiling all the data was that you often couldn't arrive at the "obvious" answer until you had gone through the entire exercise of mapping out all the possible solution sets within the confines of reasonable constraints. In other words, for many complex multi-variant problems, you had to deconstruct the problem, do an in-depth study of the possible solutions, and lay out boundaries in great detail before you could even begin to have the knowledge needed to identify an obvious solution.

I learned that advanced problem solving was a science with a breathtaking scope. The power of the PC was intoxicating to me, and I thought about potential applications for advanced problem solving coupled to massive information data bases. I believed that if we could get the data into digital format, we could gain much more understanding and insight. The ultimate elixir for me was to attempt to solve multi-dimensional problems. I therefore began taking night classes in computer science, information technology, computer programming, data base design, and graduate statistics.

I had managed to find time in my schedule to work full time doing research for Dr. Goode and also do some consulting work to help pay for my tuition and books. Since I almost all my courses were in the evenings and on weekends, I was able to pretty much be a researcher by day and a full-time grad student by night. I also tried to sell paintings to help pay for grad school, which was really expensive.

One company I had been consulting for was called ReSound Corporation. Resound had begun work to use a database of patient data to define the parameters to program a hearing aid that had digital registers to control it. In short, they were working on a true custom fit device that also used non-linear fitting. It was a stunning idea. The resulting device would be their first digitally programmable hearing aid.

ReSound Corporation had been co-founded by Dr. Rodney Perkins and Dr. Goode. The original corporate goal had been to develop the implantable hearing device concept into a commercial product.

When I first arrived at ReSound, it was in an office lab across the hall from California Ear Institute (Dr. Perkins' private practice) located on Page Mill Road right next to the Foothill Expressway. Initially, the only other person working at ReSound was Jon Winstead. A senior technician, Jon was in charge of developing the basic research needed in order to develop a concept called the EarLens into a product. He had been having trouble calibrating one particular device, the laser Doppler vibrometer. More than any other test system, this device would have a profound effect on my work.

The laser Doppler was housed within a lab inside a clean room. A soundproof chamber enclosed the entire laser Doppler system, which was suspended on a pneumatic isolation table and had a glowing red targeting laser beam. This device had much more sensitivity than the optical strobe system we had been using in Dr. Goode's lab. Rather than use photographic imaging and microscope techniques, this device leveraged the Doppler shift to detect microvibrations using a pair of laser beams. I helped Jon calibrate the system, and it was soon up and running. Over the next months, we would bring our test samples from the lab over to ReSound to develop the baseline measurements for how ears vibrate in response to sound at unprecedented levels of precision. Once we had the basic research science to a level where we understood what a hearing implant (or in the case of ReSound, an Earlens) would need to achieve to have a chance to become a successful product, then we could start working on a detailed design specification.

We put a lot of effort into the Earlens – a ton of it – often toiling away late into the night trying to make it work. At the time we all thought that this could be the answer to a direct drive hearing device. ReSound had acquired some intellectual property from AT&T (Bell Labs) and had brought in about six of the key people from Bell Labs to work at ReSound in Palo Alto. Jont Allen, Fred Waldhour, and Ed Villchur had studied the basis of the ReSound technology and figured out that actively compressing all sounds into a decreased dynamic range would make speech and other sounds much clearer and more intelligible to the hearing impaired with an active electronic system. By recognizing that the hearing impaired had not only a loss in threshold levels but also a decrease in dynamic range, the ReSound technology was able to provide a compressed signal for the audio range that was more useful to the patients. For those suffering from sensor-neural hearing loss, this was a truly significant improvement.

Almost all the modern hearing systems being used today are based in some way on advanced signal compression first pioneered by ReSound Corporation. Yet although it was a tremendous technical and clinical success, the introduction of advanced "smart" compressed signal hearing aid circuitry did not significantly alter hearing aid adoption patterns. The new devices were a true step forward in making acoustic hearing aids sound better than they had been, especially for mild to moderate hearing loss sufferers, but a majority of them still rejected hearing aids. I believe that this is because if a person does not want and will not wear a hearing aid, it does not matter how good the hearing aid is, how much it will help them, or how much it costs. If the answer to hearing aids is no, then the answer to a really good hearing aid is still no.

The basic ReSound concept was to solve the problems of the hearing impaired who suffered from sensory neural deafness in terms of the residual range of hearing they had left. The Resound team understood that the hearing impaired have an abnormal growth of loudness curve. In other words, people with sensory-neural hearing loss have decreased hearing thresholds and cannot detect lower-level sounds well or at all, but they can hear very loud sounds (jackhammers and gunshots, for example) at the same level as normal hearing patients. Amplifying all sounds equally just makes them more confusing and painfully loud. By amplifying the low-level but not the louder sounds, the sounds in between would only get a little amplification. Fred, with the help of Carlos Baez, developed a custom signal processing chip based on this technology, and ReSound was eventually able to build it into a hearing aid.

I was the first patient to be fitted with hearing aids powered by ReSound's first-generation hearing aid circuits (a.k.a. chips). Those hearing aids were the best I had ever had, and I could not wait to integrate the ReSound technology into a direct drive middle ear implant. I somehow became a star patient for ReSound and even worked the ReSound booth at trade shows. Although I was glad to help, I was also horrified that my hearing loss was now truly out in the open. But Dr. Perkins said that I if I could help just one person, it was the right thing to do, so I did it.

From the safety of my post in the ReSound research lab, I watched it grow from a small company with essentially one employee to a thriving business that employed hundreds. ReSound eventually became a successful hearing aid company selling the best instruments on the market, but there were growing pains along the way. When the first chips were put into production, there were significant yield problems, and the company went through a painful period of layoffs and restructuring. I earned extra income testing the individual chips by hand so that the company could honor their shipping schedules.

Ironically, the more success ReSound had on the hearing aid side, the less the concept of a hearing implant or Earlens or any medical device seemed to fit into their business model and regulatory strategy. While hearing aids were regulated by the FDA, the Earlens was a medical device, so it had to fulfill much higher regulatory requirements. We were making progress, but there were really only two of us trying to make the Earlens, and I was only half time.

One day ReSound brought in a young and fairly new biomedical engineer I'll call Reuben to take over and manage the EarLens project. I was excited at first, and Reuben came in with the best of intentions. My first assignment from him was to develop a series of curves for different strength magnets and shapes based on a model that he had dreamed up.

I had already tested hundreds of magnets and produced the curves based on the laser Doppler data. Now, though, I used his model and designs. When I presented my data to him, he became very upset. The curves depicted the average motion of the magnet under a set of controlled distance parameters. In each test, there were slight differences in the motion detected based on how well I was able to align the test using a micropositioning system.

I tried to explain the data to him: "These are the curves for the different magnets based on your model. Notice that this magnet has significantly more displacement than all the other magnets. The mean for the data is indicated by the dash on the plot. So I plotted the histogram and got a good shape, with the data lining up in a fairly good bell shaped curve around the mean."

Reuben was taken aback, and his face flushed as he responded, "The data should be exactly the same each time you test it! What bell curve? I do not want curves. This is not what I need!"

Part of me wanted to shout back at Reuben about what a stupid model he had chosen and how the data was perfect the way it was, but I knew he would not accept it.

"Go re-do it!" he ordered.

So I tried again. And again. And again! But each time, the results were more and more the same, and Reuben was never satisfied. In the course of similar exchanges over a period of weeks, I came to understand that Reuben wanted confirmation for what he had in his head. In other words, he thought he already had the answer, so he would only accept data that confirmed what he already believed to be true.

I finally went and asked him what he thought the numbers should really be. I then took the values, went back to the lab, printed out a table with the results that he wanted, and presented it to him.

He was thrilled "See?" he shouted. "I knew you could do it! This is right. Great work!"

But I said, "These are the numbers that you gave me before I did the experiment. Here are the real numbers." I handed him the real data. "No data ever could look that clean," I continued. "Doesn't it look absurd to you to have whole numbers like that? I did not even carry anything past the decimal point. It is just totally wrong."

Reuben was not too happy with me after that. The dilemma I had now was that what he wanted the data to be was not what the data *really was*. His idea was not working, so the obvious solution would have been to try something else. Instead, Reuben thought the problem had something to do with the person taking his data, so he came into the lab one day and sat next to me and watched the experiment. It was hard to focus with him hovering over me. When the values started coming out close to what I had been measuring, he jumped up and started tweaking my sensitive set-up.

"Oh that cannot be right! Let's adjust this ... And what about if we change the scale ... and we can move this line." His hands were jumping all over the set-up, and he began randomly twisting knobs and flipping switches.

"Dude," I said. "You just completely went off protocol, and now the equipment is all out of calibration and you are also off range. You just completely changed the set-up."

"But look! The numbers are getting better!" Reuben shouted.

"That is because you just completely changed the scale and the input levels," I replied.

"Yeah, well that is what we need to do then," he insisted.

"What? I have a better idea: Let's just make the data up out of thin air. You don't do science by arranging the equipment to get the readout you want. You set up your experiment and observe and measure what the data is."

Reuben looked me in the eye. "Hey," he said, I know what I'm doing, and those numbers look better than the numbers you have been getting!"

"Yeah, except that it is total BS data. I think we should test the device, refine the design, test again, and tweak the system until we completely understand it and how to make it better," I suggested.

"But I already know how to do it!" he screamed back at me.

Reuben was young, and I was even younger. Let's just say we just did not see eye to eye.

At the time, Dr. Goode was on the FDA panel and knew an awful lot about what biocompatibility and coatings could and could not be used in medical devices. Reuben wanted to sputter coat the magnet structure of the EarLens with titanium, an experimental technique he had read about. One day when Dr. Goode, one of the world's pre-eminent hearing device experts, came into the lab, he and Reuben got into an epic shouting match. I wanted to put the magnetic component of the EarLens in a titanium can, but Reuben had other ideas: He insisted on sputter coating it.

Dr. Goode said, "Reuben, I am on the FDA committee. We voted down sputter coating, and we will not approve it!"

Reuben replied, "No, Dr. Goode, you are wrong. It was approved."

"Reuben, I am on the committee, so I KNOW it ain't approved! And it ain't EVER going to be approved!"

"No, you're mistaken." And back and forth, over and over for what seemed like hours, the two minds battled one another.

I sat watching the exchange with my mouth open, looking on in utter amazement as a junior engineer challenged a great scientist and FDA panel member on a topic he knew better than anyone. I had already learned that Reuben did not have a lot of common sense, and knowing enough to back down when he was clearly in the wrong was painfully beyond him.

Reuben finally looked at me for backup and said, "Geoff, tell him the truth."

I made a career decision. "Sputter coating has never been used for medical devices of this type and likely never will be. I think we have to use a laser welded can, Reuben," I said.

"There, you see?" Goode said "Even the kid knows. I do not want to discuss it anymore."

After Goode left, Reuben said to me, "You and I are going to have a serious talk."

I loved the EarLens concept and was convinced that it was a great research idea, but that I doubted that it would ever be a commercial success because it required too much power and at 2.5 pounds, the entire system, which included an externally worn "neck loop," was far too heavy. You cannot treat the hearing impaired with such a heavy device. Plus, I just could not work for Reuben anymore, and since it was more than obvious that the feeling was mutual, I ended my consulting arrangement with ReSound. Reuben was going to cancel my contract anyway. Somehow he stayed on at ReSound for a lot longer than I thought he would. Reuben had made his own serious career decision by taking on Dr. Goode that day, but he found a better position in his next job anyway, so it all worked out.

Approximately two years after I left, ReSound, now under new leadership, tried out a new and improved version of the EarLens on Dr. Perkins' patients at California Ear Institute. Dr. Perkins kindly kept me as a patient in the clinical trial for the ReSound Earlens. Although the device had not changed much (it was a bit smaller now but still too big), I agreed to try it. In an office procedure, Dr. Perkins placed the tiny silicone lens with the gold-encapsulated (not sputter coated) coated magnet on my eardrum.

The beauty of the EarLens concept has always been that it does not require surgery and can be installed in an outpatient office procedure. I was then fitted with the drive unit that picked up environmental sound with a microphone and converted it to electromagnetic waves. The waves would drive the magnet back and forth, ultimately transmitting micro-vibrations to my inner ear, which could detect them as sound. When the coil of the neck loop was positioned around my neck, I could not hear anything, but when it was higher up around my ear, I heard crystal clear "direct drive" sound for the first time. It was immediately obvious that direct drive sound was infinitely better than any sound a hearing aid could ever provide. It was far superior to even the best ReSound hearing aids. This was truly something special: crisp, clear tone without distortion. The sound was really in my ear for the first time. Awesome! Trying the EarLens convinced me that the direct drive concept had been correct. The sound quality was amazing, and there was virtually no distortion. Unfortunately, the system was still significantly underpowered; in fact, I could not wear it because I could not get any significant amplification unless I wrapped the neck loop around my head. But Perkins and Goode were right: Direct drive sound was vastly superior to acoustic hearing aids. The EarLens was never successfully commercialized, but the experience convinced me of the great importance and promising future of treating hearing loss with direct drive technology. For the first time, the dream seemed real.

Dr. Goode often sent me to the library to copy the latest research publications. Every so often we also needed copies of patents. Patents are like a sneak peek at what is around the corner: They are good indicators of where the next breakthroughs might come from and which direction a field is likely to head. The only place to research patents was the Sunnyvale patent library, which was housed in a vacant school library and had all the patents issued by the United States. In the 1980's and 1990's, patent records were not available in electronic form, so hard copies had to be made and/or ordered. An inventor could only search the patents based on class, or by finding a relevant work or a specific inventor and then cross-referencing the patents. A typical patent search-and-copy mission for Dr. Goode could easily take me two days and use up fistfuls of quarters that I had to insert in the dilapidated copy machine. Whenever Dr. Goode sent me to search and copy patents, I always read them. I read everything.

The library staff was always helpful, friendly and professional. It seemed like pretty tedious work to me, but they were clearly driven by a sense that what they were doing was important. There was a little display area where they had posted the patent that had been issued as "Invention of the Month" and the "Inventor of the Year." Little did I know at the time that I would soon be the recipient of both these minor yet to me epic honors.

I always took classes in addition to working and always read whatever I could get my hands on. As I read the patent works on direct drive technology over and over, I realized that all other ways of directly stimulating the human ear that had been proposed were starting to look increasingly similar. The more I researched the subject, the more obvious their sameness was. I appreciated the designs and the merits of the competing designs, but they all had one thing in common: They all seemed to be driven from the same optimization perspective. The deeper I read, the more troubling the problem seemed. I found sentences that I thought reflected a lack of understanding of just how small the motion of the ear truly was.

And that's when it hit me: A direct drive device only has to move a few microns, an increment so small that it is like only the heart beat of an ant. That was the moment I knew I was onto something new – a new perspective that has made all the difference.

During my research years I became good friends with Dr. Charlie Long. Charlie was an MD PhD at Stanford and a surgeon and clinician who had a keener interest in research than most. His main research area was bone conduction hearing implants; in particular the Xomed Audiant, a new transcutaneous device pioneered by Dr. Hough and Dr. Dormer of the Hough Ear Institute in Oklahoma. The device was the first transcutaneous bone conduction hearing implant approved by the FDA. The implant was used to treat conductive and mixed hearing loss. It could be used to treat chronic conductive hearing loss without the need for a screw protruding from the side of the head. That sounds a bit crude, but the only competitive product to the Xomed Audiant was called the BAHA, or Bone Anchored Hearing Aid. Based on dental implant technology, the BAHA had a percutaneous screw that was affixed to the skull and a protrusion called the abutment that stuck out through the patient's skin. To me the BAHA had more in common with implants and, despite its name, was not a hearing aid. The BAHA is the only long-term percutaneous medical device used in otology today to treat hearing loss. When the system is activated, patients hear through bone conduction.

The Xomed Audiant was an attempt to solve the obvious issues of having a percutaneous screw pierce the skin by using a transcutaneous concept; in other words, no open wound. For the Audiant, a permanent magnetic component is affixed to the mastoid region of the skull during a simple outpatient procedure. An external sound processing unit worn behind the ear broadcasts an electromagnetic signal to the magnet, causing it to vibrate. The device theoretically had enough power to treat pure conductive hearing loss, but if the unit was turned up too loud, the Audiant's external unit vibrated so much that it would disconnect from the patient's head and fall to the floor.

Dr. Long was intrigued by the Audiant concept and its issues, and he thought that they could make it better. He was interested in what treatment indication range it could best be used for. He had clinical, surgical and teaching duties during the day, so he worked on research primarily at night. Charlie would often call me around 5 p.m. to see if I was up for a late night research session. I would zip over to his lab and work with him, especially on nights when he was buying pizza. He had a new idea to make an attachment scheme for the device, but he was relying on an overly complicated test system. I helped out as much as I could. Dr. Long's highly intelligent and inquisitive brain came up with some really good ideas to improve the Audiant, and we believed that with just a bit more engineering work, there was a real chance of making the design a lot better for patients.

When we could take time off, Dr. Long and I occasionally went windsurfing together, and even then we spent countless hours musing about hearing implant designs and new ways to measure them, especially on windless days. Charlie helped me work up a highly sensitive test rig that could measure and also change the pressure of the inner ear, allowing us to assess the impact on the biomechanical functions of the ear. I had not been able to get it to work and could not make the micro tips that I needed for the device, but Charlie got me back on track in a day. From then on, whenever I was stumped by anything in research, Charlie was usually the first person I would call.

Then one day Stanford let Dr. Long go. I never got the entire story, and Charlie was too upset to relate all the details to me. When I asked, he simply muttered, "Politics, priorities and politics." It was clear he did not want to go into it. My guess is that it had to do with balancing his love for science and engineering with his clinical, surgical and teaching responsibilities. He was always saying how lucky I was to get to do research full time, and he obviously felt that he was being pulled in numerous directions.

Perhaps Charlie's most important influence on me was that he taught me to believe in getting the lucky break. He always assured me that accidents and lucky mistakes were vastly underrated scientific breakthroughs. Charlie was right. I did not fully appreciate it at the time, but I really was lucky to be doing research on middle ear implants full time, I now understand that lucky breaks are, as Charlie said, underrated. I always pointed out to him that lack of luck is also underrated.

Charlie was almost prophetic in telling me how lucky I was. In the late 1980's and early 1990's, I was might have been the only researcher in the world who had the opportunity to work virtually full time on solving the middle ear implant problem largely unencumbered by additional duties. Almost all the other researchers working in the field at the time were physicians who typically only had one or two afternoons a week free in their schedules to go to their labs. I always joked that that was just enough time to turn on the lights, dust off the equipment, and perhaps even turn it on. To me, real research was a ceaseless grind that took hours of uninterrupted work.

The source of constant worry with most research work is winning research grants. Getting funding for middle ear implant labs and for clinical device programs has always been difficult. Grant money and hearing research funding in the U.S. has always seemed odd to me, with most of the basic science in hearing work primarily focused on studying hearing in animals (i.e., "How the mustached fruit bat localizes sound"), molecular biology, efforts to grow the hair cells of hearing structures (most often in chicks) and other very, very basic research. As a researcher, it was always frustrating to see that the labs, engineers and scientists working on clinical developments and applied research topics were vastly underfunded compared to the basic researchers. The lion's share of funding grants for hearing research always went to the same groups, many of which were working on projects unlikely to be relevant in the quest to help patients suffering from hearing loss in the foreseeable future, if ever. Some or perhaps most of the projects would never have application in my lifetime anyway, and though it is hard to predict where the breakthroughs in a field will come from, I am quite sure the mustached fruit bat study and its kind will never have any effect on my ability to hear better. When I attended meetings such as the American Research in Otolaryngology (ARO) each year, I came to the conclusion that many of the researchers were studying hearing almost as a hobby. Working towards developments that could actually be deployed as treatments often seemed like an afterthought or something they didn't think about at all.

But there are still diamonds in the rough. I met both Dr. Jonathan Spindel and Dr. Roger Ruth at ARO and was intrigued by their idea of using the round window membrane to stimulate hearing in the inner ear. I really did not like Dr. Spindel when I first met him. Despite the fact that he had not yet managed to actually implant a real prototype of his device in a human, he seemed overly sure of himself. Perhaps this was because he had been defending his concept data in the field for too long and had probably spent far too much time justifying his research to skeptics. I first met Jon when he was giving a talk and discussing the merits of RW drive compared with the other direct drive concepts.

"The advantage of the RW placement is that unlike other direct drive concepts, it does not require placing a transducer on the ossicular chain, which would cause necrosis," he stated.

This was a hot-button topic with me and I did not believe this to be true, so I stood up in the full lecture hall and interrupted him. "How do you know that?" I asked.

Jon stared at me in disbelief. Questions were supposed to wait until the end. Completely startled, he was slow to respond. "What? Know what?"

"What you just said," I replied.

"What?"

"That the ossicles will get necrosis if a transducer is in contact with them," I reminded him.

"Well, that is what the doctors said," Jon retorted, looking exasperated.

"Which doctors?" I pursued.

"Oh gosh, I don't know, doctors ..." Jon paused.

"Well if you are not sure, then I don't think you should be saying that."

"But that is what I was told. Look, this is not the point of this talk!" Jon exclaimed.

I sat down, and Dr. Spindel continued his lecture. After the lecture Jon was obviously not too happy with me, and I thought he was a bit of a nimrod for not answering my question. We exchanged dirty looks. It was an inauspicious start to an unlikely friendship, but he eventually became a big fan of my work and I of his.

In 1990 our grant ran out, leaving us with no funding until the next one was approved. I was not worried, though: We had written a new grant proposal, and I was quite certain that we would get funding because of Dr. Goode's excellent track record. I had just received my master's degree and was due for a break anyway.

The grant running out turned out to be a blessing because it gave me four months of unpaid leave. I decide to go on a world tour with Mickey Weems, a surfing buddy from Hawaii. I had met Mickey on one of my many surfing trips to the islands made possible by incredible American Express and United Airlines ticket deals. The University of Hawaii had a sister campus relationship with the University of Oregon, so I had sat through a couple of the anthropology courses that Mickey taught at the Manoa Campus in Honolulu. I think I liked Mickey so much because was he was so unlike me. I was into hard science, engineering and finding ways to solve problems with technology. Mickey was nothing like that: He was an expert in religious studies, anthropology, and culture and how they affected society and the individual. He could ramble on about topics I had never heard of, such as the role of communal dances in some far-off African tribe, why religious monuments were shaped the way they were, or the role of women in the early Christianity. Mickey seemed to know it all, while I had no clue.

I started off on my world adventure by traveling across the country on a Greyhound bus because I wanted to see the real USA. I got way more than I bargained for, and I do not recommend it. I experienced a minor street riot near the bus station South Los Angeles and had to step over people who had either been left unconscious or were just sleeping on the sidewalk. I was robbed in Denver and almost got stranded in the middle of Nebraska when I misheard the driver saying how long we were stopping for. A driver took a wrong turn in New York, and wound up getting the bus stuck so badly in the Bronx that we actually had to call the police to come and block a street to get it out. A guy on the bus tried to sell me Californium, which he touted as one of the rarest elements ever but which in fact looked an awful lot like a coin that had been left on train tracks. There were plenty of good times along the way, though, when I stopped to visit friends and family.

I met up with Mickey in New Hampshire, and we flew to London to start backpacking across Europe. It is not uncommon for backpackers to end up going their separate ways, but Mickey and I parted company sooner than we thought. For reasons I never really understood, Mickey wanted to go to France almost immediately after we landed in the UK, whereas I wanted to see Scotland and Ireland before heading over to the mainland. I ended up spending most of my three months in Europe with a surfer from Australia named Mark. We went everywhere: France, Sweden, Denmark, Germany, and Italy. We were just blown away by the beauty of the Swiss Alps, and I could not believe how much it looked like a model train set. I thought about how cool it would be to live in the Alps some day. We headed up to Saas, Fee and Zermatt, where I spent two weeks trying to teach an Australian to ski. By our third week of skiing, both of us were running out of money. That's when I got word from Dr. Goode that I was to return to my post at Stanford as soon as possible.

"Hey babe, get your butt back here! We got it!"

The new grant had come through, and I was soon on a plane back to work.

Rents in Sunnyvale and the surrounding areas had always been high, but as a junior scientist and part-time grad student, I couldn't even afford a small studio apartment. It looked like I had two choices: to do yard work and keep the pool clean in exchange for the right to live in the guest quarters of one of the many millionaires' homes in Palo Alto or Los Altos, or to crash in a spare room at the back of my parents' house. Thanks to the grant, however, I was promoted to Biomedical Engineer/Scientist.GS-9/3 at three times my previous salary. Dr. Goode had promised that I would be happy, and he had outdone himself. I could now afford to pay rent.

The new grant provided us with enough money to shop for our own laser Doppler vibrometer. Soon sales reps from the manufacturer were up in our lab presenting the latest and greatest laser system. They were trying to sell me the higher-priced model, but I insisted on getting the less expensive unit. The smaller unit would be easier to transport, and I had a hunch that portability would be important. If I wanted to use the laser Doppler to measure live human ears instead of just temporal bones, I needed one I could take with me.

Three months after the laser Doppler was delivered, sales representatives from the company came back to see how I was doing.

I will never forget the surprised look on their faces when they walked into the lab and saw the precious laser Doppler vibrometer suspended from the ceiling by a precarious-looking track and mounting system. They were not sure what to think at first, but I explained the system to them: I had salvaged an articulating arm from an experimental prototype laser that had been left in my basement lab and used the mirror mounts to run the LDV beam into an operating microscope. This way the LDV had three degrees of freedom of movement. The entire system could be moved anywhere and up and down within a two-meter radius.

"What it lacks in appearance it more than makes up for in function, I assure you," I explained. "It works great. I'm a function-over-form kind of guy."

"What does Dr. Goode say about it?" the sales rep asked.

"Oh, he does doesn't know. But he will once he sees the data – if I get it!"

Dr. Goode did get his data. I hired my youngest brother Michael to come and sit in a special chair I had built in the lab. I can't say he was not worried, but the $100 I promised to pay him to sit still for one afternoon reassured him. I had learned that mass was the key to good LDV work, so the chair had been weighted down by huge bags of sand that I had lugged in one weekend. Dr. Nishihara, who was our current visiting Japanese researcher, placed a small reflective target on Michael's eardrum. When we pumped sound into his ear canal via a special sealed speculum chamber, sound filled his ear canal and his eardrum vibrated. The articulating arm enabled us to direct the laser beam by changing its position and microscope position directly to the vibrating target. For the first time ever, we were able to measure the vibrational pattern of the living human ear with the LDV system. We had done it!

Once the graph was plotted, I tore off the sheet and ran down to Dr. Goode's office. I blew right passed Linda, cut through a bunch of waiting residents, and shoved the page under Dr. Goode's nose.

"Jesus! Jesus!!! You did it! How on earth ...?" Dr. Goode was bouncing around. There was nothing like really good data hot off the lab bench to get Dr. Goode pumped up, and this data this was unprecedented for us. I explained to Dr. Goode how I had accomplished the measurement.

"I fired it down the OPMI-1 beam splitter through the articulating arm that I took off that laser Stu (Harmon) left here. I made a mounting fixture and then fired the whole thing through the deal while adjusting the stand-off. The usual thing," I said.

"And it worked?!" Goode asked, obviously surprised.

"Yeah! I know what you said, but I knew it just had to."

"God. I gotta see this!" Goode was really, really happy.

We ran up to the lab, which had been completely transformed since the last time Dr. Goode had been in it. Before I opened the door, I said, "There is one more thing I should tell you before we go in. I had to hang the laser Doppler from the ceiling. But don't freak out. It has a safety."

I opened the door, and Goode saw the laser, his most precious and expensive piece of lab equipment, hanging on the track with the articulating arm hanging down and the microscope, all weighted down with the thousand pounds of sandbags I had added to the rig. A huge, heavy-duty reclining position medical chair had been bolted to the floor. Monitors and scopes were strategically positioned so they could be monitored by the systems operator. About a half million dollars worth of equipment had been made into a new custom-made system specifically for measuring live human ears to unprecedented levels of precision.

"Jesus Christ, Geoff! What did you do? What the frig did you do?"

"It works! It really works!" My brother was still there, so we showed Doctor Goode how it worked on his ear.

As he watched us direct the laser beam through the microscope onto the target we had placed on Michael's eardrum, Goode could not contain himself.

"Amazing! Amazing! This is a first! We gotta write this paper now!"

"Dr. Goode, there is one thing. We need Jont Allen to come. I really need his help on the software."

"You got it!" Goode promised.

Less than two weeks later, Jont Allen was in our lab. Jont Allen is one of the world's authorities on all things hearing. He was also one of the original members of the team that worked on the ReSound technology at Bell labs with Fred Waldhour. I considered Jont a wizard, especially on signal processing and analysis, and I am one of the very few people who know how indebted the field of hearing biomechanics is to him. I first met Jont in 1988 at ReSound, where we were both consultants, and I got to know him fairly well. He helped me with my early LDV work in the ReSound lab and had an endless flow of ideas, many of which were really helpful. I believe ReSound tried to hire Jont full time, but he just never made the move to California.

Jont was just like Dr. Goode in that you had to spend a lot of time around him before you could understand what he was saying. In fact there are probably only a few of us on the planet who can follow what Jont is talking about, and I mean that as a compliment. His was brilliant, and both Dr. Goode and I knew that he was the key we needed to take the LDV to the next level.

We had the new laser and some very crude software that I had cobbled together. It worked, but it was clumsy and it could only reduce the noise floor for the test system by about 10 decibels. I needed to get at least another 20 dB to have a system that could rapidly measure a lot of live human ears. This had never been done before, and we needed to do a large cohort (I planned to do at least 100 human ears) to lay down the vibration pattern of the ear in response to sound input. The DSP board required us to use Fortran software programming, and Fortran was a terror of a software language for me. We really, really needed Jont Allen.

Somehow Dr. Goode was able to convince Jont to come and work with us in the lab. For three days, I laid out for Jont what we needed the software to do, what we needed in order to make it self-calibrating, the signal types, the levels, what the screens should look like, and how the final data should be parsed out so that I could dump it into my analysis software. We started on a Friday morning and finished Sunday, and we got it done!

Jont's FFT software astonished me by going far beyond the 20 dB I had figured we needed and improving the system by an incredible 80dB. This system made it possible for us to measure temporal bones in a few minutes instead of hours and movements so small that they were approaching the molecular level. The funny part was that no one believed me when I told them how low our system could go.

That Sunday night, after we had finished up our work, Dr. Goode took Jont and me out for a late dinner. I was ecstatic. I could not wait to get back to lab to take this laser for a spin. I knew that I could now go beyond simply measuring the vibration patterns of the human ear; that this new tool would enable me to finally start making and measuring transducers which could be used to fix the human ear. Thanks to this new breakthrough, I could now build transducers in my father's garage and rapidly test how they worked. I alone had a machine that could rapidly test microtransducers, and in a few months, I would know more about micro hearing transducers than just about anyone.

Now I do not want to give the impression that I was just some dweeb science geek that had zero social life. Although I was married to my research work, my philosophy has always been to work hard and play harder. As young scientist, I was infamous for being out at Coyote Pointe or Waddell Creek when the wind was good for windsurfing. While I was at Stanford, the docs and I would often squeeze in a round or two at the Stanford golf course. I would stop off to hit a few balls when I passed the Stanford golf driving range. It might sound silly, but hitting buckets and buckets of golf balls is still my favorite thing to do. I would also squeeze in frequent trips to go scuba diving or head off to Hawaii when cheap tickets were available. In the winter I often went skiing in the Sierras or in Colorado. I attended parties hosted by med students, research docs, Stanford students, and of course Dr. Goode. Sometimes Dr. Goode and I would go out for dinner and drinks after work, starting out at the California Café and winding up in downtown Los Altos or at The Echo.

I have been really blessed by the many great women in my life, from my first girlfriend, Kristi, to my lovely wife, Sabina. In between, during my research days, I had a few girlfriends. One was a school teacher I had met in at the Olympics in Colorado, but that relationship ended when it became clear she was never going to move to California and I was never going to move out to Colorado and find a decent post. Another was the daughter of one of the Stanford deans, but she left to do her doctorate at University of Virginia, and her parents had understandable and largely warranted misgivings about me dating their daughter.

I also dated a fair share of the women I met through work, including a few residents and Stanford medical school students. When I think back on those days, the relationship that made the most sense and now best embodies that time was with a girl I dated on and off for a few years. For some strange reason, I cannot remember her name, but she was a student at San Jose State and worked at Chili's restaurant across the Valley in Milpitas. A perfect California girl, she had blonde hair, a dazzling smile, and a permanent tan – and she was smart. We had a lot in common: We both liked The Cure, and she even made extra money lifeguarding. We both really, really liked dancing, so we went to clubs like the Edge in Palo Alto, the One Step Beyond in Sunnyvale, DB Coopers in San Jose, the club DV8 in San Francisco, and sometimes the Catalyst in Santa Cruz or Mountain Charlie's in Los Gatos. We could get lost in the music and dancing for hours at a time while the world and our worries melted away, and we danced until they kicked us out. It was a terrific feeling, and those were good times. I am not sure why we never got serious. Maybe we just thought it would ruin the moment and the feeling of being young and alive in California, or maybe I just forgot to check the clock in the lab and spent too many late nights there. For whatever reason, we drifted apart.

To be honest, I was a bit hard to get a handle on anyway. Take music: I was a serious fan of the Grateful Dead, thanks in large part to my research buddies at Stanford. Though I never sold all my possessions and followed the band around the world selling t-shirts and toasted cheese sandwiches for money to get to the next show, I still was a bit of a Deadhead. Yet at the same time I was a modern rocker and saw no problem in trading in my tie-dyed t-shirt for parachute pants with dual belts, shiny black shoes, and a matching skinny leather tie and going to the trendiest clubs. I was a big fan of Bob Marley, yet I also liked country and was always ready to pull on a pair of boots and Wrangler jeans for a night of two stepping. In fact, the only music I could not tolerate was rap. I didn't see any real conflict in the diversity of my taste in music, and I did not establish my identity from hanging with any particular clique of people or following any specific style fashion trend.

My personality as a young man could be a bit too animated at times, to say the least. One time when I was returning from the annual American Academy of Otolaryngology meeting, I didn't find out until I was checking in at the airport that I had misread my ticket. I thought the flight I had booked by over phone was on Thursday, but it had actually been on Tuesday, two days earlier.

"I'm sorry sir. There is nothing I can do," the airline check-in clerk told me. "A one-way fare back to SFO today will cost you $1,800 plus ticketing fees."

I was stunned. That was a lot of money for me – more than four times what I had already paid – and I couldn't afford it. I took my bags and went and sat in a chair across from check-in while I tried to sort through my options. The only thing I could come up with was spending the next four days on a Greyhound bus, but I had to be back sooner. That's when I noticed that agent I had talked to had gone off on break. "Oh, what the heck?" I thought. "Let's give it another shot". I pulled my hair back so that both my giant hearing aids were clearly visible and got back in line. When it was my turn, I went to a check-in clerk who was a rather small, pleasant-looking young woman and handed her my tickets.

She looked at the tickets, frowned, and said something like, "I'm sorry, sir, but these were for last Tuesday's flight."

I steadied myself, looked her right in the eye, and shouted "Whahhhhh???" as loudly as I could. Using my best heavy hearing-impaired voice, I said "I yam hewwwing impaired!" I turned to show her my hearing aids on both sides. "I wanted tickets for a Thuuuuuuuday, not a Tueeeedaayy!" I yelled. My voice was so loud that everyone in the check-in area was staring. Then something amazing happened.

She looked at me and bellowed back, "These tickets were for last Tuesday but you wanted to fly today. I will change your tickets to today's flight!"

I was blown away by how loud she was, but it was working, so I yelled back, "Da make a mistake. Notta Tewwsdady butta Thuuuday!" Thank goodness I had purchased my tickets directly from the airline.

She changed my tickets, checked in my bags, and then shouted, "Your departure gate is gate nine!"

I was so impressed that as she handed me my tickets, I could not resist. "Gaaee five!"

"No! Gate nine! GATE NINE!" As she hollered back, she was writing the number on the boarding card with a red pen in inch-high letters and pointed to the departure gate hall.

"Dank yew!" I said, and walked off thinking how glad that I was that my ploy had worked and saved me $1800. At the same time, I was shocked to realize if people knew I was deaf, they automatically assumed that I could not read regular size lettering.

I guess most people would not have gone as far as I had and would have figured out a way to come up with the $1800. But the fact is that when I bought the tickets over the phone, I must have heard them wrong or they had heard me wrong. It t is easy to see how this could have happened because I had an almost impossible time talking on any telephone, even my special amplified ones. Overall, this incident served as another reminder of how important my work was and kept me motivated to find new treatment options for hearing loss.

But the point remains that I was a bit rough around the edges back then. At work I was sowing the seeds for a future business; at the same time I was laying down the scientific basis for the biomechanics of the ear and for a new field. If I had spare time in the evening, I often painted pictures that I hoped to sell. I was socially liberal and fiscally conservative. I was more a Democrat than a Republican, but I voted for George Bush Senior twice (not George W! never!). I was a member of the Sierra Club, yet I was (and still am) pro nuclear power. I was comfortable hanging out with my hippie friends in Santa Cruz but could put on a suit and tie and mingle with the yuppies. I might spend the morning as a deckhand on a rich guy's yacht in San Francisco Bay and go to reggae fest that evening. That was me; that was my life. I was all over the place.

One of my best friends and roommates, Dave Barnett, was an avid water skier, and we would often go to the Sacramento Delta or to one of the nearby lakes to ski. I had bought a custom ultra-surfboard on a surf trip to Hawaii and had managed to get it back to California without even having to pay for an extra bag. I used this board (the stick was a 4"10" Lightning Bolt) to surf behind the ski boat, using a short tow line. I got really good at it and eventually added fiberglass foot straps to the board so that I could jump the wake. I was wakeboarding way before real wakeboards were being made. Guess I should have patented it.

The fact of the matter, however, is that although I was clearly aware that I was seriously into medical science, I didn't realize then how much I loved doing research. I feel like research and medicine chose me back then, and they have shaped my life more than I could ever have imagined.

Lab Rats

*"Great ideas often come dressed
in the clothes of hard work."*

Thomas Edison

There was a sign on the door of Stanford lab directly across from mine that read, "If we are not here by ten, then we will be here by noon. If we are not in by two, then we will definitely be here tomorrow." Next to the sign was a printout of a lab safety warning issued by the safety officer that read, "Safety Violation. Finding: Pizza on lab bench." It was displayed on the door as sort of a merit badge.

Welcome to the world of the lab rats, a world that is home to the men and women who run the research labs of the elite institutions of the world. They are a select and special group of people who have their own unique callings, rituals, culture and a general reverence for Far Side cartoon-type of humor. They often work strange hours, and oddly enough, to the untrained eye, some of the best hardly seem to work at all. Lab rats generally loathe the trappings of bureaucracy and administrative type thinking, perhaps because the scientific method and the chronic repetition that typically accompanies research projects are exacting enough.

When I was growing up in Silicon Valley and in the early days of my research, there were a lot of (for lack of a better word) "interesting" people working in the labs. Many of them may not have fit in anywhere else. It is my firm belief that a healthy, long-term, cutting edge and economically healthy research program starts with "interesting" people. They look different and often act differently than the mainstream, yet they are the keys to innovation. "Interesting" guys need grant money, affordable housing, lab space and as little oversight as possible. What "interesting" guys hate most of all is bureaucracy, and any more than the occasional note to remind them that pizza really should not be eaten on the lab bench can cause them to run. They are generally what might be called a management challenge. But they are also brilliant, and if left alone to work on their projects, there is no telling what they may come up with.

Lab rats often are tough to figure out and sometimes almost impossible to understand, but we have to have them. When I was a boy growing up in Silicon Valley, they were omnipresent. When I worked in the Stanford labs, you could still see many of them making their daily trek to the labs in beat-up old Toyotas or Volkswagens. As affordable housing became more and more expensive in the Valley and the Upper Peninsula, they tended to move farther away, to the far reaches of commutability: the hills near La Honda or in Salinas, Santa Cruz, or Berkeley and beyond. The record holder was a guy I knew who drove in from Carmel Valley. Yet most of them showed up every day – or at least most days.

Sometimes, though, these people were just too "interesting." I remember one researcher, a medical student from Europe, who was visiting one of the labs one summer. He had somehow convinced the anatomy lab to release a full human head for research by assuring the staff at the department that we had done the paperwork and that it must have been misfiled. After using my name to get the tissue released, he put the human head into a bucket covered with only a towel and then carried it into the hospital administrator's office and joked with the secretary about it. You can only imagine my horror when I received a phone call from her.

"Hi, Geoffrey. This is Karen. You know that guy Dr. XXX? Well, he just walked into our office here with a bucket and made jokes about the fact that there was a human head in it!"

That definitely got my attention. "I am sure he was only kidding," I said. "Nobody would ever do that. Besides, we don't have any tissue like that on our request sheets right now."

"Well, OK, but he had a bucket that looked like it was heavy. You know, there is something wrong with that guy. He really gives me the creeps. Tell him to not come here anymore."

I hung up and walked up to the lab. There was Dr. XXX, in my lab of all places, removing a human head from a bucket.

"What the hell are you doing? Did you just have that in Karen's office?" I shouted.

"I was just joking," he replied.

"I don't know what you are doing with this, but you need to stop it and stop it now!" I hollered.

I was shaking with anger and shocked at the scene before me. I had to inform Dr. Goode and get the head back to the anatomy lab. I was sure that the paperwork had not been done. I left the lab and rushed down to Dr. Goode's office, uncertain what to do.

Goode was busy as usual, and I waited impatiently for my turn behind several residents in line at his office door. When I finally got into his office, I tried to explain what had happened and find out what I should do. But before I could finish, Dr. Goode got a call from one of the nurses in the operating room.

"Dr. Goode! You have a researcher who just brought a human head into the O.R. without our approval! Get up here now!"

Horrified, Dr. Goode and I rushed upstairs to the surgical suite. In O.R. 3 we found Dr. XXX, still with the head. Goode was angrier than I had ever seen him.

"You see, Dr. Goode? I told you!" I exclaimed.

Dr. XXX said, "I am doing a mock surgery and I have an approval form."

"No! No you don't" Dr. Goode bellowed. "This is not how we do things around here!"

I returned the head to the anatomy department, and Dr. XXX was returned to Europe. It was the most stupid incident I had seen in all my years of working in research. I had a talk with the autopsy chief, who told me that a new person had not been sure what to do when confronted by the demanding researcher and had apparently made a mistake. We fixed it so that could never happen again. I couldn't fathom what Dr. XXX found so funny about taking a human head into the administrator's office and joking about it with the secretary. That was just so weird. It takes all kinds, but there really is such a thing as "too interesting."

"Interesting" people should not be confused with geeks. Generally speaking, geeks are people who are totally smitten with all things high tech, and they are a legendary breed in Silicon Valley. "Interesting" people, on the other hand, love high tech, but they also love hard-core scientific research.

Take for example Dan Stein, who worked for Stanford's anesthesia research group two floors up from me in the VA research building. The first time I met him it was for lunch. I watched Dan, a strict vegan, hack up an entire bushel of cilantro, put it into the largest vat of plain yoghurt I had ever seen, and slurp the entire concoction down. Whenever I talked with Dan, the conversation would mutate into a discussion of his diet within a few minutes. I soon learned to never mention food around him.

Back in the days when Dan was a punk rocker, he had shaved his head skinhead style. Now he was into yoga and meditated whenever he could find a few minutes. If Dan took a vacation, it was never typical. He once took a month-long solo backpack trip to Guadalajara. While there he cut himself on some weird type of plant that caused his leg to swell to three times its normal size. Delirious, he ended up crawling back to a remote mountain shack and hiring some locals to carry him to the next town. He finally made it back to a remote medical outpost, where reportedly he almost died and they almost had to amputate his leg. But somehow, Dan survived. The grant Dan was working under ran out for a few months, giving him the perfect opportunity to head off to India on what was supposed to be a three-month backpack this time. He returned six months later having spent way, way too much time in an ashram. Never missing an opportunity to do something different to his hair, his head was now cleanly shaven. He wanted us to call him by some new weird Indian name that his new guru had assigned to him, but I told him I would never do that. Dan had taken to wearing read pajamas and lots of dangling beads. It took Dan a few months (and me a lot of trips up to his lab to shout, "Hey Dan! Danny boy" over and over just to remind him what his real name was) to return to a normal state after that one. Once he was re-programmed, he joined a drum group and spent hours in parks in drum circles after work.

Dan and I would sometimes brew beer together at his cottage behind a home in Menlo Park, near the VA hospital that served as the setting for *One Flew Over the Cuckoo's Nest* by Ken Kesey, who worked as a researcher. Our goal was to brew the best tasting totally organic pesticide-free beer ever. "Rasta Brau," our black, high-calorie, and high-alcohol stout, wasn't bad, but our dream of winning an amateur beer brewing award was not to be. Most of our beer tasted terrible and much of it was not even drinkable.

Dan was deeply into his research in a yin-yang, love-hate sort of way. One day he would be studying for the MCAT exam; the next he was ready to chuck it all and move to Santa Cruz and be a hippie bum devoted to drumming on the beach all day. Unlike me, Dan actually sold all his possessions at one point and followed the Grateful Dead around the country for a year. The last time I saw Dan was after a show at the Shoreline Amphitheatre, where he was out in the middle of the parking lot, drumming with a bunch of his friends. I heard he eventually did go to medical school, and I have no doubt that he is a leader in whatever field he chose. He was a truly interesting guy.

Another "interesting" person was Eric, a researcher for the ophthalmology department and a former standout on the Stanford swim team. Eric had brawn and a brain to match. He was as sharp as a tack and could talk about almost anything. He was the real deal. He wore this huge, ugly, unforgettable black Yak fabric dreadlock sweater he had picked up in Tibet, a strange garment that actually looked good on him. But Eric was tall and strapping, with broad shoulders, bleached blonde hair, and a face that was easy on the eyes, so anything would have probably have looked good on him.

Eric would work odd late-night hours since his cell cultures required round-the-clock tending. He was also an epic big wave surfer and would go out in waves so massive that they just left me standing on the beach, clutching my board in fear. Any time there was a high-surf advisory, Eric was not in lab; he was getting pounded by the Pacific Ocean. You could find his beat-up Honda Civic hidden in some pullout on the side of the Pacific Coast Highway near a surf break while he bobbed on the massive swells waiting for the next perfect wave. He was hands down the most aggressive surfer I had ever seen.

One day Eric came into lab looking particularly haggard.

"How does the other guy look? I enquired. "Looks like you had a rough night."

Eric said, "Oh, yeah. I'm really zonked. Some friends and I were hanging out by the bridge in SF, so I decided to swim under it."

"Swim what?" I asked, not sure what he meant.

"It. The Gate," he replied.

"What? You mean the Golden Gate Bridge?" I was incredulous.

"Swam right under the Golden Gate Bridge," Eric stated.

"What!? How did you get back?"

"When I got to the other side I couldn't find my friends, so I had to swim back. I got pretty cold about halfway."

I really did not know what to say. I had done more than my share of shore swims and had dreamed of one day swimming the Catalina Channel, but what Eric had just described was pure madness.

"Did you at least check the currents?" I asked him.

"Why?"

"Well, because I have sailed out there a lot, and I know that if you don't time it right, you wind up on your way to Hawaii." Eric's eyes opened wide when he realized I was not joking.

Eric had managed his Golden Gate swim in less than three hours. It was an unbelievable spur-of-the-moment stunt, but according to Eric's friend and brother, he had really pulled it off.

Eric was a sensation in the research lab, and his work was legendary because his output was so high. When his grant ran out, Eric took off on a surfing trip to Mexico. He was supposed to come back, but that was the last I heard of him.[3]

Bob Sellers was the rock star of our labs if ever there was one. Bob was the man that a lot of my fellow researchers looked up to and liked more than anyone else in the labs. He was a unique individual who in addition to his research work was an expert diver and marine photographer. Bob and his brother would fly all the way to Tahiti, fly on another few hours to some remote island, then hop aboard a dive boat and motor out for a few days of what can only be called extreme diving. The dive shots Bob brought back from his trips were the most amazing I had ever seen and featured crea-

---

3 I checked out this story because I was not sure if Eric was being truthful or not. I learned that the distance was three kilometers in each direction. I also learned that there is in fact a race for the exact same course Eric said he swam, although they work with boat traffic. Eric said he made the swim because it was so calm that day and because there were no waves to surf anywhere. I now believe that his feat was not only possible but that his story was absolutely true. It would have been possible for a swimmer as well trained as Eric to do this – assuming, of course, that he did not get run over by a boat or something.

tures I had never seen before. They were a cut above anything in any of my dive magazines or *National Geographic*. Bob's images were like the Ansel Adams equivalent of dive photography. On dives he would often separate from everyone else (a serious diving no-no), then try to minimize his bubbles and lie perfectly still on the ocean floor hoping that something would cruise by. Rather than stalk the animals themselves, Bob would try determine where their food source was and then spend hours of bottom time waiting there. There is no doubt that it worked because he had the proof on film. The other researchers looked up to Bob because he was a great person in addition to being a terrific researcher. "Bob's got it all figured out," they would say. He had this group of fans who were wannabe Bobs, and he was one of the few researchers I have known who had the equivalent of groupies. Bob had also been a founding father of the Fungus Federation of Santa Cruz (motto: "We put the *Fun* in Fungus"), and his mushroom soup was the best ever.

Then there was Bill Ebling, who worked in the anesthesiology labs upstairs with Dan. Bill was forever going on and on about an environmental issue he called the carbon problem. He always had some alarmist topic to expound on and said things like, "Everyone is talking about climate change, but nobody is talking about using up all the carbon and what that does." I think Bill was the first person any of us had ever really heard discussing the carbon problem, so we were not really sure what to say. Bill was a super sharp guy and was recruited to a new position at the National Institute of Health.

All these researchers could have easily passed as geeks if they desired, but they didn't use technology for technology's sake or aimlessly tinker with technology for the fun of it. They all used technology as a means to help solve the complexities of their studies. Bill and I had to make device drivers for our hardware and plot our data. By expediting the process, we could get much more done in less time. Without advanced technology applications, some of our more advanced research projects would have been impossible tasks and cost even more money. We all used computers to make our incredibly complicated work a bit less complicated. When we got it right, we got a lot more data and a lot more done. Dan bought a "lunch box computer" despite my begging him not to. "Look, Dan,"

I said, "it is not a stand-type machine and it is not really a portable machine either. It is the worst of both worlds." But Dan always knew better, and somehow he made it work.

I was fortunate to be working with and hanging around such a group of talented researchers, such smart and unique individuals. To say it was a stimulating environment is an understatement. Being associated with one of the top research institutions in the world also gave us all ample opportunities to attend lectures on a host of subjects, often by the many VIP speakers brought in by Stanford. The days I spent working in the labs with my colleagues were happy ones.

In 1989, the Loma Pieta earthquake just about destroyed the labs and left them a gigantic mess. Like a lot of people in the San Francisco Bay Area, I had actually gone home early that day to watch the World Series baseball game with my brother Michael and some friends. Just as the game was just getting started, the earthquake hit, and we all ran outside into my parents' backyard. The rolling and shock waves causing electric lines to zip through the air, and the water in the swimming pool was surging out in two meter waves. Once the quake stopped, we went back inside. Our house was undamaged, and we did not lose electricity or water or anything. In fact, other than the pool water flooding the backyard, we were in fine shape.

The damage to the rest of the Bay Area, though, was catastrophic. When we got to work the next day, we found a sign saying that said the labs would be closed because all the chemicals that had been shaken off the shelves had mingled and created a huge cesspool of chemical sludge. The main hospital had sustained significant damage, and all the patients had had to be evacuated. There were so many gigantic cracks throughout the facility that it was hard to find an undamaged wall. Luckily, the shaking had stopped before the buildings' foundations gave way completely. Had it continued much longer, the entire facility could have collapsed.

Bob's chemical storage locker was a particular mess. A relatively large room, it was full of fireproof storage units holding all the chemicals used in the facility. Although everything had been correctly sorted and secured, several of the storage units had ripped away from their security supports and toppled, knocking each other down in a giant game of toxic dominos. Many of the chemicals were stored in glass jars that had shattered on the floor in an array of chemical color and smell. We all had to head in wearing protective clothing. We knew that the safety officer assigned to help us manage the cleanup did not understand what we were looking at, and we also knew that we were probably the people best qualified to clean up the labs, except for the truly hazardous ones. In all honesty, we were not really sure what had spilled and what hadn't or what the chemical reactions might be, but we all knew that it could be pretty nasty, to say the least.

I ran upstairs to secure my lab, and in an hour or so I had it pretty well cleaned up. My lab was relatively easy because I had very few hazardous chemicals. Most of the damage was to the electronics equipment, and a lot of my gear was strewn across the floor in pieces.

When I was finished, I went over to help Bob, who did not have it so easy. His acid bath had flipped onto the floor, and all the chemicals, many stored in jars, had pulled through the safety brackets and broken apart. He came out of the room, took off his mask, and said, "We really need a hazmat crew. I mean a real one."

"Until we can get one, we are pretty much it," I told him. "We can't let the building catch fire or become a toxic sludge pit, so we need to step up and at least get it to the point where it does not get worse."

We scooped up as much of the chemical sludge as we could and put it in disposal vessels. We then took what we could downstairs to the disposal area that had been set up for a hazmat pick up. Bob was not too impressed with the safety officer managing the cleanup, but after a few weeks all the labs were back up and running.

Neither of us had ever been too happy with the safety officers, especially Bob. After all, it was Bob who posted all the warnings on his door, including the one about pizza on lab bench. One day a few months after the earthquake, I heard Bob talking much more loudly than normal. This was odd, because he was normally a gentle, soft-spoken man. I stepped out in the hallway, and there stood Bob, confronting an individual holding a clipboard in one hand. In the other he had a bright red plastic bucket with the inscription "SAFETY" in bold letters. Bob was standing between the man and the lab safety shower.

"Now listen to me!" Bob bellowed. "After the earthquake and cleanup, I don't need any more excitement. I am telling you now: Do *NOT* pull the lever again!"

"But they fixed it!" the young man replied.

"That's what the last guy said before he pulled the lever the last time. They did not fix it," Bob said very sternly.

The point of concern was the labs eyewash and shower system. In theory, if someone was ever doused in chemicals or caught on fire or got acid in their eyes, they could run out in the hallway and wash it off with a big dose of H20 by pulling the handle on the emergency wash station. The fact that there was no drain for the water had been a minor construction oversight. The 5,000 gallon water tank on the roof of our building had a one-way valve that once released would not caused reset until the entire 5,000 gallons had emptied out through the shower, flooding the halls and soaking the building's electrical wiring.

Bob finally prevailed, and the safety officer slunk off. I followed Bob into his lab.

"Can you believe these guys?!" Bob asked. "They pulled that handle a couple of years ago and just about electrocuted the guys down stairs, and ..."

A loud "Twaannngggg!" sound came from the hallway.

We both looked out into the hallway, and there was the safety guy standing under the shower with the bucket. Water was rushing out of the shower.

"OHHHH MYYY FRIGGGINNNN GAWWDDDD!" Bob shouted. He bolted for the stairs to run down and shut off the power before someone got electrocuted.

Not sure what to do myself, I watched the safety officer. As the bucket filled, he tried to shut off the valve, but water kept pouring out of the system. Desperate, the safety officer ran into the bathroom, poured the full bucket down the toilet, and ran back. There was already water everywhere.

Bob returned and shouted at me, "Go get a mop and whatever you can find! We need to direct the flow down the stairwell and keep it away from the elevator shaft! Grab a flashlight too." I grabbed my flashlight and a mop and began pushing the water down the staircase.

By this time the poor safety officer was practically crying. Shame and disbelief were etched on his face as he kept rushing back and forth, filling the bucket and pouring the contents down the restroom toilet. But he had unleashed a deluge: 5,000 gallons of water, the equivalent of a small swimming pool, was streaming through our shower. The first "Bam! Bam! Bam!" from the shorts hit just as Bob killed the main power. The lights went off, and the few emergency back-up lights dimly lit the corridor. After that episode, the safety people avoided Bob and me as much as possible.

Following the earthquake, the safety committee had a construction company install safety doors on all the shelves, as well as lassos for all the books and binders in all the labs. There was only one chemical in my lab that gave me slight cause for concern: an acid called flux that I used during soldering. I only had 5cc's of the stuff, though, stored in a syringe that I kept in a little box right next to the soldering station.

Not long after the safety doors had been installed, I was working at my soldering station one day. I opened up one of the new doors, which promptly fell off its track. The door landed directly on the syringe full of flux and, overcoming sheer statistical and common mechanical principals, somehow managed to turn the syringe around 180 degrees, point it up at a 45 degree angle, and depress the plunger completely. In one amazingly swift motion, a jet stream sprayed the entire syringe full of flux directly into my left eye. I froze, stunned by the sheer physical impossibility of being attacked by the newly installed safety feature and by the sheer mathematical improbability of the moment. What were the odds? Finally my brain kicked in: *Move! Move! Move!* it screamed. I ran out in to the hallway to the safety shower and eye wash, which was still attached to the 5,000 gallon drum on the roof. I looked at it and then thought to myself, *Well, crikey! It's the one time in my life I've ever needed an emergency eye wash, but I'm not about to dump 5,000 gallons into the building again!* I ran down to the ophthalmology clinic as fast as I could, grabbed the first resident I could find, and had him set me up an emergency saline drip. I spent the rest of the afternoon in the clinic flushing out my eye. At that moment, I hated safety people.

As research dollars got tighter and the field for grants more competitive, the "interesting" people were the big losers. Grants and funding are generally awarded to the more well-heeled and high-visibility projects, the research labs that are best equipped and have the staff to write the best grant proposals. Today, there are far fewer "interesting" people to be seen around the labs where I used to work. I fear we have lost a key economic and scientific leading edge. Sure, many of the "interesting" research people were so far out on the cutting edge of their fields that they may have fallen off, but now good labs and certainly people with good ideas were being left behind, hurting the chances of finding that one-in-a-million needle in the hay stack or the researcher who comes up with the next Nobel Prize winning or concept that becomes the next big idea. I'm convinced that the key to really good research is hiring the best "interesting" people. We need them more than we know.

FMT Eureka

*"This FMT ... jumps like
a Willys in four wheel drive!"*

Dr. David Foyt

The primary goal of my work was to develop a new kind of hearing system that could be implanted to treat hearing loss. As a hearing loss patient myself, I wanted something new; the next new thing. I and the millions of others with hearing loss like me wanted something different, something that worked. I wanted to be fixed.

Non-inventors seem to think that the process of invention involves and leads to a "Eureka! moment, but the truth is that inventions do not suddenly materialize out of thin air unless someone has invested a lot of time, work and hard thinking. If there is a moment where the light bulb goes on, the brain fires up, the idea presents itself, and the inventor says, "By Jove, I think I've got it!" it usually comes after years of effort.

Any good device requires a good invention. And a good invention always has its share of good stories along the way. I can recall one day I was in Dr. Rodney Perkins' office as a patient, and we were finishing the exam and reviewing my test results.

"What about surgery? I asked him. "Is there anything you can do to fix me up?"

"No, nothing that would help your loss," he replied.

So I said "What about a hearing implant, an implanted device like one of those cochlear implants?"

He answered, "No, those won't help you, but we are working on something that might be a possibility in a couple years."

I could not have envisioned that only a few short years later I would be employed by his colleague Dr. Richard Goode and working on that very project, and that hearing implants and the sciences surrounding this field would become my life's work. I also had no idea how far in the future the realization of a new hearing implant that could be used to treat my hearing loss would be.

My laser Doppler was not only a great tool for measuring and defining the biomechanical structures of the ear; it was also ideally suited to measuring devices that could be used to repair and stimulate ears. It was a terrific way to measure small devices that, in theory, could be used to fix ears. The new laser system, with Jont Allen's software running it, was the instrument that made it possible for me to start building and testing microdevices that I had never imagined before. It also allowed me to test them to unprecedented levels of precision and understand how they operated in all the key audio ranges. I needed a good place to make the devices, and that would be my father's garage.

Inventing the Floating Mass Transducer took many years. First I had to understand the problem, study the ear, complete countless dissections, and spend hours doing basic research. Then I had to do live human studies to identify the vibrational patterns and use cadavers to try out different ideas and concepts. Along the way, I had to adapt and perfect several test methods and create measurement devices and instruments. I eventually had to develop bench testing protocols and, ultimately, manufacturing tests for the incredibly small and sensitive devices required for direct drive of the middle ear. I had to design and build new transducers, often by hand in my father's workshop late at night. I tried hundreds of variants, but they all failed for one reason or another. All of them had one or more shortcomings or did not work at all – except for one.

In graduate school I had taken a class in linear programming, so I tried to set up the problem of middle ear implants as a linear programming model. One of the key outputs of linear programming is not the actual quantitative result; it is the revelations that can occur during the act of setting up the problem. Linear programming requires a researcher to begin to clearly think about and then re-evaluate the design constraints, the desired inputs and outputs, and the design maximization and minimization goals. It can be a very tedious process. Now I wish I could say that I packed all the equations into a linear programming software package that spat out a picture of my invention, but that is not how it worked.

With the linear programming exercise in mind, I went back and evaluated all the ideas I had previously tried. By this time I had a much clearer understanding of how little force and displacement (0.1 microns = 110 dB @ 1.0 kHz) are actually required to drive the vibratory structure of the ear. I fully understood how small a micron really is, and I had known for a long time that at the heart of solving the middle ear implant problem was a strange arena of microphysics at a sub-cellular level. I started trying new ideas, and I tried to discard everything I had previously read regarding middle ear device design. In order to start with a clean slate, I had to try to force all my previous misconceptions and all the work I had read about into a file in my brain labeled "questionable information." I began trying radically different designs that had new tracks and possibilities for a new transducer design.

It was not long before I built the first FMT, or Floating Mass Transducer. When I first started building the first of this new class of devices, I was surprised that they kept working and could not understand why. On paper, conventional theory showed that many or most of the first units would not work, yet they did! How was that possible? It made no sense! So I did the most illogical thing: I started trying to build these FMT's to *not* work. And they got better. What? And when I tried really, really hard to build them so that they absolutely could not work, the high frequencies got so loud that even I could hear them ringing with sound. At first I was sure I was observing an anomaly. These early devices did have one key attribute that most of my other ideas had lacked: They could be made very small and biocompatible.

I talked to my colleagues at Stanford and tried to explain this new device concept, and they came up with even more reasons than I had as to why the devices would not work: they would cancel out, the fields were not optimized, the mass was not right, if the devices were made smaller the anomaly would go away, it was a waste of time, etc, etc. Everything they said made perfect sense. So one evening when I had been making more devices out in my father's garage, I went into the house to tell him what I was seeing and why I could not understand it. I explained that no matter how I made them, they always worked, even though we all knew they should not. Then I said, "Dad, you know, it is really strange: These devices – they're like little Floating Mass Transducers or something." And when I said that, it was immediately clear to both of us what these devices were. "It's the FMT!" he exclaimed. We went straight out to the garage and worked into the wee hours making device after device after device. They all worked, and now that I knew what I was doing and why they were working, they all kept getting better and better and smaller and smaller.

The next day I showed Dr. Goode several optimized FMT device designs, and he agreed to let me have the technology transfer office sign over the rights of the design to me. The papers were filed the next day.

The FMT is a transducer that includes a housing that is mounted to a vibratory structure of an ear (nominally the ossicular chain). A mass that is mechanically coupled to the housing vibrates in direct response to an externally generated electric signal. The vibration of the mass in turn causes inertial vibration of the housing in order to stimulate the vibratory structure of the ear. The FTM is made using biocompatible materials that must all be perfectly made and assembled, and it is smaller than a grain of rice.

It took about a year for the technology transfer office to assign me the rights to the technology.[4] Since I was working under a federally funded grant at the time, the release had to be issued by the United States government. The VA granted me full rights to the technology. The day that the FMT technology transfer papers landed on my desk, I had another one of those memorable moments. Dr. Tim Wild, who was working with me in the lab, said to me, "Geoff! What about the middle ear?"

"Tim," I replied, "it is for the middle ear!"

---

4   Any inventor who is gainfully employed must typically get a release from his/her employer for the technology that he/she invented. Even if the invention was made outside working hours or is in a different field, it is absolutely essential to secure a statement from the employer stating that they have no rights and/or waive all rights to it. It is hard to argue that you are the inventor and owner of a technology if you do not have a release from your employer. I could never have claimed rights to the FMT without having the technology transfer.

"I know," he said. "I just wanted to be the one that said that to you so someday you can put it in your book." And so here it is.

It may sound strange, but it was at that moment that I fully realized what a big idea the FMT was. In Silicon Valley, there is no higher honor than for colleagues to rib you about your idea or project. I knew then that the device was going to be around for a while.

The goal to develop a superior electronic hearing system for the hearing-impaired has quite a history. Collins patented his first electronic hearing aid in 1899. It featured a battery supply, an amplifier, and crude signal processing circuitry that drove a speaker (a.k.a. receiver) positioned in the ear canal. His device was rudimentary, but it had all the primary functional blocks of the modern hearing aids in use today. Despite his successful work on microphones, electronics, amplifiers and batteries, Thomas Edison, arguably the greatest inventor ever, also worked on but never commercialized an electronic hearing aid. In fact, Edison was very hard of hearing himself. He thought that this was an advantage as he was able to concentrate better and ignore interruptions.

Work on hearing aids from the early 1900's through the 1980's focused on reducing their size and improving the packaging and functional performance of the components. The pioneering work of Villchur and Waldhaur, which facilitated the introduction of active compression circuits and was the key breakthrough in modern hearing aid design, was introduced first by the ReSound corporation in 1988.

Since the 1970's, hearing aid owners have accounted for 21 to 23 percent of all of hearing-impaired people This means that more than 75 percent of hearing loss sufferers who could and should benefit from amplification do not even own a device. A large portion of those who do own hearing aids do not even use them once a year. The number of truly active hearing aid owners who use their devices for four or more hours every day is 10 percent or less of the total hearing-impaired population.

The reasons why a clear majority of hearing loss sufferers rejects hearing instruments are complicated. First, there is the strange and outdated stigma of hearing loss and wearing a hearing aid. Patients' perceived lack of technology benefit is often cited as a main reason for not using amplification. Many people who have seen and heard a friend or family member struggling with and complaining about their hearing aids think, "Well if they didn't work for them, then they probably won't work for me either." Patients who owned hearing aids in the past but for whatever reason did not like them or get good benefit and sound quality are unlikely to be willing to try them again. Unfortunately, some firms that sell hearing aids are unscrupulous, offering inferior technology and service at vastly inflated prices. Many patients who do have the appropriate technology have been unable to fully benefit from it due to inappropriate instrument fitting and programming. An all-too-common example: The hearing aids of patients with high-frequency loss should be programmed to treat that, but instead they are programmed for low-frequency hearing loss. Getting the appropriate device is one matter; getting it adjusted so that it provides maximum benefit is another.

Direct drive middle ear implants offered the potential to solve most if not all the major problems associated with acoustic hearing aids. A surgically implanted device would allow the transducer to be positioned in much closer proximity to the ultimate target structure, the cochlea. Such a device could in theory deliver a superior signal without feedback and could offer improvements in cosmetics and ease of use for patients. Critics of this approach argue that these devices require surgery, that feedback suppression circuitry solves the feedback issue, and that the smaller, new-open fit devices largely solve the cosmetic and ease of use arguments.

The problem is that the critics are wrong. Most patients still have issues with hearing aids, and the complaints are largely the same as they have always been. I have always found it interesting that most proponents of acoustic hearing aids do not actually have them, so how can they really know? There is no doubt that many patients can and should use hearing aids and that hearing aids are better now than ever, but they will never be an acceptable solution for many patients. There are medical or anatomic reasons why hundreds of thousands of patients cannot actively wear acoustic hearing aids, and in many of those cases, middle ear implants can and do offer the best chance of treating hearing loss. Conventional hearing aids also have limited benefits for many suffering from conductive and mixed types of hearing deafness. Proponents of alternative treatment options such as middle ear implants suggest that the many improvements and gains that can be achieved with this technology benefit patients. The more options, the better.

Ironically, I believe that the most significant issue confronting the field of hearing today is not the technology challenges; it is what I call the "treatment model." Being diagnosed with hearing loss necessitates a multitude of appointments – being referred to an otologist, then going back to the audiology clinic, and then to a hearing aid store – and considerable expense. It is not an uplifting experience, to say the least. I hope that for most people the process is better than what I experienced as a young child, but I have my doubts. I was so lucky to have Mansfield Smith as my ear doc. Even though he was seeing and treating patients with life-threatening conditions, he still treated me and my hearing loss with the seriousness that it deserved. To me, as a patient, hearing loss seemed like the end of the world, and Dr. Smith understood that.

With some 80 percent or so of the hearing impaired rejecting amplification, hearing loss is the single largest chronic sensory condition that remains untreated in the developed world today. The need and demand for alternative options will only increase as the population increases and as we live longer, more productive lives.

The field of ophthalmology, in contrast, offers a host of alternative products and treatment options for vision impairment, from standard eyewear to contact lenses to surgical options for vision correction. The point is that for a majority of visual impairments, patients have more than one treatment option, none of which carries the same stigma as wearing hearing aids. The referral model and treatment pattern for vision impairments results in millions of surgical vision corrections each year. A hearing implant or other real alternative to acoustic hearing aids would have the same kind of success. Ironically, a lot of people also really look good in and get excellent benefit from eyeglasses. It is rare to find someone with a vision issue who is not using correction. Can you imagine what driving would be like if 80 percent of the people who needed vision correction rejected treatment? That would be interesting.

Now that I knew the basic design for the FMT, I needed to get it built. Getting the first real devices into implantable form would require a tremendous amount of work and money. There would need to be clinical trials for approval in Europe and the United States. I figured that the clinical trial effort would be very expensive and that the rest of the approval costs would also be high. A junior scientist could never hope to raise the kind of money it would take to build even one single FMT through academic channels or through grants. I had no choice but to start my own business.

In 1992 I started a company called *Imag*, for implantable magnetic transducer. It was not a great name, but I thought it was at least a starting point. I had some business cards printed and put together my first business plan using some Nolo press materials. The results of my first attempts at writing a business plan certainly could have been a lot better, but it was an eye-opening experience. In researching the material for the business plan, it dawned on me that hearing loss was not only one of the largest medical needs; it was also an enormous market opportunity. I went over and over the figures, and the numbers kept checking out. Were there enough surgeons and centers? Were there enough audiologists to program the devices? Were there enough people who could afford them? The only number that I did not have was the rejection rate for surgery. How many patients would not be willing to undergo the surgery to have the device installed? With millions of laser eye surgeries and breast augmentation surgeries being done every year, the surgical requirement, in my view, could actually be a selling point. Even if a majority rejected surgery, there were still plenty of patients. I focused on a plan for just the people suffering from conductive and mixed loss who would need some type of surgery to hear, and the numbers were still strong. Even if I limited it to only those patients who had tried a hearing aid and returned it after the 30-day free trial, the market was still huge and I still had a great business opportunity. Now I truly understood why Dr. Perkins and ReSound had been chasing the EarLens concept for so many years.

I sent my business plan to Hans Camenzind. Hans, who had been my first CEO back in the InterDesign days, was now running his own consulting business, and I figured he would be a good place to start. If nothing else, he could at least steer me in the right direction. Although I was still awaiting the technology transfer office to assign the rights, I had been assured that it was merely a matter of time, so in early 1993 I got serious about trying to get funding and started preparing my presentation.

After reading my business plan, Hans agreed to lead the effort to develop the FMT. He also helped me finalize my patent filings and arranged for a patent attorney. It was a stroke of good luck that one of the leading European physicians in the field at the time was Professor Dr. Ugo Fisch, who practiced at the ORL-Klinik UniversitätsSpital Zürich and like Hans was also Swiss. We had determined that it would be much faster and less expensive to start the initial trials for the device in Europe. Hans contacted Professor Fisch, and they discussed the new technology. Professor Fisch was impressed enough to volunteer to be the principal Investigator for the project. He became the founding member of my surgical advisory committee in Europe and played a key role in the development of my product from 1993 until his retirement in 1999.

Hans was a strong believer in the technology of the FMT and suggested that I arrange a meeting with Dr. Rodney Perkins. I tried several times, but I could not set up an appointment. I also sent him a letter but received no response. Dr. Perkins was an incredibly busy person, and I could only imagine the demands on his time. He was involved with a lot of companies in addition to running California Ear Institute, so he no doubt had a full schedule. One time I saw him driving up the Foothill Expressway in the lane next to me, and I wished I had my business plan with me so I could toss it in his window. It was disappointing that I could not even manage a meeting.[5]

Starting any company is a long shot, and the goal posts for success are narrow. Dr. Angelos Dellaporta was one of the eye docs who

---

5   Years later Dr. Perkins said I certainly should have pushed harder for this, but at the time it seemed to me that I had done all that I could. Perhaps I should have scheduled an appointment as a patient and then handed him a copy of my business plan, but I did not think of it until just now.

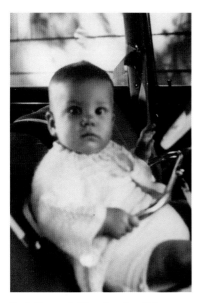

Me in the purple Mercedes, circa 1965

Soccer boy, 1970

1526 Kingsgate, 1970

Party at Vasona Park, 1972

With friends, 1972

Baseball player, 1972

Front page of the Sunnyvale Scribe, 1975

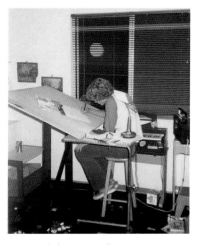

Me at work designing T-shirts

My swim team, 1983

Me in Yosemite, 1984

With Dave Barnett, 1985

San Francisco, 1985

In front of Mount Shasta, 1985

My parents and I at 3047
Orchard PW, 1985

Symphonix Design Team,
1994

Dr. Don Van Rossen
and his wife Virginia,
University of Oregon,
1987

Sabina Ball with Harry Robbins
(CEO Symphonix) on our wedding day

The first person implanted
with the Vibrant
Soundbridge, 1997

My dad in the garage with
Radesh Najran and Markus
Nagl from MED-El
showing them the first
versions of the FMT, 2009

Vibrant MED-EL Team, 2004

Vibrant MED-EL Team, 2010

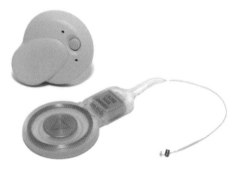

Vibrant Soundbridge Middle Ear Implant System

worked in the VA ophthalmology clinic on Fridays, and he asked to see a copy of my business plan. At this time I was not too happy with how my project was going. I was struggling to get my FMT business off the ground and figured that business school could only help. I told him I had decided to apply to the Stanford School of Business to get my MBA. As I explained to Dr. Dellaporta, "If I want to do a really big project and do it well, it has to be done in the corporate world, because the market is so big and the development costs are so high."

After Dr. Dellaporta had read my business plan he said, "You should not give up on this. I think you might be ready to speak to some of my friends. Just wait and we will see."

Applying to business school seemed like good plan. I was bummed about how little had happened and I also knew that most new business concepts rarely got funded, even if they were good. Besides, an MBA from Stanford would be an invaluable asset to me.

I applied but did not get in. Instead, I got a letter followed by a call from a PhD at the business school saying, "We saw your application for the MBA program and would like you to come talk to us about a position in the PhD program." I went over, but I had little desire to start a five-year PhD program. I thought a doctoral degree would steer me toward exclusively teaching in academia, when what I really wanted to do was make devices that could help people. I wanted to build things, start a company, do trials, and get devices approved. Be careful what you wish for.

At this point I had just been turned down by the Stanford Business School, I had lost Hans as my first CEO due to the idiotic actions of newly fired junior researcher, and I had no money. All I had was a dream.

The time had come to make a bold decision: whether or not to start a business. I could continue to work at the Goode lab at a job I loved, or I could go out on my own and risk it all. I was burning through a lot of cash to support the fledging FMT project: I had bought a cell phone and a fax (neither cheap back then), and I had copying, paper and legal fees piling up. It became clear to me that if I was to have a chance as a real full time business, I would have to start running it like one. I hired part-time administrative help and became one of Kinko's copy center's best and most frequent customers. The largest asset I had was a stellar credit rating, so every time an offer from Master Card, Visa or Discover came in the mail, I got the card. Within a couple of weeks I had a stack of credit cards with a total limit of $55,000.

"That will hold me for a while," I told my roommate, Dave Barnett, waving the stack of cards at him.

"Well, it better," Dave said. "You'll never be able to pay all that off!"

He had a point. I only prayed that he was wrong.

Not long after that, Dr. Dellaporta called me in the middle of the week, which was really unusual for him. "Geoffrey! Come to my office! Can you come right now?"

"Sure. Be there in a flash."

I headed over to the campus area, where Dr. Dellaporta had an office next to the main Stanford medical buildings. When I got to his office, he practically pulled me inside. I was sure that he simply needed me to help him with his computer again, but that was not what he had called me over for this time.

"I have spoken to Ron Antipa and showed him your business plan. And you know, he really, really likes it! He wants to meet you. He works for Alex Brown in San Francisco," Dr. Dellaporta told me.

"Really?" I asked. I had no idea who Ron Antipa was.

"Yes. He's coming to see you next week!" Dellaporta said excitedly.

This was really good news. I did not know who Ron Antipa was, but I definitely knew that Alex Brown was one of the leading investment banks at the time.

The next week I worked on putting the best window dressing I could on my business plan, even forking out an extra whopping five dollars a page for color copies. I updated the slides for my presentation. The week after that, I met Ron Antipa at a restaurant in the Stanford Mall. I was impressed with Ron. he was a broker with Alex Brown, had a lot of business contacts, and was smooth and polished.

At the end of the meeting, Ron said to me, "So are you ready to start what could be the best time of your life?"

"More than ready," I replied.

Ron arranged my first "dog and pony" presentation at Alex Brown headquarters at the top of the 101 building on California Street in San Francisco. When I arrived for the late afternoon meeting, the sun was setting over the Pacific Ocean, and the view of the city in the twilight was absolutely stunning. The Alex Brown board room was equally imposing, with a gleaming mahogany board table that seated up to thirty people. It was the first real big-time board room I had ever been in, and I was impressed. In attendance were Peter Carroll, an intellectual property lawyer with Medlen Carroll; Howard Ervin, a lawyer with Cooley Goodward; Steve Issacs and Lorance Corash of Steritech (now CERS); and a few administrators. Ron had set up this meeting to get buy-in from this group of contacts if they believed it was a good idea. If they did, Ron would continue to work on the deal; if not, then it would be "nice meeting you." I was well aware that I had to pass this test. I put my old slide projector in the middle of the board table and ran through my presentation, using used my new laser pointer to explain the concept and how it would work. I outlined the plan, the financials, the regulatory path, the budgets, and the patent strategy. At the end, I answered questions.

Before he left, Peter Carroll said, "Geoff, well done. I think you really have something here. Have your attorneys send your files over to me for the IP (intellectual property), and I will take on your patent file free of charge until you get this deal financed." The other attendees agreed. I had passed the test!

Ron agreed to arrange the next meetings but wanted to get the business plan in even better shape. We worked back and forth on it via fax for the next few weeks. He also helped me polish my presentation. Basically, Ron helped me get my act together and prepare to make pitches to potential investors. He also renamed the company Ehos, which as I understood it, is a Greek word meaning beautiful or angelic sound. I never could verify how this made any sense. In fact, to this day I have never found a solid reference to the term anywhere.

When I told him the good news, Dr. Angelos Dellaporta, my wise mentor from Stanford, said, "That is great, Geoffrey, but remember: Do not trust anyone, including yourself." He was referring to the fact that it is all too common for a real inventor or a real researcher to have their work stolen or misappropriated, and for others to try to take credit for work they had not actually done.

"There are too many leeches out there," he continued. "They lie and they wait for someone bright to come along, like you, and then they suck everything you know out of you and take it for themselves."

It was an ominous warning. I knew what he was saying but never expected to see it happen up close and first hand. It is mind-boggling to think of all the good, well-intended researchers, scientists and inventors who have not protected their work by following their NDA's (non-disclosure agreements) and have trusted others too much, only to see their work stolen or copied and taken by someone else.

The one time that this happened to me, the person stole the mistakes of an early unfinished manuscript that I had not yet corrected. The charts were actually way off due to a beginner's mistake I had made entering the data. In a weird way it was kind of funny to realize that this person would later present this work and years after that still not realize that the data was wrong. It was right there, so obviously wrong, and yet this person has no clue to this day. But in my case, except for a few amusing moments, no real harm was done. I can only imagine what it feels like to watch others walk off with your intellectual baby, one you worked on and nourished for years. It must be awful. I would change Dr. Dellaporta's warning to "Trust everyone, including yourself, and stay positive, but always get an NDA, always talk to your attorney, and always document, document, document."

My main issue at the time was raising funding for the FMT concept, and I needed to have someone that potential investors could call and talk to about the surgery and the clinical need; someone that potential investors could go to with questions about the pros and con or about my data; someone who could verify that the device could be installed and answer any other questions regarding my data and so on. I needed surgical experts with device experience. At Ron's suggestion, I made a trip to the Hough Ear Institute in Oklahoma City to meet Dr. Hough and Dr. Dormer and their team. In the field of hearing implants, they were the only team that at the time had enjoyed success with vibratory hearing implants following their work to pioneer the Xomed Audiant. I had them sign a NDA first thing; then Dr. Hough opened the meeting by having us all stand in a circle. "Please bow your heads," he began. "Dear Heavenly Father ..." he continued, leading us in prayer. I thought that was strange for a business meeting, but it was the beginning of what I would have to call an odd bedfellows relationship with Dr. Hough and his team.

It was also the first time I would be presenting the FMT to a room full of otologists, with Dr. Stan Baker, obviously a keen and intelligent person, sitting in. Afterwards we went out to dinner. The restaurant they chose was located at the top of a revolving tower that provided us with sweeping views of the American heartland during dinner. Dr. Hough made a toast to a new invention, a great day, and a promising future, and he thanked me for coming. It was a good meeting, and they agreed to help me.

Ron introduced me to Peter McNerney, a former Baxter executive now with a venture capital firm named Coral Ventures. Soon after that I met Karen Bozie, who was assigned to my deal. Ron also set up a meeting with Don Lucas, a private venture capitalist who had hired a consultant named Wayne Rudmose to evaluate my technology. I drove to the offices that Don shared with B. J. Cassin on Sand Hill Road. I made my presentation to Don, Wayne, and Don's son, Don Lucas Jr. Peter McNerney and B. J. Cassin also sat in. The amount that I was requesting was an initial cash investment that would run the company for two years based on my budgets. My pre-money valuation of $3.5 million may seem like a cute amount now, but in 1993, it was a lot of money for a startup and an awful lot for a kid from Sunnyvale.

After I finished my dog and pony show, I spent several hours with Mr. Rudmose (he had signed my NDA), explaining to him the inner workings of the FMT, the way the audio processor functioned, and how I could leverage the telemetry scheme and Hochmair technology. Wayne had a PhD in physics and some background in sound suppression systems for military helicopters. He was impressed with the FMT design. "You've solved a major physics problem here," he said. "How did you work it out?" I told him about my work with temporal bones and laser Dopplers and how small the vibration output really needed to be, about the linear programming modeling that I had worked with, and so on. It seemed odd to me at the time that Wayne kept pressing me for answers as to which microphone I had chosen for the external processor. I told him several times that I would use one of the Knowles microphones and liked the EK series, but that I had not decided which one to use because I had yet to lay out the final circuits and design the audio processor packaging. "Right now I'm more concerned about getting the full first formal device specification finished and starting board layouts. Once I get these underway, then I can worry about the exact microphone model. Knowles has hundreds of designs I could use." He still kept coming back to the microphone topic, but at the end he told me, "I can assure you I will write up a positive report for Don."

When I left after three or four hours, I was ecstatic and absolutely sure that I nailed it. I told Ron, and he was really happy as well.

"Just remember," he said, "I get to buy stock!"

"No worries, Ron. No worries." I replied

The next day I got a call from Don Lucas' office telling me to meet with Don Sr. that afternoon at five. I was so pumped! It had not even been 24 hours, and I had already received a call-back. I was sure my deal was going to get done. I called Ron, who agreed with me. Ron could not make it to the meeting, but he said, "Pretty soon you're going to be working your butt off, living in an apartment across the street from your new company, and surrounded by amazing people"

Later that afternoon I reported to Don's office. Don Lucas is an amazing and successful person whose presence makes him seem three times larger than he already is. I waited outside his office while he was meeting with Joe Costello of Cadence Design.

I had attended a lecture Joe gave and found him to be highly intelligent and an accomplished speaker. Cadence had been involved in a software scandal that at that time had already dragged on for years. Based on the laughter I heard coming from Dan's office, I thought maybe I should buy stock in Cadence.

The meeting wound down. I said hello to Joe as he left and then sat down in Don's office. The office was full "tombstones," mementos of all the companies he had invested in and/or had taken public. Tombstones are fancy models usually made of acrylic that have the company logo and stock offering date on them. They are the signature award of the venture trade. There were also trophies and awards from previous successful deals everywhere. Don had been called the godfather of the Silicon Valley startup scene, and if you looked at his track record, evident from all the plaques and awards all over his office, the title was fitting. In fact, Don was one of the original Valley venture capitalists.

"Geoff! How are you doing? You know we just got the report from Wayne, and it is really good. But he is concerned about the microphone – that you have not picked one yet!" he boomed.

What? This is nuts! I thought to myself. Being able to get a good microphone was the least of my concerns. They were the one component that was ready off the shelf, and many good quality devices were available.

I said, "Don, there are so many microphones and more than one supplier, so I can get several. There are many possibilities. If it will help, I'll gladly choose one to start with, but I cannot promise it will be the one I end up using because I still have to make the final device package. It will definitely be a Knowles microphone, though."

Don Sr. held up his hand, shook his head, and replied, "Wayne says that this is the most important part and he's worried that you have not made a selection yet. To him, it is the most crucial part in making the design work. I went to a 49ers game this weekend with B.J., and we were down on the field and this huge guy, I mean a *huge* guy from the offensive line walks by and you just thought to yourself. Whoa! This guy is a big guy! And then another player walks by, and he's even bigger! And I mean those 49ers, they have some big guys!"

I had been told that Don often spoke in riddles and that when he did it was sometimes a bit hard to follow. I struggled to keep up.

"I really like you, he continued, getting back to the topic, "and I like your deal. It's small technology. We like things small: the smaller, the better. You're a good guy and someday you are going to be a big guy, but right now you're not. So we're off the table. But B.J. wants to see you on your way out."

I was crushed. My head was spinning as I tried to understand what had just happened. One side of my brain was in a state of disbelief.

How could I be losing my funding because I had not picked a micro-phone before I had a design specification? The other side was think-ing, *What? Do I need to start lifting more weights? Am I really not getting the money because I am not a huge football player? What did he mean?* There was a knot in my throat the size of a football. It was all I could do to hold back the tears. I had lost the deal and Don was "off the table" because of the stupid microphone? The microphone!

At that moment I was really pissed off at Wayne Rudmose, but I sucked it up the best I could. "Thank you, Don. Thank you very much for your time and your interest. I could follow up with Wayne a bit more ..."

Don shook my hand and said firmly, "Go see B.J."

So I collected my things and I walked across the office to wait outside B.J.'s office. I chatted with his secretary until B.J. got off the phone call.

"So Geoff, did you talk to Don?" B.J. asked.

"Yeah, but I guess I could have done better. It sounds like I need to get the design further along," I replied.

"Don't worry. Pete McNerney at Coral is still very interested, and I have some other irons in the fire. Don't get too discouraged. It's still too early for that."

Thoughts of what an idiot I was for not having had at least a rough spec sheet for my favorite microphone types with me came to a screeching halt. Were they good-cop, bad-copping me?

"Geoff, I need you to start talking to these people about getting some research space. Do it tomorrow," B.J. said, handing me a card for the real estate agency. "Space is tight and some good places might close up soon, so get right on it." I was stunned. "And don't worry about Don. He'll come around." B.J. smiled.

I walked out to my car and watched the beautiful and familiar twilight glow over the western hills of the Santa Cruz Mountains. I wasn't sure what to think. I punched in Ron's number on my new cell phone as I was driving back towards the Valley on Interstate 280 but, as often happened, could get no reception. The entire way back to Sunnyvale I wondered whether I was in or out. Was my project a go or not?

I was almost home when the cell phone rang and I picked up. "Peter McNerney here. Heard things went pretty well today. You should be proud!"

Right after Pete hung up, Ron called. "Way to go, kid! Looks like Pete is going to lead the deal!" It was really, really good to hear that from Ron.

"Dude, this is really crazy, really crazy stuff!" I said.

"It's your first venture deal, kid! Welcome to the bigs."

A week went by and not much happened with my deal. I met B.J.'s real estate people, and one of them was a bit surprised when I told her how much space I had in mind.

"I need 15–20,000 square feet of basic R&D and a small clean room or room for one would be terrific, hopefully at a rate of $1.50 a square foot a month."

The pretty and smartly dressed real estate woman looked at me, paused, and then asked, "Umm, can I ask you how old you are?"

I said, "Uh, yeah. I'm 29."

"You look even younger. So what you are doing with B.J.?"

"I can't say. We're in the quiet phase."

"Oh, I see. So you're one of those," she said.

I was not sure what she meant, but yes, I reckon I was "one of those." We found some likely facilities. One was off Page Mill Road across from where the *Wall Street Journal* offices had been, another was down near California Ave in Palo Alto, and a third was in North Sunnyvale by Moffett field. They were all possibilities. The one in North Sunnyvale had a good space for a clean room but would need some capital improvements.

In the venture capital business, one VC is selected as the lead on a particular deal, and Pete McNerney was positioned to be the lead on mine. The lead makes the lion's share (50 percent or more) of the upfront investment and then tries to get two or three other VC firms to take parts of the rest. This helps to spread the risk and also increases the deal flow for a venture firm by allowing them to place side bets on deals where they were not the lead.

VC is a tough business, and it is not for the faint of heart. VC partners are paid very well, but to get to that level, a new MBA right out of business school is expected to work incredible hours, show utter devotion, and have the ability to generate deal flow. Even though VCs have a technical area of specialization, they have to deal with inventors and teams that are often not good at explaining their new idea, concept or technology, so it is difficult for them to get the details of each deal. VCs may look at a hundred new deals each year, but for each new company and inventor that comes through, it is usually their one and only deal, and it is hard for them to know what points are really important for the VCs. After my microphone experience, I can only say that all the points are important. You just never know. A young VC, or for that matter any VC, does not want to get burned on a real sucker of a deal.

In addition to doing deals, VCs can also be very instructive and helpful to new companies starting out. They can be instrumental in finding and hiring executive staff, and they can be an incredible resource. But they also make mistakes. I can remember one startup surgical device company that had only been in existence for two years. There was an offer from Medtronic on the table to purchase the entire company for $600 million, but the management and the lead VC on the deal turned it down. A year later the company went belly up, and the lead VC ended up leaving the firm.

VCs also have to contend with boom-bust cycles. Some years are really good, and some years are phenomenal. During really bad years, though, they cannot execute their exit strategies and disburse payouts and stock to the fund investors due to a shutdown of the IPO pipeline or a slowdown in acquisitions by larger firms. To make matters worse, they also know that weak periods, when the economy is bad and it is tough to get deals done, are often the times when it is most important to get things done in preparation for when the markets improve. VCs also know that good ideas coming down the chute are not timed to economic cycles. Sometimes the companies that go public in bad economic times are some of the better companies. By bundling deals together and working with institutional investors, venture capitalists provide a key function: They turn concepts and research and development concepts that are beyond the scope and level of other funding options into business opportunities that provide jobs and stimulate the economy. For inventors, loans from banks and small business funding are typically too time-consuming and cannot provide enough financing to give the concept the treatment it deserves. A good return for a VC fund is at least 20 percent per annum. Although the actual numbers and performance for individual funds are closely kept secrets, there is no doubt that some funds lose money. One key is to get in with good fund managers; another is to have enough capital to be able to get into a good fund. Venture firms typically require very high minimum investments.

Some argue that on average, venture funds do not do better than conventional investments in stocks. VC firms generally require a management fee of two to five percent, so if a VC firm has $100 million under management in one fund, in theory they get $2.5 million or more for setting it up. The venture partners can and generally also do participate in each fund, and the individual partners often invest some of their own capital in hot deals. But the order for VC firms is still steep: Ten-year venture capital funds are expected to repay investors up six times (6 ×) their investment. This means that two or three of the companies out of every ten have to make a 30 × return (on average) to provide the fund with a 20 percent compounded investment gain – and that is for an average fund. Again, some return less or nothing, but some funds are the next Netscape and have the ability to create enormous returns on investments.

Venture capital firms have been a key factor in the success of Silicon Valley. Venture capitalists also provide a vital macroeconomic service: They allow huge pension funds and other institutions the opportunity to invest in higher-risk opportunities by packing these investments in such a way that the risks and valuations are more reliable and therefore more fundable. In my case, I could not raise the money I needed for my research from Stanford, but the Stanford pension funds could invest in one of the VC funds that ultimately would fund me. Many of the sons and daughters of retirees work for startups, purchase goods and services, and either pay rent or buy housing. In short, although VC firms make up a relatively small slice of the total investment capital, their contributions to long-term economic stimulation and capital circulation through all levels of the economy should not be underestimated.

The venture capital community creates a hidden cultural or societal asset. It breeds a class of people who become successful entrepreneurs. The proximity to successful entrepreneurs and startups sows the seeds of belief among other would-be entrepreneurs, convincing them that they may also have a real chance to make it. This belief creates a positive reinforcement phenomenon. In Silicon Valley it also decreases the degrees of separation from someone who has been involved in a successful startup. It is nearly impossible to live in a place like Sunnyvale for five years and not to know someone who has directly benefited from or been employed by a startup.

Many countries in Europe have been late getting into the VC game and now realize that not enough of their GDP and capital resources are being directed towards such ventures and into R & D. Getting VC funding and starting a business can be accomplished in a matter of weeks in the U.S., whereas the process can take up to a year or more in many bureaucracy-heavy countries.

The VC firms offer an enticing opportunity for many young and up-and-coming MBA's, and for the few who become partners of a well-managed fund, the economic rewards can be significant. They do pay a price, however: The hours (especially for cubs) are incredibly long, the travel for funds specializing in internationals can be extensive, and the work never, ever stops. Both the pressure and the personalities can be difficult to deal with. Some would argue that VC's can do good things for society, and many are major contributors to cancer research and other types of organizations. Don Lucas, for example, has contributed heavily to the prostate cancer research programs at Stanford. Venture capitalists would also argue that they can help steer the direction of more altruistic and environmental efforts by funding green technology such as solar power, electric cars, and so on. But the fact remains that they are all about the bottom line. It may sound tough, but it is smart in the long run. Developing a class of superstar entrepreneurs and an associated group of talented people who are familiar with and have experience in the startup game results in a cross-pollination that fertilizes the chances for other successful startups to follow. It enables other inventors to get funded and show what they can do, even when they may not be great at explaining it or have not selected the perfect microphone.

After a couple more weeks ticked by, I got a message from Ron on my answering machine.

"Hey, Ron here. Just wanted to check in and see how you are. B.J. mentioned that Harry Robbins, CardioRhythm's CEO, might be calling. Hang in there, sport."

Harry Robbins? The name rang a bell, but where had I heard it before? I searched my notes and racked my brain. It turns out that I had met Harry a couple of years earlier, at the Laserscope booth at the American Academy of Otolaryngology annual meeting in New Orleans. Harry had been the VP of sales at Laserscope, which at the time was one of Dr. Perkins' companies. Harry, along with Peter Hertzmann, had been instrumental in the company's sales and marketing success. After Laserscope, he had gone on to be a member of the founding team of CardioRhythm, a startup that made a steerable cardiac ablation device that they had recently sold to Medtronic.

A few days later, B.J., Harry and I met for an hour at B.J.'s office at Sand Hill. I gave my presentation again, and then we had lunch at the Sundeck restaurant across the street. Even though I had just gotten to know Harry, we clicked. I really liked him and remembered how impressed I was the first time we had met. I thought, *This guy is the real deal. He would be a super CEO for me.*

"I see the potential in your deal," Harry said. "I like it. I like it a lot! I like you and your FMT. This could be huge! I hate the Ehos name, but the real question I have is, what about Rodney?" (Harry was referring to Dr. Rodney Perkins.)

"I tried to get a meeting with him but I couldn't," I told Harry. "He never got back to me."

Harry said "I want to get this deal set up. Don't talk to Rodney yet. We need to try and get him in. I want to call Petri Vainio at Sierra."

B.J. said he could make the call to Rodney when the time was right and added, "I am in the deal if Harry is CEO. Is that OK with the both of you?"

"I'm in if Dr. Geoffrey will hire me!" Harry promised.

I almost choked on my blackened chicken sandwich.

"Absolutely. If you're serious. Really?" I sputtered.

Harry said, "Good-bye, retirement. Looks like another venture deal."

After the meeting ended I called Ron. "Hey, I think I just hired my own boss," I told him.

"Really? You got Harry?! You really got Harry?" He sounded very surprised

"Looks like it!"

"Well, kiddo, you're really on your way now!"

Harry was right: The name Ehos was a loser. Nobody got it, not even people who knew Greek. I had been playing with names for a year now, trying to come up with a new one. I had finally come to like the name Harmonics, spelled HarmoniX. The X on the end was supposed to stand for prescription, as in Rx. I thought Harmonix was good, but Harry didn't like it because it had the word "harm" in it. "We can't be harming people if we have a medical device company," he argued.

I kept playing around with names until finally, one day as I was driving down 101 towards Pete's Harbor on a date, the name Symphonics came to me. "Write this down! Write this down!" I yelled to my date. I knew that this was a good one. I called Harry from the restaurant.

"Symphonics," I said loudly into the phone.

"I like it!" Harry said. "Spell it."

"S-Y-M-P-H-O-N-I-C-S. Got it? It sounds great, doesn't it?"

"So lemme see," Harry said "You know what we can do? Let's change the *cs* to an *x* like we had with the other one. Now we have S-Y-M-P-H-O-N-I-X. I like that! That is it! We got a name! We got a name! Let me call Peter and call you back."

The phone rang during lunch. It was Harry

"Peter (Hertzmann) says it's great, and he says it checks out. He says we can do all types of lettering with it. We have a name!"

Symphonix was born. We finally had a name.

Harry lived up in Saratoga, in a large estate that I nicknamed "Robbins' Roost" overlooking the Valley near Villa Montalvo. Both his house and the views looking out through its fine French doors were impressive. You could see all the way to Moffett field.

"On really clear days we can see the Bay Bridge, but just barely," Harry said as he showed me around the sprawling place.

The time I first drove up his long and twisting driveway, Harry and his wife Susan were doing extensive remodeling, and the entire back of the house was on stilts. It was impossible not to be amazed by his home, and the remodel was equally impressive. They had dug out the hillside to make the home even bigger by putting in a large basement below it. Harry knew the names of all the plants in the garden and had quite a collection of native and non-native specimens. He had all the latest electronic gadgets, marble floors, soaring ceilings, and a pool with a waterfall that was straight out of the Disneyland play book.

Harry and I re-worked my business plan in his office. I was beginning to wonder how many times in my life I was going to re-work the plan instead of actually getting down to business. We figured out what percentage of stock venture people would get in exchange for the $6M in upfront investment we now had determined that we needed. We fine-tuned the details of the business plan and the R&D project time lines. We made room in the budget for a few more staff positions. It seemed to me like the more input we got and the more we improved the business plan, the bigger the budgets got.

After a few hours we had it done. Harry stood up, gathered up all the plans and changes, and then without skipping a beat rushed out the door. "I need to get these over to Peter so that he can start on getting this all together."

"Peter? Who is Peter?" I enquired.

"Peter Hertzmann is the guy we are going to hire for marketing. He will pay his own salary in his graphics arts ability alone!"

Excited, Harry hurried off in his car, and I followed him down the hill in mine. It was pretty clear that Harry Robbins was an enthusiastic, fast-moving guy.

The next day I drove back up to Harry's home again. This time he was not looking so happy to see me; in fact, he looked really angry. I was a bit worried and hoped he was not going to quit. *Oh great*, I thought. *It has only been a few days and he's pissed off at me already.* One thing was for darned sure: People like Harry do not wait out in front of their homes unless something big is up.

I got out of the car, and Harry bounced over to me, holding his nose.

"Friggin' bees! I got stung by a bee!"

"What?!"

" Friggin' bees. I hate the friggin' bees!" Harry was stomping around and waving his arms.

"On your nose?" I asked.

'Yeah! Right on the end of my friggin' nose!"

"Just now?"

"Yeah, I was pounding frogs and they friggin' stung me!" Harry was walking fast in tiny circles.

"What frogs?"

"I hate the friggin' frogs! They kept me up all night, so I was bashin' 'em. Oh, I gotta call Susan. Let's go inside." Harry headed toward the side entry that led into his office.

Once inside, Harry showed me what he and Peter had done with the plan and the new slides they had made. It was really good work. The new graphics for the device were unbelievable, with medical textbook quality graphics. The text read perfectly, and the slides were even better.

"Peter really knows his stuff, doesn't he?" Harry asked as he punched a number in the speed-dial of his phone.

"Susan! I got stung by a bee! On my nose. I was out in the garden and it just stung me. Yeah, yeah, yeah, okay. I'm going right now."

Harry hung up the phone then got up and rushed off in a flurry of arms and wails.

"I'm going to the clinic and Susan is meeting me there," he said. Here is the code for the gate. Let yourself out."

"Can I make a copy of these?"

"Yeah. Just let yourself out when you're done. We meet Petri tomorrow at Sierra four o' clock."

And that was that. Harry was gone.

Now I thought that my business plan had really improved over the past few months, but what Harry and Peter had produced was on an entirely new level. The narrative and the figures and details were largely the same, but they now read perfectly. The layout was much improved, and the graphics alone told the story so compellingly that it was much clearer than it had been in my previous plans that had said essentially the same thing. It had evolved into a really great business plan.

Harry survived his bee attack. He was not allergic to bee stings, so both he and his nose were fine. The next day we met with Petri Vainio at the offices of Sierra Ventures, located across the way from B.J. and Don's offices at Sand Hill. I thought Don and B.J.'s offices were quite something, but Sierras offices were really, really gorgeous. The impression was rock solid serious. The first thing visitors saw was a reception desk that appeared to have been chiseled from a huge granite boulder. There was serious art in extra heavy and large frames, and the decor communicated that this was a place of real business. When I showed up, it was obvious that Harry and Petri had already been meeting for much longer.

I was greeted by a handsome tall man with immaculately coiffed blonde hair.

"Geoffrey, I'm Petri Vainio," Petri said by way of introduction.

"He means Dr. Vainio," Harry chimed in.

"So, Petri, this is Dr. Geoffrey!" Harry said.

"Nice to meet you, Petri. Too bad you have to work in a place with such inferior office furniture. Must be tough!' I said, joking.

"Nice, isn't it, Dr. Geoffrey?" Harry said. "It's what happens when you have a few good years and make millions for your clients."

Petri said, "In our business, when investors are trusting us with lots of money, it is important to do everything we can to make them feel that they are putting it into a solid firm."

Petri told me all about Sierra, how he knew Harry, and how they stood behind their clients and businesses. Petri gave me a copy of the firm's information materials and information about himself as well. Petri had an MBA from Stanford and was also an MD. I could not help but be impressed.

"So you got your MBA from Stanford?" I asked. "You know, in the interest of full disclosure, I have tell you that I did not get in."

"It is really not easy," Petri replied.

"But they wanted me to get a PhD in business."

"Geoff, if we get this deal done, I think the experience will be far more useful to you. I really like the deal. I like the concept, the technology, and the market potential. And I really like the name Symphonix," Petri said.

"So Harry, what do we think about Petri and Sierra?" I asked.

Harry perked up. "Petri has agreed to lead the deal, and Sierra is in!"

"Yes. That would be our intention at this point – if this would be OK with you," Petri added.

"What do you say to that, Dr. Geoffrey? Sierra! Not bad for your first deal!"

"Well, it sounds good to me. But what about Pete? I thought his firm wanted to be the lead, and I thought that was what B.J. wanted as well."

Harry said, "Pete has been working with you for what, months now? Not much has happened. With Petri we will start to work on the term sheet today, and we are looking to close the deal in a matter of weeks. B.J. is in."

Petri continued, "I assure you Sierra has nothing but the highest regard for B.J. Cassin and Don Lucas. They will be in the deal. Maybe we can also get space for Coral."

"Sounds good, then!" I replied.

"So we all agree?" Petri asked.

"We're all in!" Harry confirmed

Symphonix was on its way to finally getting its money.

The next morning I was back at Sierra to work on the deal points. Petri had all the figures for our deal worked out, and Harry and Petri were both poring over the calculator when I walked in. There was a lot of back and forth as they tried to agree on the pre-money and post-money deal valuations. We went over the deal points in detail. Harry and I would get roughly an equal number of shares, Harry would get slightly more, and we had a stock pool for the employees. They had put together an employment contract for me, and there was a list of other deal points to work out. Harry and I would have the negotiations for our side handled by the law firm of Wilson Sonnsni Goodrich & Rossotti, and Petri and the other investors would use Venture Law Group for representation to close the deal. Closing could be in about two months, maybe sooner.

"Is there anything else that you need, Geoff?" Petri asked. "It is really important to us as investors that you feel good and stay motivated."

"Yeah, actually there is. I have run up almost $40,000 of credit card debt to run this for the past year, and it would be great if I could pay it off."

"No problem," Petri said. "As long as you have the receipts and they are for business expenses, they can all be paid."

This was good news. In fact, it was great news!

"The other thing is that Ron Antipa has been helping me, and I promised to get him some stock."

Harry's head jerked up and he sprang out of his chair. "What? B.J.'s stock broker? Forget about it! Just forget about it! I will talk to B.J. about it." Harry was incredibly animated on that last point. I didn't get it, but it was obvious that Ron Anitpa had not made the list of Harry's top ten favorite people.

As I left them both at Sierra, Harry shouted after me, "You need to go to Stanford and meet my suit guy over at Nordies (Nordstrom's menswear). He knows you're coming. Do it now! We are meeting Mayfield on Wednesday."

Later that evening after I went to get my new suits fitted. When I got back to Sunnyvale and went up to my apartment, my answering machine light was flashing, and I had 13 messages.

"Geoff, Pete McNerney here. Just checking to see how you and Harry are making out. Great move on Harry, by the way. Call me back as soon as you can." Beep!

"Geoff, Pete again. Call me soon. Bye." Beep!

"Geoff, it's Ron. What's up with you and Harry?" Beep!

"Geoff. Hi. It's Karen, Karen Bozie. Please call me when you have a chance." Beep!

"Geoff. Hi, it's your mother. How did it go with Harry today? Call me back! Love you." Beep!

"Geoff. Ron again. Call me. Urgent!" Beep!

"Hi, Geoff. B.J. Cassin here. Glad to hear things went well with Petri and Harry today. Congratulations to you, and good work!

Looks like we have a deal here, and we all excited for it and you. Keep up the good work! Bye." Beep!

Wow, I thought. *I guess if you want to fill up the answering machine, you just have to spend one afternoon shopping for suits at Nordstrom.*

I looked down and noticed that the battery on my beeper was dead.[6] In all the months that I was supposed to be working on my deal with Coral, they had usually been slow getting back to me. This was something entirely new. Clearly Pete had somehow surmised that I was meeting with Petri, and that Petri was now pushing to lead the deal. Even though B.J. was fine with this new change in events, Peter McNerney apparently was not.

I called Ron. "Hey! What is up with all the messages from everyone? Peter hardly ever calls."

"Geoff, look. I need to know: Did you talk to Petri and is Sierra leading the deal now?"

"Yeah," I told him.

"And B.J. said he was OK with it?" Ron asked.

"Just got a message from him. It is fine with him."

Long pause.

"Really? He said that?"

"Really. And Petri already has the deal points pretty much nailed down."

Another long pause.

"Well, that is good news. Congratulations!" Ron said "Anything else?"

"Well. Uh ... Yeah. Look, I uh ... Well, I mentioned that you wanted to participate and that since you have helped me so much, you should have a chance to get stock in the deal and ... It does not look good at this point, Ron. I will try again. But it really does not look like it is going to be possible. I am really sorry. Maybe you can talk to B.J."

6 Yes, I carried a beeper. It drove Ron Antipa crazy. At the time I could not use cell phones as they interfered with my hearing aids and were nowhere near loud enough for me to hear. So I admit I had a beeper. I also had a fax machine that switched lines, but this never worked either.

Longer pause.

"Ron, you there?"

"Sorry. It's just that this is a real disappointment. Really upsetting. How am I going to tell Pete that he lost the lead?"

At that point I now understood that Ron had been trying to push Pete along behind the scenes and was probably just as frustrated as I was as to how slow matters had progressed, if not more so.

"You know, Ron, I think that Coral can still participate as investors," I offered.

It turned out that Coral was able to participate as "Round A" investor in the deal. In the end I was never able to get Ron founders' stock in the deal. For years I tried to make amends to Ron by trying to transfer some of my own shares, but my boss repeatedly made it clear to me that he would not approve this. It would not be the last time that I was caught in a Catch-22 situation, where I know I should do something but can't. I was never able to make it up to Ron, and I still regret it.

Petri raced through all the due diligence work. They checked up on me and chased down all my references. He called the team in Oklahoma, he called my patent attorneys, and he had Jim Heslin of Townsend, Townsend and Crew do a freedom to operate analysis of my work to make sure I was not infringing. Jim Heslin reviewed all the other works and wrote that in his opinion the FMT was novel, likely to gain a patent, and did not infringe on any other prior art that he could find. Petri had other attorneys call Hans and Professor Fisch, review all the previous documents, and so on. It all checked out.

Petri told us that we were to make exactly four pitches to four other VC firms. Petri wanted two more VC firms in the Symphonix deal. B.J. had gotten Pete and Coral a slot of the investment money, which Harry did not like at all, so we pitched the deal to the other firms.

The buzz in the VC firms up on Sand Hill Road was that Symphonix was a hot deal. We went to pitch the deal to Mayfield Venture Partners. On the way to the Mayfield offices, Harry looked up at the building and said, "Mayfield. How times change." He was beaming.

We walked into Mayfield's conference room, and Harry looked around as I was setting up my old trusty slide projector. "I can't believe you showed up at Mayfield with that piece of shit!" Harry was so irritated by the sight of it that he bought a new slide projector the next day.

Harry handed me a note that read, "Don't say anything confidential. The rooms could have microphones."

I looked up at Harry and asked in a loud voice, "What kind of microphones do you think they would be using, Harry? Because if I know one thing, it's that you can never be too choosy about the kind of microphone you pick."

Harry looked at me with horror in his eyes. "Just don't say anything!" he hissed.

Clearly, the joke was lost on Harry.

Boy, we must have been a really hot deal, because everyone from Mayfield attended the Symphonix presentation. It was standing room only. They had even brought in the human resources administrators. Harry nailed his presentation, and I guess I did OK. Harry and I were barely out of Mayfield's driveway and back on Sand Hill Road on our way back to Sierra when Petri called. "Mayfield is in!"

Harry and I high-fived each other, and Harry was ecstatic.

"Mayfield! We got Mayfield! How the world has changed!" he exclaimed.

We ended up doing the presentation for a few more groups, including bankers and the Venture Law Group attorneys. In only two weeks, Symphonix went from having no funding to having to turn money away because there was not enough room in our deal for everyone who wanted to put money into it. We were done – for now.

The Mayfield team was in, but they wanted to meet Dr. Goode and see the lab and the laser Doppler. Harry had come over to my labs earlier with Peter Hertzmann, and I showed them my laser track system and the prototypes. Peter wanted to see me pulverize some ossicles with one of Stu Harmon's lasers, so we did that. When the ossicles disappeared in a puff of smoke, they were both as giddy as two school kids. The Mayfield people came in and were all business. They gathered in our small conference room, where Dr. Goode did his recitation of the history of hearing implants, ReSound, and the pros and cons of middle ear implants. Mike Levinthal of Mayfield asked, "Why is it that ReSound and you and Dr. Perkins aren't interested in the FMT?"

"OK, look," Dr. Goode said. "I'll be straight with you guys. I think the thing will work, but at ReSound we decided to take a strategic position to stay out of the middle ear. To stay out of surgery. That is just what the board decided, and so this doesn't fit with our strategy. And Geoff has taken this concept a lot farther along. I do not think that this will be the next Microsoft, but I can see it becoming a good business, like cochlear implants." That answered all their questions.

Looking back now, this is when Symphonix may have made a key tactical error. Calls inviting Dr. Perkins to join Symphonix as both an investor and a board member were made, but with no success. It is not clear to me when the calls were made, but Dr. Perkins later told me that in his view, the calls came much too late. "They called me after they had everything set up," he later told me. I assured him that I had made several attempts to set up an appointment with him much earlier but had been unable to do so. He indicated he was not aware of this. Dr. Perkins was asked to be on the board, but since he was on ReSound's board and still working on the EarLens, there was a conflict of interest. This was a valid reason at the time, but I still think that there were other reasons that may have had more significant weight. I will never really know. But I still think that had Dr. Perkins been on the board, the future of Symphonix might have been much better.

Harry and I spent the next couple weeks buzzing around in Harry's beastly Mercedes looking at locations for Symphonix. Harry would go out and chase down a bunch of leads with his realtor and then have me look at the choice findings of the day. Harry had already panned all my choices for locating the company in Sunnyvale or Palo Alto. "I know the venture people want us up that way, but we can save a lot of money down here. Besides, they need a reason to get their wheels on the road anyway," Harry said.

Harry was not an easy customer, though, and there was always something wrong with each facility we looked at. We ended up whittling the list down to one place in North Santa Clara and two in North San Jose, both off North First Street. Harry asked me to think about which one would be the best for R & D over the weekend. I said that they all had pros and cons, but they all had possibilities. At 9 a.m. the following Monday, Harry called me up. " Dr. Geoffrey! I just signed the lease on Orchard Parkway! Come on over! I'm standing in your new office!"

"You're kidding!" I was surprised.

"No. Come over. It's great!" Harry was excited.

"But Harry, don't you think you we should at least wait until we close the deal and get the money?"

"Nah! It's all right. She took a check for the deposit and promised not to cash it for two weeks."

"Are we closing?" I enquired.

"Two weeks! Petri got the date moved up, and the attorneys will have all the paperwork done." Harry told me to get over there and hung up.

Matters had plodded along for a long time, but now that Petri and Harry were involved, things were really moving. I had my first new building and was going to get my first venture deal done. I hopped into my car and zipped up Montague expressway towards Orchard Parkway, which was just off North First Street.

Harry was beaming. His friend Jeff was already had his tape out, measuring the place.

"OK, so Harry, whaddya want over here?" Jeff asked.

"We want cubes right up here along these windows, then one big one here, and then we need desks for all these offices here, and up here," Harry ordered, pointing here and waving there.

"Is this the board room?" Jeff asked Harry.

"No that's over there. And this is where we need the board room table, and I want a big, solid one, not two pieces." Harry kept hopping around, pointing out things.

"This here is Dr. Geoffrey's office, and we need a credenza in back of the desk and two chairs in front and then a meeting table over here so that we can have up to four people." Jeff and Harry marched out through the building, and I sat there in my office on a box that had been left behind. It was really happening. We were a real startup. The white walls and the empty space and the R & D labs waiting for benches reminded me of the scene from my youth when InterDesign was moving into its first building. Now this one would be mine. How the world had changed!

Having to resign from my post at Dr. Goode's lab was really hard. I loved working for Dr. Goode and knew that no matter what, the chance to work with him had been an invaluable experience. He certainly left his imprint on me and the field of hearing will certainly have his mark on it. He was polite and wished me well. Most of my colleagues were happy for me, and I was assured that I would have a place to come back to if I needed to.

Dr. Goode said "Write everything down so the new guy won't struggle too much." The strange thing is that even now, years later, I still somehow feel that I'm working for Dr. Goode. I guess I always will be.

Soon after my resignation, I had a large party at my parent's house to celebrate the birth of Symphonix. I hired a nine-piece mariachi band and brought in a lot of Mexican food. We must have had nearly a hundred people over for a barbecue by the pool. All my friends and lab mates came, as did Harry and his wife Susan, Dr. Goode, and the Camenzinds, including Hans. A surprise guest was Mr. Harvey Day, my high school hearing-impaired teacher. "Geoff! You have come a long way. I am proud of you!" he said. It was a fine day.

It would have been October 1994 when Harry and I finally closed the Symphonix deal. We officially moved into the new building and began setting up the company. We had a lot of interviews to schedule and a lot of hires to make in order to staff up team Symphonix. Harry was really happy. In fact, the only thing he still didn't like was that Pete McNerney had worked with B.J. and Petri and that Coral was one of VC firms to be included in the deal.

I never really understood what Harry had against Pete and Coral Ventures. Pete McNerney seemed like a nice enough guy to me and he was no longer the lead, so I thought that whatever grudge Harry had would slowly die down. Wrong. It remained sore spot with him for a reason I did not know, or perhaps for no reason in particular. Karen Bozie, who was one of the junior associates working with Coral Ventures at the time, also had no clue. When I asked her about it, she shrugged and said, "You know, I have no idea. You can never tell what happens in these deals. People can get caught up in the passion of the moment. Sometimes things get blown out of proportion or out of context. Too much about very little." Harry was undoubtedly one passionate guy.

One day, Harry had just gotten off the phone with the Coral people, who had asked him to send some documents over. As he sent the documents over on the fax machine, he told me, "You know, it's all your friend's little stockbroker's fault that I have these people to deal with!"

I tried a few more times to get Ron some founders' shares, and finally one day B.J. said to me, "Look, Ron's my stockbroker. I'll take care of it."

From then on, when Harry got irritated with me he would bring up Ron Antipa. I learned strictly avoid two topics around Harry: one was Coral and the other was Ron Antipa. Every so often Ron would call me up and ask about the stock shares and if there were any for him. I would tell him. "Talk to B.J. I just can't go near it". One day I got a call from Don Lucas Jr., who was starting his own venture group at the time. "I need you to give Ron some of your stock. I think 50,000 shares is about right." I was floored. That was a lot of stock. I did not even know if this could be done, and by now I was getting really tired of the whole thing as well. When I told Harry about the call, he went non-linear. "Jesus!" he screamed at me. "I am sick of this! Lemme get Don Sr. on the phone!" He slammed his office door, and I heard him day yelling on the phone. Harry really had a temper.

He finally came out and said, "Look, for the last time, I took care of Antipa, and I don't want to hear any more about it." "Message received," I answered, even though I already knew that. I was not in a position to piss off my new CEO any more about this and certainly not before the ink was on the closing documents.

I called Ron and told him what had happened with Harry and as politely as I could, asked him to drop it. I was surprised when Ron told me that B.J. had not gotten him any stock from the McNerney/

Coral side of the deal. *Had Coral also shut Ron out?* I wondered. I felt bad, but what could I do?

We had an all-day closing meeting for Symphonix to finally get its funding. The signing was held at WSGR's offices on Page Mill road. Since the meeting started at 8 a.m., we had a buffet breakfast. Harry and I and each set of attorneys spent six hours signing documents: founders' agreements, stock options agreements, dissolution agreements, and incorporation documents. There were 30 or more copies for each set, and they all had to be signed. B. J. was there in the morning, but he left as soon as they had rushed him through the ones he needed to sign. It was a good thing we had our consul in the room to make sure that we were not signing the wrong terms. The other consul and ours would make notes, agree to future changes, and clarify points.

After it was all done, one of the attorneys came out and gave Harry and me three checks for a total of six million dollars. When the meeting was over, we took the checks out to Harry's car. I was shaking. It was a lot of money and represented a lot of work to this point, and there was much more to come.

Harry stammered, "We need to go to Silicon Valley Bank right now and deposit these. Right away."

"Or we can go to cash them and move to Belize," I joked.

"Nah, nah, I'd much rather go to the Caymans!" Harry exclaimed.

As I was following Harry on the drive down Highway 280 back to the Valley with six million from our first-round closing, my car overheated. I had to stop and leave it at my parent's house in Sunnyvale, then ride with the rest of the way with Harry in his beastly Mercedes.

"Dr. Geoffrey, I think we need to get you a new car. Maybe Kenny at Silicon Valley Bank can help you out."

I said, "Six million ought to cover it," and Kenny did help me get a new car.

Symphonix

"I had nothing to do with the damn leads!"

Bob Katz, in his interview with Geoff and Harry

Harry Robbins was CEO and Chairman of the Board for Symphonix. I was Vice President and Chief Technology Officer and Director. We had a huge empty office building. For the next two weeks after the closings, Harry and I spent the mornings running around to Office Depot, furniture stores, art shops, plant stores and you name it to get everything the company needed. We would stuff Harry's car full of whatever we could and had the rest delivered. Our lives were full of catalogs and trips to stores for bookcases, copiers and fax machines, the hardware of business. Harry bought all the art and hung it up throughout the building.

Before the new furniture arrived, I spent two weeks in the corner of our building sitting on one cardboard box that I used as a chair placed next to another cardboard box that I was using as a table to hold my clipboard and my cell phone. I had to be there to let workmen in to install cubes, carpeting, windows and doors. I had to make sure that the right items were delivered and sign the paperwork for them. I also had to review resumes and try to schedule interviews, and I was starting to buy the lab benches and equipment we would need. Whenever a workman came over to install carpeting or to paint, I let them in and made sure they were doing the right job. I got a lot of strange looks.

One of the workers came in, took a hard look at me and then said, "So you in here in this building all by yourself?"

"Yes sir. Well, at the moment anyway," I replied.

"You sittin' on that box?" he asked.

"Yes sir"

"Well, I ain't never seen nothin' like that before."

As I said, he was not the only one to give me strange looks.

Word that we were setting up shop traveled with lightning speed. I would get cold calls from people selling everything a new company could possibly need. I must have had eight calls from different phone companies and more from the long distance providers. Harry put me in charge of selecting the phone system until I chose one that he didn't like because it didn't have some feature that he wanted but that I believed he would never use anyway. We found a different one. We installed all the lighting. The furniture finally came in, and I got my office chair (I still have it and am sitting on it as I write this 16 years later). Harry had all the desks for the future engineers, and they all had fluorescent magnifying light stands because, in Harry's words, "The engineers, they all love those friggin' things!" The truth is that all engineers actually hate them. Framed art prints were hung on the walls, artificial plants were brought in, and the break room was set up. The look of it all reminded me of the first day of school back at Serra Elementary: everything neat and tidy and all laid out. "Just waiting for the kids to arrive!" Harry would joke. But I had a problem. I needed my key project leader.

Though Harry was a bit animated at times and may have yelled and screamed a bit more than many might like, I *got* Harry, and we clicked. I hated it when he would stick it to me on topics such as the Antipa matter or pick up on some other point and nail me with it. But the fact is that Harry was a super guy, and I could not have picked a better, more dynamic CEO for a startup. I would much rather have an supercharged, high- energy CEO who tends to gets in my face than one who sits in the corner office reading CNN on the internet all day. Harry was a great speaker and an awesome motivator. He was smart and he got the job done. Harry certainly had many critics, but most of them never worked with him as closely as I have. Was Harry too fond of money and of serving his own self interest? Maybe, but not compared to what we see today on Wall Street, that is for sure. Harry wished for financial success, but he also wanted success for Symphonix and its employees. Most of all, he wanted to help people who needed the Symphonix implant. Harry was a true startup guy. He was honest about himself, and with Harry, what you see is exactly what you get. He made no bones about it. I was proud to work with Harry and I would gladly serve with him again. He ranks me.

It would not be right to staff up the operation for the design and development team until we had the right person to lead the formal development project. I had been interviewing, and we had the recruiters looking for our executive staff positions, but it was slow going.

Symphonix employee number three was Harry's buddy Peter Hertzmann. Peter would be VP of Clinical Affairs and Marketing. This job title combination is so unusual that even today, years later, it's hard for me to believe that it was his title. But Peter was highly talented individual (he had donated the "Peter Hertzmann Library of Historic Chinese Cook Books" to UC Berkeley), and he made it work. I had first met Peter in the Symphonix building when Harry introduced us: "Peter, this is Dr. Ball, the inventor."

I happened to be wearing blue pleated trousers, and as we shook hands, Peter said to me, "Nice pants! They make you look like a bus driver."

"Umm ... OK ... Like, whatever then," I muttered, thinking to myself, *What an ass!*

Peter did not make the best first impression, to say the least. He could be that way. But he would turn out to be a key asset to the development of Symphonix in the early days, initiating our clinical work in addition to creating excellent surgical manuals and images. With input from physicians, he also developed the entire procedure to install the Soundbridge. So we had Peter, but that was all. Thanks to Peter I never wore blue trousers again, ever.

Peter, Harry and I would go to lunch each day, and Harry talked about the Laserscope days, all the CardioRhythm deal stories, and Medtronic, and on and on. He seemed to know everyone, and he could hold a room with his stories and levity. Peter and I would just sit there and listen. With Harry it was tough to get a word in.

Good candidates for the VP of Research and Development were hard tough to find. We had almost closed a deal on a former Medtronic executive, but when his wife saw that Silicon Valley real estate prices were approximately triple those of the Minneapolis area, she turned right around, flew home, and made it clear she was not coming back. We had wasted almost six weeks on this guy, who had led us to believe he was very likely to accept an offer. Our recruiter was really upset when I broke the news to him.

"I hate that guy! I cannot believe he did that to us! He promised me that it would be OK. I hate it when people lie to me! I friggin' hate it!" the recruiter screamed down the phone at me.

Finally after we had gone through a few more candidates, he found us Bob Katz. Bob was based in Colorado working for Teletronix, a pacemaker implant company going through a rough spot. We flew Bob out and showed him the facility. Bob laughed when he saw the Styrofoam peanut dispenser Harry had bought hanging from the ceiling in the shipping area.

"Who the heck bought that thing?" Bob enquired

I rolled my eyes, pointed at Harry, and answered, "He did!"

"Whatcha' gonna use it for, Harry?" Bob prodded.

"Oh come on, you guys. You know. It's for filling up the boxes, you know, when they want to pack stuff and they need filler," Harry defended himself.

Bob and I looked at each other. Bob winked at me and said, "Well, Harry, if you're the boss and that's what you say, then I have NOOO problem with that."

"Thank you!" Harry replied.

I broke in, "And you know Bob, after you come work for us, whenever you have a box you need shipped, Harry here will personally fill it with Styrofoam peanuts so that there won't be a bunch of extra ..."

Harry interrupted: "Now you shut it! Geez! What is with you guys!? Can't I have a Styrofoam peanut dispenser if I want one? Bob, don't you start in on me. I get enough of it from Dr. Geoffrey!"[7]

We took Bob up to the board room, and the first thing he said was, "I want to make sure you understand one thing: I had nothing to do with the damn leads, so please don't ask me about them." Tele, his former employer, had had a major problem with the pacing leads that it had produced for its pacemaker system. We had read

---

7 We never did use the peanut dispenser, but the hopper hung over the shipping area for years as a tribute to Harry.

about it, and it was one heck of a mess. Harry winked at me, and then I looked Bob in the eye and said, "Bob, Harry and I ... well, we were just wondering if you could tell us anything about the leads."

Bob stared ahead blankly, looking like he had just seen a ghost. Harry started cracking up, then so did I. Bob sat there looking at us like we were a couple of maniacs who had just flown him out from Colorado for the specific purpose to making fun of him. When he started cracking up too, we knew we had found our guy.

Once Bob loosened up, he was the best interviewee I have had to this day. He was smart and quick and he knew what we needed done. We sent him up to the VC's to interview with them so they could explain the level of commitment behind Symphonix. They were impressed as well. Bob was young, but we felt he was ready to step up and to make the project happen. Bob joined the team and relocated to California in record time. In fact, the very next week, Bob was the fourth person to move into our offices. I had moved into the Orchard Parkway Apartments right across the street from Symphonix, and Bob moved in there as well. Ron had been right: I would be living across the street from my new company, and I was now surrounded by amazingly talented people.

Harry, Bob and I then started staffing the engineering unit. We hired Tim Dietz, Craig Mar, and Chris Julian to start on the transducer team and work on the implant portion of the device. We staffed the electronics and signal processing side with Bruce Arthur (who had worked with Bob at Tele), Jim Culp, John Salisbury Eric Jaeger, Dan Wallace, and Duane Tumlinson. Steve Trebotich, whom I knew from ReSound, soon joined our CAD department. These were the core guys who would build the device. Pat Rimroth was hired to staff the manufacturing side. At our first holiday party, held at the San Jose Downtown Hyatt, about twenty employees and all the board members were in attendance.

The goal of Symphonix was to build and commercialize the world's first middle ear implant. We named the product the Vibrant Soundbridge. The purpose of the Vibrant Soundbridge is to provide therapy for hearing loss for patients who are either dissatisfied with conventional acoustic hearing aids or cannot use them for medical reasons. The Vibrant Soundbridge is a direct drive middle ear implant that amplifies the mechanical vibrations of the middle ear ossicular chain, thereby providing an amplified signal to the cochlea. Utilizing mechanical energy instead of acoustic sound presents the opportunity to deliver a more accurate and higher quality signal to the inner ear. Direct drive devices can provide this signal without feedback or occlusion and offer the user significant benefit that may contribute to a significantly enhanced life quality.

At this time we had all the information from my original patent filing and the data from my early prototype designs, but that was about it. The goal was to take the concepts in my original patents and to build them into a device that actually did what we said it could, that could be implanted in a patient's head, and that would last a lifetime. Easy to say, but honestly, as confident as we were and as good as the technology looked on paper and in the patents, we would never know if we could really make it happen until we had given it our best shot.

On February 2, 1995, I received notification from Peter Carroll that the patent for the Floating Mass Transducer had been allowed by the United States Patent office. It was my first patent, and I was awarded a stunning 56 claims. The device had not been invented until 1992, and now, only three years later, it had an issued patent. Harry bought everyone lunch, and we had a great little office celebration at Symphonix headquarters. I was thrilled.

It had been a long time coming, but now I was surrounded by people working to make the world's first middle ear implant a reality. It was a fine moment for me and for the millions of patients that desperately needed an implant in order to hear.

The Vibrant Soundbridge

"You seek a great fortune, you three who are now in chains.
You will find a fortune, though it will not be the one you seek.
But first ... first you must travel a long and difficult road,
a road fraught with peril. Mm-hmm.
You shall see things wonderful to tell."

The prophet in *O Brother Where Art Thou?*

Rather than use acoustic energy to vibrate the tympanic membrane to stimulate the middle ear, direct drive devices vibrate the ossicular chain directly with mechanical energy. We call this "direct drive" hearing. Direct drive makes it possible to deliver a higher quality signal closer to the inner ear, the target structure. The successful implementation of this type of device can solve many of the issues inherent in conventional acoustic devices by reducing occlusion and feedback while providing significant levels of amplified signal over a wider frequency spectrum.

The team had to build all the main components of the system. The first task was to build the first r*eal* Floating Mass Transducers. When finished, the FMT would be the smallest hi-fidelity transducer ever built. It would have to be about the size of a grain of rice and capable of delivering the equivalent of 115 decibels of equivalent sound stimulation to the ear but only use 100 microwatts of input power. This was a lofty goal. Many would say laughable. The FMT also had to be completely hermetically sealed and 100 % biocompatible. But the Symphonix team did not blink. They made it happen.

We began testing the first FMT's as soon as the team had finished. They had managed to build a device that was approximately 2.0 mm in length and 1.5 mm in diameter, with a total mass of only 25 mgs. The Symphonix FMT is a solenoid comprised of two coils wound around a hermetically sealed, titanium alloy, bobbin-shaped housing. The hermetically sealed titanium transducer housing contains a samarium cobalt rare earth magnet suspended on a set of silicone elastomer springs. The coil wire is polyamide-coated gold, and a thin coating of medical grade epoxy provides a secondary layer of mechanical protection. Though tiny, lightweight and powerful, the FMT turned out to be remarkably robust. In fact, to this day it has never failed.

The FMT was a key component of what we named the Vorp, which was the implant portion of the device. The implant and FMT had to be installed in the recipient's middle ear by a surgeon in a one to two hour outpatient/short stay procedure.

An external unit called the audio processor (AP) had to supply the input signal and voltage to drive the implant unit. The AP consists of a microphone, signal processing electronics, a telemetry coil, and a battery. It picks up a sound signal, amplifies the signal to the correct level for a specific patient's hearing loss, and then sends an amplitude modulated signal across the skin to the receive coil of the Vorp. Magnetic attraction holds the AP in position post-auricularly on the outside of the head during normal use.

Rather than use acoustic sound as the drive force, the Vibrant Soundbridge delivers mechanical energy to the ossicular chain. In the partially implantable Soundbridge, the microphone of the externally worn audio processor picks up sound. The audio processor is held in position under a patient's ear by magnetic attraction. The AP's microphone picks up sound, amplifies the resultant electronic signal, and sends the resultant signal to the internally located receiver portion of the implant. The signal is passed down the conductor link to the FMT located on the most distal portion of the VORP. The FMT then delivers mechanical motion to the ear.

The advantage of a system that has minimal effect on patient's residual hearing cannot be overstated. As with any medical technology, no matter how well tested in advance, a thorough clinical study had to be conducted to reveal the true strengths and weaknesses of the Vibrant Soundbridge.

The young Symphonix engineering and manufacturing teams faced the daunting task of designing a device that consisted of the smallest high fidelity transducer ever conceived and figuring out whether and how it could be built. We also had to make it small enough to fit and hang on one of the tiniest bones in the human body, the one that resides within the middle ear. Next, we would have to get the device through the incredibly challenging rigors of clinical trials. After that, we would have to win FDA approval and then market and sell the device faster than any of the other teams working in the field. We also needed to get our scientific advisory boards up to full speed to help us organize and design the clinical trials. Up to this point we really only had Professor Fisch.

In early January 1995 Bob and I walked into Symphonix headquarters and found Petri and Harry in Harry's office.

"We closed the deal with Dr. Hough!" Harry said excitedly.

"For what?"

"To do the animal testing and the clinical trials. Dr. Hough agreed to be the chairman of our United States Scientific Advisory Board!"

It turned out that both Harry and Petri had snuck off to meet with Dr. Hough and Dr. Dormer and the team to close a deal to get the Oklahoma team working for us. Bob and I had not been aware of their intent. At first Bob was miffed, and then he got angry. Harry and Petri had gone out and made a deal with a key research group for R & D that could significantly impact his project timelines, and they had done it without our input. They had also committed a significant portion of his budget, and it was going to be expensive. In theory, it was a good idea, but Bob had not even met these people yet. Bob and Bruce hopped on a plane and took off for Oklahoma to go meet the new research team. Harry, Petri and I took off to go to Zurich to meet with Professor Ugo Fisch, who as the chair of our advisory board in Europe would help us select the other members and plan our European clinical trials.

When Harry, Petri and I arrived in Zurich, we took a cab up the hill to the ORL-Klinik UniversitätsSpital ENT clinic and rode the elevators up to Professor Fisch's office. The purpose of the meeting was to get a final blueprint of the clinical trials he would do and hopefully to convince him to be in charge of the European Scientific Advisory Board. He had agreed in principle to this with me before, but we wanted to close the deal, and Harry and Petri both wanted to meet him face to face I wanted to have him review the latest device plans and the new drawings that we had as well as the mock-ups for the sizes and the latest device configuration.

When Dr. Fisch opened the door, Harry introduced himself and Petri and then said, "And you know Dr. Geoffrey here."

They were both surprised when Fisch said, "Yes, Geoffrey. Actually I have never met Dr. Ball. It's my pleasure."

For some reason they thought I knew Dr. Fisch quite well, when in fact up until that time all of my work and correspondence with him had been via fax, letters and phone calls. Hans Camenzind had met with Professor Fisch in Zurich; I had not. Meeting Professor Fisch was a transformative experience. He had terrific insights into the design and indicated to me what he wanted changed, what shape it should be, how it should bend, how long the lead should be, and other input. He ticked off the design aspects he liked and said politely, "This really looks quite good. If you make these changes, I think it will be quite fine". Then he asked, "When will you be done? We have already started to find patients. Your work here is most important, and it can help so many."

Though we had only just met, I felt like I was talking to a longtime friend. Professor Fisch was earnest, and his dedication to the field was top notch.

Before we left that day, he asked me, "Dr. Ball, is it your intention to get one of these for your own hearing loss?"

"I would love to have one," I said.

"I think it speaks well of the invention that the inventor believes in it enough to have it himself," Harry chimed in. "Dr. Geoffrey here is gonna be one of our first patients!"

Petri left for another meeting with one of his other European startup companies, and Harry and I stayed behind in Zurich. We had two days to kill before we had to go to a meeting in Neuchatel, which was only a few hours away. Harry and I toured the city, taking long walks, checking out all the shops, and eating at Zurich's great restaurants. Harry had a great time making endless fun of me. I made fun of Harry and of his making fun of me at my expense. It was great to have a boss who, though admittedly a bit high strung, both respected me and was fun to be around. At one point Harry said, "Dr. Geoffrey, you're going to do all right!"

Those two downtime days with my new boss were a highlight of my time with Symphonix, and I thoroughly enjoyed them. In a way, that interlude was the calm before the storm. In the years to come, Harry and I would sail some rough seas together. With

Harry at the helm of the good ship Symphonix, the rest of us were not always sure where we would land, or exactly when, but thanks to Harry, we all believed it would be someplace great.

Bob did a fantastic job of running the development project. He also turned out to be the second hardest worker I ever met, ranking only behind Ingeborg Hochmair, the CEO of MED-EL, a cochlear implant company in Austria. As we had anticipated, the transducers turned out to be the main design challenge. The first key task for the implant team was to replicate all the transducers I had built. The engineers watched everything I did to build the devices and took copious notes. Then they built the FMT's themselves and were stunned that they worked so well. The main issue turned out to be building devices that were small enough and could be hermetically sealed. Chris Julian, working with Dan Wallace and Tim Dietz, solved the problems: together, they proved to suppliers that it was in fact possible to build parts as small as we needed Initially, the suppliers had thought what we were proposing for the FMT was impossible. Dan Wallace developed my laser Doppler vibrometer test into an excellent test system for the FMT.

The key development issue had been a phenomenon we called drop out. The transducer's output, as measured with the LDV, would go into a non-linear mode in the low frequencies, especially at low input levels. The drop out problem was solved in a series of late-night testing sessions that Dan, Chris, Bob, and I, along with Tim Dietz, conducted. Once we had it solved, we were ready for our first acute testing of the device.

In February of 1995, Silicon Valley got so much rain that many roads were closed. Late one night I was driving back from a meeting up at Sand Hill when I heard on the radio that the Guadalupe River near our facility had overrun its banks. *Jesus*, I thought. *We just installed the computer network! If we get flooded now, it could set us back months!*

At Symphonix, the situation was much worse than I thought. I had to park on the expressway and wade the rest of the way to the building in waist-deep water. The parking lots were completely submerged, and the water was six inches away from the front and back doors and still rising. I was really freaked out. I ran through the building, disconnected all the PC's, and put them up as high as I could. I then did the same with all the servers and network equipment. I moved all the files and paperwork I could find to higher ground too. I wasn't sure it would do any good, but I had heard that the city engineers were working to get the pumps started in order to move the water back into the San Francisco Bay. It was clear that the floors would get wet, but at least we could keep working or move everything temporarily if we had to. By the time I left, the water had come right up to the doorway and was beginning to flood the lobby.

I called Harry. "I got the Network up as high as I could," I told him. "Do you know anyone who has a boat? Because we are going to need one."

"You're kidding me!" Harry screamed into the phone.

"No, I'm not." The sounds Harry was making on the other end of the line reminded me of when he had been stung by a bee.

Finally I said, "Now, Harry, just settle down. If they get the pumps working, we should be OK, and if not, we will figure it out." I hung up. I had not made Harry's night, that was for sure.

It was days before the city got the pumps working. However, the levees lining the Guadalupe River did not breach, and the rain eventually tapered off enough that the water could slowly begin to recede. The staff had to park around the corner or way up on the street and wade through Lake Symphonix, but we survived with just a bit of damp carpeting.

At Symphonix we had many late nights and hundreds of meetings. We ran hundreds of tests, wrote thousands of documents, and made thousands of drawings. It was a significant undertaking to implement the quality system that ensured that we had validated, verified and well-documented the top-tier systems in place. We had many long and sometimes heated debates. At the same time the R & D engineers were building, testing, and refining the devices, our manufacturing team, led by Pat Rimroth, was working on figuring out how to build a manufacturing line that could produce the implants and audio processors.

Like all early startups, there were a lot of late nights with pizza for dinner at work. We often did not get home until late in the evening. We would catch a few hours of sleep and then get up and go back to Symphonix early the next morning. Meanwhile, the clinical staff was working on protocols and site approvals for the clinical trials. Peter Hertzmann led the herculean task of gearing up for the first implants and trials. We also had more than our share of VIP visitors, frequently current and potential investors and collaborators. Throughout it all, Bob was most impressive. He was almost always the first one in the building in the morning and the last to leave at night. There was so much testing to do. Many Saturdays were basically full work days. The only real day off was Sunday, but even then, Jim Culp or Eric Jaeger or someone else could often be found burning the weekend oil.

I had my own research lab at Symphonix, and when I had a chance, I would try to work on new stuff in addition to doing the laser Doppler testing and validation work for the device. I built the first implantable microphones that really worked and made a totally implantable device possible for the first time.

On November 6, 1996, only 18 months after the Vibrant Soundbridge was invented. Dr. Ugo Fisch implanted the first one in a patient at the ORL-Klinik UniversitätsSpital Zürich, and European research institutes followed suit. The surgeries were a success, and the first patients were found to have significant hearing improvement and reported excellent sound quality. The device worked!

However, as promising as the results were, I was a bit disappointed. I thought that the device could do even better and that we were missing more than just a little of the system's maximum output level, yet we had no more headroom on the electronics. In other words, the system should be a lot louder than it was. A top concern for the design team had been to not make the device with too much output or too loud. We had been warned over and over to not make it too loud, and we had obviously been overly cautious when we backed it off. Even though a key reason for running a trial was to fine-tune and finalize the performance, it sure did not make us feel real good at the time. Too much output could further damage a patient's hearing, and of course we did not want this to happen. We had a bit of a crisis when we had to go back to the lab and adjust and refine the audio processor to have a higher signal level, but Bob and his team achieved this in record time. Looking back,

Harry was really a good and calm supporter during our first patient results. The Symphonix team worked it all out with amazing speed. The next patient results came in from our higher output audio processors, and they were stellar. At our clinical trials sites all across Europe, surgeons had begun implanting more and more devices. We had met our targets. The Soundbridge worked! It really did!

Going from the start of a company to a successful surgical implant for a Class III medical device in 18 months has to be some kind of record. To have made this happen in such a short time is unprecedented because the regulations for active implantable medical devices are among the most stringent in the world. At Symphonix we had cut no corners, but we managed to get it done.

Shortly after the initial success of our first implants, Harry and I made the first of several trips to Japan to try to start the Japanese approval process with their ministry of health. We needed to find the right consulting team to help us coordinate all the trials and submissions. We were confident that with my contacts, including Dr. Suzukin and Dr. Yanigihara and the Ehime clinic, our chances were good. A couple of years and several false starts later, I came to the conclusion that we were actually many years away from any success in Japan. Today, as I write this nearly fifteen years later, I still have not won approval in Japan and am still working on clinical trials. Despite assurances from the Japanese that they would accept FDA trial data, they are still insisting on clinical trials in Japan.

Harry had taken some pictures of us on our Japan trip, and my mother got copies to show off her son to the other nurses at El Camino hospital where she worked. One of the younger nurses told my mother she had an extra ticket to a performance of "The Nutcracker" because a friend of hers had cancelled, and she asked Mom if she thought if I would be interested in going. It was the holiday season, and I was not dating anyone at the time, so I let myself be persuaded by my mother's urgings to give the nurse, Sabina, a call. The fact was that I had already seen "The Nutcracker" way too many times and thought it was a real snoozer. I called Sabina anyway to make arrangements and suggested that maybe we could meet for coffee beforehand. I went to pick her up at her apartment near San Jose State and was pleasantly surprised when a tall, very attractive young woman greeted me at the door.

"Hi, Geoff. I'm Sabina."

Wow! I thought to myself. *This could turn out to be much better than I thought! She's gorgeous!*

We headed down to The Bear in Los Gatos for coffee creams (sort of like a coffee milkshake) and had such a good time talking that we decided to go out salsa dancing. We clicked and had a fantastic time, to say the least. I loved her style and her strong European accent. When I dropped Sabina off back at her apartment later that evening, her roommate asked her how the date had gone. "That's the man I am going to marry!" Sabine told her. Her roommate naturally thought Sabina had lost her mind, but she had not.

Peter Hertzmann and his staff had finished the EU clinical trial, and all the patient data was complete. We would quickly win approval to market and sell the Vibrant Soundbridge in Europe, and we opened our EU offices in Basel, Switzerland.

In the United States, the Vibrant Soundbridge had a much tougher time winning approval from the United States Food and Drug Administration Every medical device in the United States must have FDA approval before it can be marketed for patient use. Before any trial can start, the new device must be presented to the FDA at what is called a pre-IDE meeting. I presented the technology, and Earle Canty, our regulatory affairs officer, also presented. Our clinical staff outlined the clinical trial design. Dr. Hough was there with Stan Baker to present the surgery for the device. The meeting with FDA went as well as could be hoped.

After I presented the device design, one of the FDA staff engineers said, "This one looks like it's really going to work. It's about time!"

His colleagues frowned. FDA meetings are not generally supposed include displays of exuberance over device design.

"The Vibrant Soundbridge is racing towards kids," said one of the FDAers. "There is such a tremendous need that we are going to have to be extraordinarily diligent." The FDA was right: The pediatric market for the Vibrant Soundbridge would be significant, but the device would not be approved for use in the pediatric market until 2009, and then only in Europe. To me it is ironic that to date, the Vibrant Soundbridge has still not been approved for pediatric use in the United States. To my knowledge, no children in the U.S. have ever been implanted with the technology.

The FDA was keenly aware of the breakthrough Symphonix had made. In one sense, that was good, but it definitely attracted a big spot light. Perhaps too big. The FDA gave us approval to do our first clinical trial patients in late 1996. The first patients in the United States had been completed by Dr. Charlie Leutje in Kansas City, and the results were fantastic.

I was the last of the first five subjects to be implanted with the Vibrant Soundbridge in the U.S. by Dr. Derald Brackmann at House Ear Institute in Los Angeles. My surgery was supposed to start early in the day, but Dr. Brackmann had too many cases. They had a full film crew there, so everything had to be done twice. Sabina and I were engaged at the time, and she was there with me. The film crew had us hold hands, kiss, and do all sorts of embarrassingly contrived things for the cameras. I had been sedated, and the film crew had taped a microphone to the inside of my loose-fitting hospital gown. They were really concerned about the microphone because it was a very expensive RF transmission type system. I had also been hooked up to an IV. There must have been eight people crammed into my small hospital room.

After a few hours of waiting, I had to pee, so I got up and pulled the IV stand along as I negotiated my way around all the people and equipment. Despite my heavily sedated and slightly goofy state, I made it into the bathroom. I closed the door, pulled up my gown, and let it flow.

Now in case you should ever find yourself in a similar situation – where you have to use the toilet and the next room is full of audio visual technicians and a microphone is taped to your surgical gown – I have some recommendations. First, if you are fitted with a remote RF type microphone, you should make sure that the microphone is turned off before you start to pee. If you forget, like I did, the audio equipment will record the entire event for all to hear. The second thing you should do is to make sure that the tape holding the expensive microphone to the gown is in fact sticking.

Otherwise it, like mine, will come unstuck and fall into the toilet bowl. And should your expensive RF microphone system actually fall into the toilet, my third recommendation is that you try with all your might to stop peeing before you lurch down to try and grab it. If you don't do this, you may find that during the effort you unintentionally shed your hospital gown and pee all over it. If this happens, you will surely find, as I did, that you have made a complete and utter mess that requires a new gown. Oh, and by the way, if you should ever find yourself in a sedated state hooked up to an IV and manage to drop your expensive RF microphone into the toilet and at the same time pee all over it and everything else, accept the fact that the microphone is shot and it is pretty much a total waste of time to try and dry it off. Pretending nothing happened will not work either.

It would be several hours more (thankfully with no more microphone incidents) until Dr. Brackmann finally had me wheeled down to the surgical prep area. By this time I had been receiving sedatives for nearly six hours, so I was in a pretty pleasant mood to say the least. I was really excited and at the same time feeling pretty goofy.

In the prep area, the scrub nurse had to shave off the hair around the incision site, but as they had never done a Vibrant Soundbridge implant at House Ear Institute, she had no clue exactly where or how much to shave. She asked me to show her where it should go, and I did my best to outline the area behind my ear where the incision would be made. She started shaving away the hair behind my ear and then asked, "How high up should I go?"

Forgetting that House Ear Institute was a Catholic hospital, I said, "Just stop when you get to the 666."

Whoops! Guess they had me on some really good drugs.

I finally made it to the O.R., where Dr. Brackmann was waiting. I was wheeled in, I reached into my gown pocket and handed him a detailed note that I must have written in the afternoon while I was still lucid. Dr. Brackmann later told the story:

"So they wheel in Geoffrey, and he pops upright, looks me in the eye, and says, 'Here is how I want the surgery done and make sure it is in good contact with the incus!' And then he hands me this note even though we had him pretty well knocked down for the surgery. It was the only time in my career where a patient gets into the OR and hands me a detailed set of handwritten instructions telling me how he wants his surgery done."

I have no memory of that part, but the surgery was well documented. In fact it was broadcast to a conference room where a roomful of other surgeons and my fiancée watched it live via an audio-video link. According to Dr. David Foyt, as soon as the surgery was complete and the general anesthesia was wearing off, I immediately popped up again and asked the stunned O.R. staff, "Is it in contact with the incus?" They assured me that it was, and I lay back down on the gurney. I cannot recall that part either.

My surgery was on Friday, and Dr. Brackmann wanted me back for a quick check up on Monday morning, but meanwhile Sabina and I headed down to San Diego for the weekend. We lay by the pool and read books, went out to eat, and generally took it easy, though we did buy some long boards and do a bit of skateboarding on the beach paths.

We met Dr. Brackmann on Monday morning for the post-op follow up and more video and camera mugging. Dr. Brackmann told me the surgery had gone well and added, "I followed all the instructions on your note."

It was still early in the morning, so Sabina wanted to go to Disneyland before driving back up to San Jose. I had dreamed of having an implanted hearing device since I was a kid. Now I had one, and I had invented it.

Not bad! Not too bad at all. And now I was going to Disneyland too!

The Implant

*"I had the ambition not only to
go farther than man had gone before,
but to go as far as it was possible to go."*

Captain James Cook

My implant was activated by positioning the audio processor over the implant and thus turning on the device. The first time this happened, it was truly a magical experience for me. For the first time ever I could hear loud, clear, distortion-free sound that felt like it was truly inside my ear. The clarity was awesome. It was far better and a more surreal experience than I could have ever imagined.

During the activation, which was done at House Ear Institute, we had to do interviews with about five news agencies. The coverage was broadcast primarily through the Los Angeles radio stations. My story also got on CNN with the irony that the clip ran mostly in the international markets in Europe and not in the U.S.

Even though I had a lot of public speaking training and official media training arranged by our PR consultants, Harry would find fault with whatever I said or would wish I had tried to put a different spin on it. The new devices sounded terrific, and when they were activated I could hear sounds I had never heard before. These were the most amazing and most noticeable to me. One of the first sounds I heard was the wind rushing through the trees. I had never really heard this before, and now I noticed that the swooshing is accompanied by little flute-type sounds as the wind wraps around the branches. I had no idea trees were like mini symphonies of sound. Rain was another new sound: I heard raindrops as they plinked and plonked on the windshield and roof of the car and pittered and pattered other places. Listening to birds singing, waves crashing on the beach, and music was simply elating. All my life, I had experienced sound as a flat, dull landscape that was full of distortion. Now, for the first time, sound had taken on an indescribable three-dimensional quality.

During interviews, I was asked questions like, "What types of sounds are you hearing now that you couldn't hear before?"

I would answer, "I really never heard birds before. I never knew that the wind could sound the way it does. Music is absolutely amazing now, and the clarity of voices, including my own, is tremendous."

That drove Harry crazy! He wanted me to say something totally scripted like, "My quality of life has dramatically improved, and my speech recognition scores have increased significantly. Insurance companies should cover the device, and audiologists should learn all they can about it and recommend it for their patients." So I tried to work comments like that into my talking points, but the media was much more interested in the personal story angle. If 19 out of 20 statements I made in an interview were ones that Harry would have approved of, the one statement that they ended up using was invariably the one that would make Harry crazy.

To add to my confusion, the public relations consultants were thrilled with how the media events were going and how well my "sound bites" were being received. In contrast, Harry hated almost all my sound bites and rode me so hard that he started sitting in on interviews, taking a seat across from me and telling me what to say by mouthing the answers. This had the effect of making me nervous and changing my natural speaking quality into an unnatural scripted sound, which it was. The PR consultants thought that the quality was going down. "Geoff has a natural way of articulating what people in our audience want to hear, and that is what we need for the story," they would tell Harry. "If we over-coach him and give him a script, we'll lose that." But Harry was adamant. I understood his point, and I understood the PR folks' points as well. I was in a tough spot.

A few weeks after my activation, I received a call from Scotty Reid, a thirteen-year-old working on a school project.

"Is this Mr. Ball?" a smallish voice asked.

"Yes."

"Is this *the Mr. Ball*?"

"I guess so. I work at Symphonix."

"I'm writing a report about you for my class, and I wanted to know how old you were when you thought of making an implant for yourself."

"I guess the first time I thought about implants I was about your age – maybe 13 or 14. But I found out that the ones they had then would not work for me."

"I thought so. So you were 13 when you decided to make implants for yourself."

"Well no, not exactly. It was lot more complicated than that ..."

"You know you are the only living cyborg," Scotty interrupted, "and I was wondering what you think about that."

"What? Think about what?"

"You know. Being a cyborg, a being that re-animates itself when one of its functions is disabled, like in battle, and then it fixes and repairs itself. You are the only living one. So what does it feel like?"

"Oh! Yeah. Right, Scotty! Absolutely! Yes! Being a cyborg is awesome! Yeah, it is really, really cool and, this is just the start! Now we hope to quickly assimilate more cyborgs into the collective. It's going to be great!"

"That's what I thought!"

So we chatted some more about Star Trek and the differences between cyborgs and bionic beings, and whether I was really a cyborg maybe just a borg. I knew two things about thirteen-year-old boys: They rarely change their minds, and you can never win an argument with them. Scotty promised to send me a copy of his report, but he never did. If he had, I could have used his full name and quoted from his report. Scotty had a point, though, so I will be sure to put being cyborg on my resume.[8]

---

8   Full disclosure: When I wrote the first drafts of this book I was pretty happy with the "cyborg" part, which is all true. Being a cyborg actually seemed kind of funny and kind of cool. In fact, I originally even had cyborg worked in to the chapter title. But before I finished the final edits, I saw an episode of "The Cyborg" on VBS.TV (www.VBS.TV.Com). It was about a guy who implanted the equivalent of a "smart card" in his arm in 1999 and could use it to turn on lights in his office. After seeing the episode, I decided that being a cyborg was not funny: the VBS show had ruined the entire concept for me and made it seem stupid. Oh well.

One of my many responsibilities at Symphonix was to keep an eye on the competition and monitor the industry. I also made a lot of scientific presentations and supported key research projects. I attended almost every hearing conference there was in the United States and Europe. Harry and the board were so worried that someone would "scoop" Symphonix, so I produced monthly updates on the competition.

In 1996 there was a conference at Asilomar in Monterrey, California, that was focused primarily on cochlear implants. I went and took copious notes. It was the best cochlear implant conference I had yet attended, and I found it to be incredibly high on the scientific exchange barometer.

At the conference dinner I sat next to a gentleman I had never seen before, and we began talking. Shortly thereafter, a beautiful young woman came and sat next to him. I introduced myself, and the man, speaking with a German accent, introduced himself to me.

"I am Erwin Hochmair," he said.

I was stunned. My fork froze in midair. "Erwin Hochmair!" I practically shouted with excitement. "I have read all of your and your brother's work! You are the key to making the telemetry I use. Do people realize how important your work has been to the field!?"

Erwin looked at me with a confused and concerned expression on his face. "What brother?" he asked.

I spoke a little more slowly, thinking that maybe he could not understand. "You know, you and your brother Ingeborg," I explained.

At this point he looked surprised and startled. "Oh! You mean my wife, Ingeborg! May I introduce you to Ingeborg Hochmair?" And he motioned to the woman sitting next to him.

"You mean to tell me that for all these years I thought you and Ingeborg were brothers and now I find out that Ingeborg is a beautiful woman and your wife? You know, that just about says it all for me!"

Thank goodness both of the Hochmairs had a good sense of humor and thought it was hilarious. Like any serious skier, I knew Ingemar Stenmark was on the Swedish men's Olympic ski team in the 70's and 80's and perhaps the greatest slalom skier of all time. I had also known of a few teams of brothers working together in research, including one working at Stanford. I also must admit that in all the engineering classes I had taken, I could count the total number of women on one hand, so I plead guilty to being male biased. But still, I was astonished by the fact that they were married. To me it was the equivalent of a chance meeting with Marie and Pierre Curie. That is how highly I regarded their work.

They say that you never get a second chance to make a first impression. I had definitely made a first impression, but not the one I wanted. Had I known at the time how important they would be in my life later on, I would definitely have tried to do it better but at least they would remember me.

I proposed to Sabina at the Cash Store restaurant in Davenport, California, across the street from the old Davenport pier. After she said yes, we celebrated in Capitola. A few months later, on September 13, 1997, we were married at the Monterrey Plaza Hotel on Cannery Row in Monterrey. It was a perfect day: 75 degrees with crystal clear views of the bay all the way to Santa Cruz, where my familiar surf breaks were. The nuptials were held on a pier above the shoreline where I had gone diving many times. I must say it was a fine day and a great wedding. It was also a corporate celebration: In addition to Harry and almost the entire staff of Symphonix, our guests included the board of directors and even a few of our key investors.

Symphonix employed approximately 80 people worldwide. We were approved in Europe in early 1998, and our clinical trial in the U.S. was running well. Harry and the board thought it would be a good time to look to the public markets for additional funding rather than to continue to do private financing rounds. We put together all of our slide shows, but the markets were not ready to take the company public. The issue with being a VC-funded company is that the venture funds basically have only two ways of paying their investors a return: The first is to sell the new company through a merger or acquisition and then distribute the proceeds to the investors. The second is to take a company to the public markets via an initial public offering and then distribute the shares to the individual investors. The point is that they need to have an exit strategy.

In the late 90's, the IPO was viewed as an ideal way for investors to see a return on their investment. An IPO gave a company a terrific way to raise the cash required to expand its operation and to start investing more funds in new products. On the other hand, there is no guarantee that companies with an excellent track record in R & D but poor sales will be able to execute on the sales and marketing of their products. Or worse, in the case of truly breakthrough concepts, the market adoption can often be unbearably slow. Wall Street is not too patient with a young company that does not achieve its sales targets.

In 1999 Harry did a deal with the division of Siemens Hearing that created hearing aids. The deal allowed Symphonix to use the Siemens digital signal processing technology and their programming software. Siemens would distribute the Vibrant Soundbridge throughout Europe.

Shortly thereafter, the Symphonix Basel office closed and our European employees were put on Siemens' payroll. The concept was that Symphonix could leverage Siemens' distribution expertise in Europe and drive the business. On the upside, we would gain a huge foothold and customer networks in Europe. Among the downsides were that the transfer price and other deal points were not the best terms for Symphonix. In hindsight, there was little Symphonix could do if sales targets were not achieved.

Sales in Europe for the Vibrant Soundbridge did not grow at anywhere near the projected rates. There are many opinions as to why sales were so sluggish. One was that the European markets expected reimbursement and that it took several years to win positive reimbursement decisions in each country. The second was that there were not enough sales and customer support staff. Siemens added approximately four field people to the team of six that Symphonix had primarily in Germany, but some argued that it should have been many more. I cannot know everything that happened, and I can only imagine what the view inside Siemens truly was. But I know for a fact that soon after the Symphonix deal, there were different people on the team that had made it happen on the Siemens side. This was very odd. The new team may have had different views about the wisdom of the Symphonix deal, and they didn't seem to understand it as well as the original Siemens team. The Vibrant Soundbridge represented a tremendous breakthrough in terms of product offerings, but when there is no predicate product in a market space, it is often difficult to gain initial sales traction.

The curse of the Soundbridge was that we were first; that there had never been a hearing implant of its type. This was good for creating interest but bad because there was no prior experience base. Audiologists had rarely had to refer patients to surgeons for a device, and surgeons had rarely had to sell patients on technology. In other words, audiologists were good at selling hearing aids and surgeons were good at doing surgery, but neither had experience in selling a patient on a surgery or getting a patient referred to a physician. To make matters worse, in some countries the audiologist-surgeon relationship is not as positive as it could be. In too many other cases the relationship between audiologists and surgeons was either nonexistent or negative. Many audiologists were afraid that if they referred their patients to a surgeon to have an implant installed, the surgeon would not send them back to purchase the audio processor. In many cases, our technical staff could manage and improve this relationship by supporting the process in the beginning stages. We had always known that the audiologist-surgeon relationship would need work, but it needed a lot more work than we planned for.

The second curse of the Soundbridge was the time factor. Once Symphonix won approval, we needed implants to be done at a reasonable rate. The numbers of implants required in order for us to achieve stellar success were not astronomical. We would only need centers new to do three to six implants in the first year, then 15–20 in the next year, then five to ten per month thereafter, and so on. There were already plenty of centers to help make this happen. When you consider that hearing loss is so prevalent and generally untreated, these rates seemed conservative. We were wrong.

It generally took a new Vibrant Soundbridge center three to six months to find their first two patients. The activations were not until eight weeks later. Six months post surgery, they would bring the patients back for a final test session. If all went well, then they would start to look for their next three or four patients. Instead of doing three to six implants in their first year, centers were taking the whole year to do only two. Then and only then would they start looking for their next subjects. We were astonished.

Each new center was in fact running its own mini clinical trial. To make matters worse, they were generally starting with a cohort of fewer than five or six subjects, which had been a typical number for sites in our clinical trials. As with anything new, there is always a learning curve, and if there were going to be issues, they were most likely to be with the first one or two subjects. But we had not built such long time horizons into our business models and did not have this extra year for each new site in Europe.

Siemens experienced this curse in Europe, and Symphonix would see it again in the U.S. after FDA approval. My competitors also saw it. The middle ear implant industry appeared to be cursed.

In 1998, Silicon Valley was caught up in the dotcom mania. My commuting time across the Valley to San Jose had doubled because of all the extra traffic created by the tech bubble economy. Symphonix was caught up in the hoopla. One morning one of the Symphonix engineers joked, "Maybe we should call it 'Symphonix dot com'!" Everywhere we looked, companies were going public. Symphonix was a technical success: The devices were being implanted, and clinical trials were running and going well in the U.S. We were getting coverage in most media outlets and had feature pieces in big business magazines and the *Wall Street Journal*.

Engineers never win Nobel prizes (unless one generously counts the awards to Von Bekesy and perhaps Shockley), so when I won what I consider the next best thing, Grand Prize in the Engineer of the Year Award for Excellence in Design in 1999, I was thrilled, too say the least. Our device was being hailed as revolutionary, and we had literally blown right past competitors that did not have the FMT design. Although all our competitors had started well before us, we had beaten them in the race to be the first and only device approved in Europe, and now we were on track to be the first in the United States.

Building a totally implantable device and getting it approved would be a daunting and expensive effort, and it would require additional full rounds of clinical trials. We believed that if we used the same FMT, we had a better chance of winning faster approval. A totally implantable system would require doubling our R&D capacity and hiring a lot of additional resources to get it manufactured. We were also gearing up to launch in the United States once we got approval. In order to meet our projections for product requirements, we would need to greatly expand our manufacturing capacity. To do all this, we needed a much larger facility than Orchard Parkway, a lot more people, and a lot more money.

Ours the first commercial middle ear implant with any success. Repeating that technical success and building the world's first totally implantable system seemed too good *not* to do. Our bankers and our consul told us that the capital markets were extremely good and that the window was open to raise additional funds. However, they warned, we could not rely on the window being open forever, so we either had to go public now or wait a long time for another opportunity.

We brought in bankers and began interviewing banking firms to evaluate our business and our chances of success if we went public. Since we were just starting out with our sales in Europe and with Siemens, we did not have a long sales record to go on, so Symphonix would be a speculation investment or a spec stock. In 1999, dotcom companies were going public with far less than what Symphonix had achieved. We had had significant technical success where many others had tried and failed. We had one of the largest market opportunities in a medical field with unmet needs. The bankers were bullish on our chances. One told us, "This will be a gem in a field of dotcom tech stocks. Symphonix offers something new and a lot more real."

Successful completion of a Symphonix stock offering to the capital markets would mean the public and our competition would get a good look at what was going on with our business. But there was also a downside for me personally as an inventor. One banker told me, "They are going to lock you up like you would not believe," meaning that I would not be able to sell stock on the offering or for a long time after the offering was complete. I had been working on this all of my professional life, for more than 15 years, and was sure they would let me sell a few shares on the opening. But it was not to be.

At the time, going public seemed like the best thing for the company, for the investors, and for the hearing impaired who could benefit from our technology and from the additional innovative products this step would allow us to develop. I always believed that the more we focused on building and delivering the technology that would benefit the hearing impaired, the better our chances of becoming a very good company.

We interviewed our bankers and evaluated their pitches. They were extremely positive about our chances on the markets. We selected Cowan as the bank that would lead our deal, and George Montgomery took over managing the Symphonix deal to go public. George and his team managed the process of drafting of our "red herring" (a prospectus that describes the company, the technology, the market and the risk factors) and IPO documentation with the help of our attorneys at Wilson Sonnsini. Soon we were in drafting sessions that would detail our business financials, the stock disposition, the use of funds, and the risk factors. It took many months to finalize the document.

I only disagreed with a few of the decisions we made at Symphonix. One was when we decided to move just around the corner to a larger and much more expensive building, also in San Jose. Commercial rent rates and building prices were exorbitant. On the consumer side, the picture was equally horrific. The cost of buying a home in Sunnyvale was too high for most of us. Sabina and I ended up purchasing a tear-down house in the Los Gatos hills priced well below market value and fixing it up. Some of my engineers watched their rents double in the course of just a few years during the peak of the dotcom bubble. We paid good salaries, but we could not keep up with real estate market inflation. I thought we should consider moving out to the Central Valley or much farther south, where housing was much more affordable, but I was alone in my thinking.

Once we had all the necessary initial public offering documentation filed and finalized, Harry, Alf Merriweather (our CFO), the banking team from Cowen and I took off on the Symphonix IPO road show. We travelled across the U.S. and through Europe for four weeks to meet and present to all the investment bankers and potential purchasers of our stock. Our goal was to fill the book with commitments to purchase shares so that there would be enough orders to buy the stock we intended to sell on the open market. Symphonix stock would be traded on the NASDAQ. On February 13, 1998, Symphonix went public. The IPO was $12 a share, which rose to $17 in short order. The Symphonix IPO was a success.

Siemens had now taken over the European operations, and Bill Perry, chief of the Symphonix European Division, elected not to stay on with them. Bill was originally from the U.S. and had been in Europe for several years, but now he wanted to move his family back. I thought Bill was the perfect candidate for the slot of VP for marketing and sales in the United States. In another of the few key decisions Symphonix made that I was at odds with, we hired a former West Pointer with an MBA to fill the slot and develop our North American market. This person, who shall remain nameless, was supposed to be a great, and his resume was not bad all. What seemed a bit odd to me was had been that he had so much – too much – military-related work in his background.

"This guy is all military," I told Harry. "Not that there is anything wrong with a military background, but I still think Bill is the better man for the job."

"That ship has sailed," Harry said.

The dream of all inventors is to make a great invention, to see it become successful in the market, and hopefully to make some money. At the peak of its NASDAQ run, the market cap of Symphonix totaled around $300 million when the stock was trading at $17 a share. After the Symphonix IPO, I was worth millions on paper. However, the amount of Symphonix that I owned had been diluted down to a minor percentage. I had no issues with that as I always believed that it is better to own a small piece of something big than a big piece of nothing. It is rare, certainly, for a medical device company to be privately held and to have a high market cap. It is rarer still for inventors to hold more than five or ten percent of it after all is said and done. It was virtually unheard of for the inventors and original management team of a publicly traded company to own more that 50 percent of the stock.

Despite my best efforts, I was not allowed to sell stock on the initial offering. As much as I believed in the future of Symphonix, it was in my own family's best future financial interest to diversify my holdings. There were specified windows when I would be allowed to sell small portions of my stock as long as there were no material events that the SEC could perceive as insider trading. But there was a catch: Every time the window was open, I would walk over to Alf's office and ask him if I could sell some shares. Alf would call the attorneys, and the answer was always no. Or I would call and place a sell order with my investment banker, who would call our consul and/or Alf and then call me back and say, "No, the window is closed." So I was never able to sell, nor was Harry.

As our stock price began to decrease, the "no's" became more adamant. I was only ever allowed to sell a small amount of stock one time. It was nowhere near enough to start a retirement account.

Harry was in a similar position. I was and still am a startup guy, but we all knew that Harry was the real startup CEO. In fact, I had originally thought Harry would start the company and then transfer out in two years, but he stayed on as we transitioned into a "mid stage" company. I believe that Harry stayed on as long as he did because the Symphonix deal turned out to be a lot more to his liking than he had envisioned. There is a saying that the original team members of a Silicon Valley startup will work harder and put in more hours in two years than the average person will work in a lifetime. Harry had been one of the key founding members of Laserscope and then a founder and CEO of his startup, CardioRhythm, which had been sold to Medtronic prior to his joining Symphonix. That deal had had more than its share of challenges. Symphonix was Harry's third startup company in a row, so I guess one way to look at it is that Harry had in fact already put in three lifetimes of work into startups in only seven years.

Harry was great leader and a true inspiration, and he had been a key driving force in the company. But being highly strung and driven in addition to all the stress of running a startup and taking it public is bound to take its toll. Harry was understandably in need of emotional and physical relief. He and his wife also wanted to relocate back to the East Coast and retire. We all knew it was inevitable, and though we did not like it, we knew that it was time for a change. Harry deserved a break.

Harry Robbins was the most entertaining and truly fun CEO I have ever worked with and at times the most frustrating. Like everyone, he had his good days and bad days. He was quite the character. Say what you will about Harry Robbins, but the one thing he did better than almost all other CEO's was the one thing that is without a doubt the key function of that role: hiring talent. Harry had the knack, the initiative, the resources and the connections to make great hires as well as the personality to attract the best talent. To this day I am still amazed by his bird dog nose for sniffing out great talent and getting them signed on.

I pushed to make Bob Katz the CEO of Symphonix, but the not all other Symphonix VP's shared my opinion. Some might wonder why I did not want the coveted CEO spot myself. The fact is that I knew that Bob was a better candidate at the time. Bob was older, he had an MBA and more experience, and he was ready. At the time I didn't feel I was the right fit for the role. I also loved my lab and the inventing and research side too much. I felt, as did others, that I still had to grow a lot before I could take on the CEO role, especially now that Symphonix was publicly traded. My dream of running my own company some day would have to wait a few more years.

When Harry left the company in 1999, the board felt that moving Bob up would create too much friction among the other VP's, so they hired Kirk Davis as our new CEO. I was sorry to see Harry go. He had taught me a lot, and being around him was perhaps better training for me than any MBA would have been. For Harry, the good thing about leaving was that he was no longer employed by Symphonix, which meant he could trade his shares and diversify his holdings.

As the window for me to sell shares was always closed, it became clear that the only way that I could sell and significantly diversify my stock holdings was to follow Harry's lead and leave the company too. This was the only way I could get out from under the lock up rules. I had not even been allowed to start a programmed trading plan. It was a terrible predicament: On the one hand, I loved Symphonix and the people; I loved the technology and the work. It was great place to work, and it was my baby. On the other hand, I realized this might be my one and only chance to make a significant amount of money. Sabina and I were trying to start a family, and future kids were a primary consideration.

Symphonix was my 23rd employer but my first shot at making real money. I know that it is rare to get a second chance and rarer still to get a third. Comments such as, "This is your first venture deal. There will be others." did not sit well with me. I knew how unusual it was to get a company to the point where Symphonix was. I knew the odds were stacked against me.

Few businesses really make it. Typically, of every 100,000 people who have a good idea or invention, only 5,000 will try to write a business plan or get even halfway serious about pursuing their idea or business. Four thousand of them abandon their business idea once they realize how much work and expense are involved and how many significant obstacles they will have to overcome. That leaves a thousand who actually get some type of financing and start a company. Of those thousand start-ups, 90 percent will fail in the first two years. Over the next five years, eighty of the remaining hundred will either have closed or been sold. Only one or two of the twenty surviving businesses will have a market value of more than $100 million. The goal posts for achieving a business success are narrow indeed.

I was afraid of how it would look if I left my dream and took the money and ran, and I talked to my wife about our predicament. I told her that the stock kept leveling off, then moving down, and then coming back up a bit; that seemed like every time this happened, the window was closed again. I did not want to leave the company like Harry; I really wanted to stay. I also had this other crazy dream of being able to start and fund my own lab and work on another idea I had. In my dream, I operated the lab as a product incubator for Symphonix.

Sabina said, "This is your life's work. It is what you do and what you love, and you aren't finished yet. It's not about money; it never has been for you. This is your mission. Whatever happens, we will be fine. Don't give up your dream. We will find a way to make it no matter what, so don't worry about us."

I talked to my own attorney. Alf was also worried what the impact would be on the stock if the CTO rushed for the exit so soon after the CEO had left. At the end of the day I stayed because I knew it was the right thing to do, but I also knew it might be a terrible financial decision, perhaps the worst I could possibly make.

We were just finishing up our submission for FDA approval. The results with all our subjects were terrific: With all the European data and all the U.S. patients, we had almost 100 patients done. We had a remarkably clean clinical trial. We were starting to work on pulling together the panel packs that would be sent to each of the FDA Ear Nose and Throat Panel members in advance of our approval meeting. Michael Crompton was leading the regulatory department, and he was doing a stellar job in terms of moving us toward FDA approval in the United States.

Then the devices started failing. We had seen a few devices fail in the field in Europe, but these were due to mishandling or trauma to the implant during surgery. We felt that we had taken appropriate measures. Suddenly devices started coming back after having been explanted. They had simply failed. At first it was only two, but soon there were five and then 10, and we were freaking out. We had a problem that had to be fixed. We found the root cause and took all the corrective actions to fix it. We tested all the new devices and submitted all the documentation to the FDA. Even though the fix for the design was a simple design change, it was costly in terms of the time it would take us to make sure we had it corrected the problem. The FDA had us do more patients in order to show that the problem had in fact been fixed. We ended up doing another 50 patients, which delayed our U.S. launch plans. It would also delay our planned market launch at the American Academy of Otolaryngology meeting. It was more than a bit maddening.

Kirk Davis was a seasoned medical executive out of Baxter. He had a picture-perfect resume, and when I first met him for our interview, I thought he was a super guy. I also thought that it was interesting that this would be the second time I would be involved in hiring my own boss. Kirk had always wanted to run his own company, and he certainly had the right skill set, background, and leadership qualities for it. He took over in 1999, just as we had gotten the FDA ENT panel to recommend our device for approval, and we were all really happy to have him. According to Kirk, during all the interviews that he had with our executives and directors, nobody had told him that our launch date was delayed due to the problem with the device. I guess everyone on the interview committee assumed that someone else would have mentioned it. At the time I can see how this had happened: We had "the fix" identified and were moving quickly to solve it and get the data in to the FDA.

The FDA panel meeting granted approval for the Vibrant Soundbridge in late 2000. The new VP of marketing and sales, the former military commander, had come in and assembled an excellent team of sales and clinical managers to cover five regions of the U.S. The goal of the sales managers was to drive sales, while the responsibility of the clinical managers was to support the sites and the patients for programming and to help identify and work with patient candidates.

After the approval order came, we had an executive staff meeting to review the plan and materials for the product launch; in other words, what product we going to launch the product in the U.S. and how we were we going to launch it. Our e-staff normally met for one hour on Monday mornings, and the meetings were generally positive and productive. Since we now had approval, this meeting should have been a happy and congratulatory affair too, but it wasn't.

It still seems impossible to me as I write this, but the VP for sales and marketing basically said, "There is no plan."

"What materials do we have?" Kirk asked.

The VP produced newer versions of the same materials that Peter Hertzmann had done previously. There was not much there and certainly nothing new. What had he been doing for the past six months? He had the field personnel, but most of them had been hired by the director of field operations.

"I have a good team, and they are motivated," he said in exasperation. But he did not have a launch plan and he had not produced any materials. I was stunned. Clearly the approval from

FDA coming when it did had caught him off guard. Obviously he thought he had more time, but he was wrong. Maybe having an MBA was overrated.

We missed our chance to launch the product in 2000 in any real and effective way. With few materials and a strategy that was lacking in depth and detail, our new field staff had little direction. It was true that the field support staff was an excellent team, but soon I was having meetings with key people, good professional people, and recent hires who felt compelled to come in and discuss their serious reservations about the direction their boss the marketing VP was taking. Tragically, some of these same people began to resign. We lost our field director, then one of the top sales managers. Our key marketing staff people left, one saying she "could not take it anymore." We knew we were in trouble when we had not even launched and already had people jumping overboard. Our sales and marketing effort was in total disarray. We were losing precious time and resources.

We finally managed to execute a mini-launch of the VSB at the spring COSM meeting in Palm Desert in early 2001. This meeting was not as well attended as the larger American Academy meeting, but we still had important customers and a decent booth, and our field staff was in attendance. It was not all that it could have been, though, and the VP of sales and marketing was let go shortly thereafter.

With the dot com boom at its epic all-time high, we could not find a new VP for the sales and marketing department quickly. Good talent, always in short supply, was now harder than ever to find. I again pushed for Bill Perry, and he actually came down and spoke with Kirk. Bill had found a position that he was happy with, but at least he was willing to talk. It may have been that Kirk was not impressed, but once again, the hire did not happen.

May, June, and July 2000 went by. We had few candidates to interview, none of them a good fit. We had brought in Robert Baker, formerly of ReSound, to help with the marketing while the VP spot remained open. We hired John Luna, and he and Robert did a remarkable job of getting the sales staff trained and updated. We were without a VP in sales and marketing for nearly six months until the board hired "our new marketing guy."

This was the third decision I took issue with at Symphonix. I was against hiring the new marketing guy to fill the vacant VP position not because I thought he was incapable, but because he was a former executive of a hearing aid company that I did not like. I knew the chance of someone from that company being a good fit was very unlikely, and I felt the new marketing guy was the wrong choice. I told Kirk that while I appreciated the guy's enthusiasm and drive, I had a really bad feeling about hiring him. Kirk was polite and said he understood, but that the decision had been made and that he needed me to get on board with it. We were out of time. I reluctantly agreed to support the decision and hoped that I would not regret it. Another issue I had with this hire that with was that he did not want to move his family to California right away. By this time in my career, I knew that not wanting to move *right away* was a clear red flag warning. It indicated to me that it was more than likely that he and his wife were not going to relocate to California any time soon, if ever. Instead, he would take a small apartment and commute back to Wisconsin twice a month.

I told Kirk, "The fact that his family is not moving here right away is not a good sign. We need someone who is committed 100 percent. How would you feel working in California for someone who lived in another state? What would that communicate to you?"

I believe Bob Katz was perhaps the least impressed of all. Shortly after the new marketing guy was hired, Bob decided it was time to leave the company. The reason for his departure might well have been that he didn't like the direction of the company was taking on the sales and marketing side. It is true that Bob had been offered a terrific new opportunity, and I think that he might have thought that he was the best man for the CEO role. After all, he had left his mark on every aspect of Symphonix and had driven the development effort that made the Soundbridge a reality. Along the way, Bob had become an expert in the field of hearing, and he had excellent connections with physicians and audiologists. He had become an excellent speaker, and he had a firm, effective team approach to problem solving that the employees appreciated. While Bob Katz was at Symphonix, it was the company that could do nothing wrong. We had positive energy and could always find a solution to any obstacle. Symphonix was a stimulating and fun place to work.

When Bob left, I lost a dear friend and my sounding board. Carlos Baez, whom I had worked with years ago at ReSound, was put in charge of the day to day running of Symphonix R&D.

It was frightening how quickly the corporate culture changed after Bob left. Almost overnight, the company that could do nothing wrong turned into an organization that could do nothing right. Symphonix had always had the drive to find a solution to any problem or issue, but suddenly problems appeared impossible to solve. Bob and I had been quite a team on the R&D side, but once he left, a barrage of arrows started coming my way from the other departments. Carlos did his best, but filling Bob's position and role in the company culture was not easy. Then a virus I call stinking thinking spread throughout the organization. It was most virulent on days when our stock price was lower than usual and slightly less noticeable when the stock was up even just a bit.

An example of the damage stinking thinking caused was extreme negativity that pervaded the company. Dr. Jon Spindel and I had spent several weeks in my lab studying a new position for the FMT. Dr. Spindel had long been a proponent of placing a transducer such as the FMT on the round window of the inner ear. The beauty of that concept was that it transmitted mechanical auditory energy directly into the cochlea. In other words, the Soundbridge was a type of mechanical cochlear implant. The solid data we had collected over weeks of painstaking work revealed that we could more than adequately drive the inner ear with the FMT, and that this could be used for hearing loss that was beyond the current indication range approved by the FDA. That meant the Soundbridge could be used to treat even more patients. Our data was awesome, and we believed we had a new product concept.

We presented our findings to the Symphonix executive staff. We proposed that we attempt to develop the method further, solicit input from our scientific advisory board, and start a project to do a clinical investigation. The response from our regulatory staff was, "You want to put the FMT on the round window in a live human patient? Over our dead bodies!"

The clinical and regulatory folks then ticked off a list of reasons why the application of the FMT on the round window would never work and should never be used on human subjects. To their credit, the regulatory and clinical folks did appreciate the value of our work. They admitted that it was "very good science" but said it had "no clinical value."

Dr. Spindel and I were deflated, to say the least, when we were told that even though our data was good and clearly revealed the value of the approach, we had a lot more work to do before we could even think about trying the new approach on human patients Ultimately, however, we arrived at the conclusion that the clinical and regulatory folks were probably right. In doing so, we also became the victims of stinking thinking and part of the new corporate culture of finding problems rather than solutions. The idea of using the FMT on the round window became just a neat little research finding and not much more. Sadly, we never even published a paper on our results.

I believe that the round window data would never have been shot down the way it was had Bob Katz still been in the building. He had tried on several occasions as early as 1995 to work with the University of Virginia team that included Roger Ruth and Dr. Spindel on the concept of using the round window. Bob, who had listened closely to the expert otologists and Symphonix SAB members, also believed that the FMT could drive the oval window of the inner ear. Dr. Charlie Leutje, the first surgeon in the U.S. to use the VSB, had been arguing for such approach for the Vibrant Sound-bridge since he first saw the design in 1994. Now we had data that absolutely showed the potential, but the concept fell on deaf ears in the post-Katz Symphonix. One of the problems of being first with a concept is that you end up spending countless hours trying to explain how your device works rather than focusing on how to get it adopted as quickly as possible. From a technology explanation point of view, is far easier to be number two. As the saying goes, "Sometimes the early bird turns out to be the worm."

Another example of stinking thinking was the direct drive stimulation (DDS) development debacle. Before Bob left, we had had a project in the works to build a system that could demonstrate the FMT's capability to generate epic hi-fidelity sound before a patient was implanted. Although documentation proved that the FMT was at the time the smallest hi-fidelity transducer ever built up to that time, most people working in the field, and certainly prospective patients, could not be expected to sit down and read and understand the technology and data that validated the value of the FMT. In fact, my own writings on its fantastic sound would be likely to put most people to sleep.

We had a problem: We had the FMT, a fantastic design that made the best direct drive sound ever, but only a few people in the world truly understood how it worked. Bob and I wanted to build a device and then show everyone how good it was rather than simply tell them.

The concept for the DDS (direct drive simulator) was to use an FMT that would be held in the ear canal of a prospective patient or anyone that wanted to hear the fidelity of the FMT. A small amount of warm water would then be introduced into the ear canal. Without getting too technical about the biomechanics of how all this works, the person would then hear epic direct drive quality sound produced by the FMT. We put soft silicon on the ends of the FMT's, and physicians could then use a bit of mineral oil and hold the device next to the patient's eardrum. The reports were fantastic, and everyone who tried it was amazed.

We produced a quick yet adequate system that was ready to go just after Bob left Symphonix. Everyone appreciated the significance of being able to demonstrate the value of the FMT to patients and their family members without the need for surgery. The chance to test drive the FMT would be an excellent additional way to help increase our patient flow, not to mention that it was incredibly cool. But the new marketing guy wanted the system to look much fancier: He insisted that it should be built into a custom box and have easier-to-use knobs. Regulatory wanted to do a submission, and clinical wanted more data, and on and on.

"We can do all of the tasks, we can make it into a fancy box, and we can put it into a super snazzy format, but it will take time and cost a lot of money," I countered. "On the other hand, if we submit what we have today, which I admit is no frills and basic, we could get it out in matter of months. If we do it the other way, it will take nearly a year, a year where we could be using something instead of nothing." The decision was made to try to build the super snazzy system, and the basic no-frills system was abandoned. I was to go out of house to try and get a supplier to get it done within six months. I did, but as with most projects requiring regulatory submission, it took a year before it was complete. Once stinking thinking starts, it spreads like a virus and it contaminates almost everything. The DDS was the single most frustrating project I ever worked on, but we got it done.

Despite all this, we were ready for the big launch of the Vibrant Soundbridge. There can be no doubt that everyone on our marketing team did their utmost with the abilities they had. To their credit, they put together our first real United States launch of the Vibrant Soundbridge at the most important convention of the year, the American Academy of Otolaryngology meeting held in Denver, Colorado in the fall of 2001. The agendas were all printed, the tasks were all laid out; and the booth was awesome. All hands were on deck, and the excitement was palpable. Everyone – our investors, our employees, and most importantly the field – was watching as Symphonix made its real main stage debut. It was our turn to dance. I was beginning to think that my reservations about the new marketing guy had been all wrong.

We had all the key people from the Symphonix and all our key scientific advisory board members in attendance. We had flown in all our field staff and must have had 40 people from the company at the meeting. We had our full booth with all our new displays. We had materials and sales tools. We had a plan! We had set up a huge temporal bone workshop at the University of Denver with 50 stations where the surgeons could be trained and practice the installation of the Vibrant Soundbridge. We had 50 programming stations where we could train audiologists how to program the device. We had flown in five of our patients who were successful users to talk to physicians and audiologists about how the implant had changed their lives for the better and answer their questions. I was pumped. We were all pumped. Our presence was great, our people looked great, and the booth was fantastic. This was the big launch! *Ten, nine, eight, seven, six* ...

The agenda of the launch day was to have a combined morning session with the audiologists and the physicians. Then in the afternoon the surgeons would be formally trained in the surgical technique. The audiologists would have hands-on programming training and a Q & A session with experienced Soundbridge programmers and real patients. *Five, four, three* ... Then there would be a cocktail reception followed by a gala dinner event. *Two!*

At 10:30 a.m., we came out of the morning session for a scheduled coffee break. That was when normalcy abruptly ended. There was a small television out in the lobby area, and people were crowded around it. There were looks of utter disbelief, tears, and a strange stoic silence as everyone tried to listen to the broadcast. The launch of the Vibrant Soundbridge, the most unsuccessful launch of a new medical device in history, had been scheduled for the worst day imaginable. *Stop the countdown.* It was September 11, 2001.

There was a gasp, and someone called out, "The World Trade Center just collapsed! The United States is under attack!" I ran over and watched in horror and disbelief. Many of the bankers who had helped take us public had offices in the World Trade Center, and some of them were now dead or dying. I was shaking.

I found Kirk Davis. "We have a lot of people here," I told him. "You and I need to go right now and rent every rental car we can find so that we can at least get these people home. Obviously, the rest of the day is not going to happen."

"It is going to be OK," Kirk assured me. "We will be able to get out of here in a day or two."

I was flabbergasted, and the thoughts that went through my mind at that moment are not fit to print. "Someone just used two planes as weapons to take down the World Trade Center. We can forget about airplanes for weeks, if not months! We need to go rent cars immediately, before they are all gone. The launch is over for us."

Kirk thought I was crazy. "Geoff. Look, just settle down."

I knew we did not have any time to waste. I ran outside, got a taxi and took it to the nearest Hertz rental site.

I walked in and said, "I need ten rental cars."

The agent looked at me, astonished. "You want what?" she asked incredulously.

"Oh, and two vans."

She looked at me and said, "I only have six." She added that she had never had anyone ask to rent six cars before.

"This is not a normal day," I told her.

My brain was racing a million miles an hour, yet in a surreal way my thinking was crystal clear. It was almost like I was having an out-of-body experience. I thought to myself, *Someone just attacked the U.S. with airplanes. We are now at war with someone, and thousands have perished. Our launch is finished. The stock market is going to take a huge hit, as will our stock. Symphonix is in big, big trouble. We all are.*

I thought of the people in those towers that I had met. It ultimately turned out to be far worse than I imagined. It was a nightmare.

On September 11,, 2001, I watched with the rest of the world in horror as the World Trade Centers fell. I did not know that in a strange and bizarre way, that tragedy would forever change my dreams for Symphonix. My company essentially died that day, and with it a part of me along with the plans and dreams that I had for the future. I had to change my dreams and find a new way and a new beginning. Compared to those who lost their lives and loved ones on that tragic day and the countless other people who had to remake their futures after the attacks, though, I had been lucky and was grateful to have a second chance. When I got back to the conference center, I was not surprised to find that all the remaining events had canceled. The conference was effectively over. The gala dinner would not take place. There was not a rental car left to be had in the entire city of Denver.

At five p.m., we glumly assembled the Symphonix team in the lobby of the conference hotel. We all sat and stared at each other. The largest rental car would head northeast and drop people off along the way. I had another car head southwest. Kirk and I would drive two rental cars back to California, and the other two cars would head south and then out to Los Angeles. We packed all our gear in the cars and said our goodbyes. I drove for most of the long trip back to California. The entire way, I had a surreal feeling of dread and my stomach was tied up in knots.

On the one hand, I knew that my company had an even tougher if not impossible year ahead of it now. Today's events could wipe out all our hard work and success. It made the fifteen years of work I had personally invested seem useless. At the same time, my concerns seemed petty and selfish in light of what had happened in New York and Washington and Pennsylvania that day. All night, we listened to the reports on the radio of the rental car that was one of the tens of thousands crisscrossing the United States in the early hours of September 12. How could my company, my baby, survive this?

I had an uncanny experience as we were crossing the great deserts of the American Southwest. It was the middle of the night, and the road was dark and empty: no lights anywhere except for distant lightning and no other traffic. The others were asleep, and I was driving, lost in my thoughts about the attacks. Suddenly, without warning, there was an ear-splitting sound as a bolt of lightning struck. Then another. "Wham!" *We really have our work cut out for us now,* I thought. "Wham!" *It is going to be a tough year.* "Wham! Wham! Wham!" *I have no idea what the future will bring.* Each "Wham!" was like God making a point.

Two weeks prior to September 11, Sabina and I had been in Monterrey, California, to attend a wedding of the daughter of my good friend and golfing buddy Rick Adams and his wife, Myra. The groom had been on the plane that hit the second tower. His bride was devastated. In the light of such tragedies, it seems unfitting to point out that Symphonix, along with many other young companies, were also casualties of that event. Prior to 9/11, the dotcom bubble was already a reality. 'Spec stocks,' companies that may have been years away from commercial success, were being hammered particularly hard in the capital markets. Prior to September 11, Symphonix, which had been falling since its peak of $17, had been trading at around six dollars a share. When the markets re-opened after September 11, our stock cratered and would never come back. Worse, for six months post 9/11, people were not thinking about getting hearing treatment. It seemed that the whole country was suffering post-traumatic stress.

To make matters worse, a new form of the middle ear implant curse took shape. After September 11, when our stock price was so low (less than two dollars a share) that we were facing de-listing from the NASDAQ exchange, some of our doctors had issues implanting the VSB because they no longer believed that Symphonix would be around. In other words, they had lost faith in the company because they thought we were going out of business. The irony was that if they implanted even modest numbers of the patients that could benefit, then we would be around for years and years, and in theory our stock price would someday rise. By assuming that Symphonix would not be around anymore and not using the product because of our stock price, they were creating a self-fulfilling prophecy. The same would hold true for any product. If, for example, there was a number one pacemaker company in the world, and if all doctors decided at the same time to stop using those pacemakers because they doubted that the company was going to be around much longer, then guess what? The pacemaker company's stock price would fall, and with no sales at some point the company would cease to exist.

As far as I know, the only good thing to come out of the fiscal crisis of 2010 is that I can now talk about short selling in the stock market and the effect that I believe it had on the Symphonix stock without sounding like a paranoid crazy person. Between 2006 and 2007, Goldman Sachs and others placed short bets against products that they themselves were placing with clients. At the same time, they were hedging these bets via insurance through amazingly complicated transactions. Take-home message: They fanned the fire of the United States mortgage meltdown and almost ruined the world economy. So what was the point?

Now back to Symphonix after its IPO. At that time, Symphonix was the only publicly traded middle-ear hearing device company. Being public has the advantage of allowing companies to raise cash in the offering and to raise additional funds when the stock price is high. The bad thing is that the company's books are open to the public. If a company is in a tough spot, even if it is just a temporary rough cycle, it can be unduly punished in the stock markets. Companies can also be overvalued, so short selling does, in theory, help companies remain closer to their more realistic valuations.

Symphonix had gone public in 1998. Shortly thereafter, the creation of the Yahoo finance and other similar pages made it possible for anyone with an e-mail account to post anonymous comments. The message boards for Symphonix (NASDAQ:SMPX) were lightning rods for short sellers. Almost from the day SMPX started trading, the boards were lit up. I had tracked stocks before and seen the message boards, so I knew that there had already been cases of internet activity "pumping and dumping" penny stocks. ReSound stock had also been hard hit by the short sellers at one time. But what happened to Symphonix was something else. Symphonix must have set some kind of record for message exchanges on all the boards from the shorts. I can still recall the online handles.

JAWS: "SMPX is going down, down, down. CEO out. Who's next??!!! Short this stinker!"

SSHORTX: "This dog has no bark but I have a bite. I'm short while the suckers go."

It was endless and relentless, but it was legal.

It was also legal for our competitors to trade in our shares. Businesses that had an interest in making Symphonix go away could short the SMPX stock and run it down to drive down the price. This would ruin any decent prospects for future financing and to create a bad image for the company that could further reduce sales.

Do I have the receipts and the transaction records to show that competitive companies shorted SMPX? No. Can I get them? No. Why not? Because those trades are completely legal, and there are no disclosure requirements. It was technically legal for big firms to take shorts on positions that they sold to customers, and our competitors also had no problem shorting SMPX stock. Is it legal to maliciously use message boards to help drive the price down? Maybe. But in 1999 through 2001, how on earth could SMPX go and track this down and put a stop to it even if it was not?

So am I saying this happened? To this day that I have no doubt that my competitors traded in my stock and that some might have even taken a long bet on it trading up. I am saying any decent MBA could arrive at the conclusion that if they wanted to make a company like SMPX go away for good, it would only cost them one or two million dollars to do it and possibly make a lot of money at the same time. They could even leverage and hedge the bet into an even more significant position. A modest payment to one of the firms specializing in filling up the chat rooms, message boards and rumor mills was all it would take to drive the company stock down.

Over the years, I have heard countless rumors about such monkey business. I am not sure what to believe, but I know what I saw. I am not an expert on the stock market or short stock positions, but the message boards and the volume of the shorts were truly unbelievable and seemed way out of line in comparison to what was going on with similar companies. Where there is smoke, there is fire, and what I saw was a blaze that was out of control. If wanting Symphonix to go away was good for your business model, if it was not too expensive to do, if it was legal, and if there was a chance to make some money, why wouldn't you do it? It is good business. It is smart business. Do I agree with it? No. Am I upset? Of course I am: It was my company. But I understand it was part of our capital markets, and if it was legal, what can I say?

In the future, spec stocks there will hopefully be regulated by laws that stipulate how and when short positions can be taken. The laws limiting stock manipulation that are currently in place need to be enforced. In my opinion, predatory short selling activities must be abolished, and it is high time to stop the pumping and dumping of stocks and other market manipulation. Corporations and insiders should never be able to trade stocks in their own field. Ever. Period.[9] This is especially important for startup and mid-stage companies new to the public markets. Even though I believe my company was a casualty of short selling, I recognize that it can serve an economically valuable purpose by keeping markets and individual stocks from becoming overvalued and markets from becoming overheated. Who can take such positions and when and how they can take them needs to be closely examined, in my view. I do believe, however, that it should be against the law for competitors to trade and to take positions in the very industry they work with. Goldman Sachs should never have been allowed to trade the stock of other investment institutions, nor should they have been allowed to sell shorts on the housing bubble. That was like pouring liquid oxygen directly onto a fire, and you just do not do that. How on earth could they have traded without insider information?

---

9 For example, an executive for car company Y should never be allowed to own shares in car company X, its competitor.

The impact of limited sales in the U.S. and the Siemens team also struggling in Europe became a nightmare. The short sellers were making a killing on SMPX. To make matters worse, physicians began to call in with comments such as, "I think Symphonix will be going out of business, and I can't implant a device that I am not sure will be supported." Kirk, along with our new CFO Terry Griffin, had raised more capital. But with our balance sheets bleeding red and the post-9/11 climate contributing to the failure of our cash inflow to reach our projections, it became clear that we were going to have cut our burn rate. Kirk wanted to keep working on the totally implantable technology platform, which at the time was about 60 percent complete and would presumably be ready for clinical trials in nine months. Kirk believed that the totally implantable platform was critical to our success and did not want to abandon it. Adele Olivia, one of the newer directors on the Symphonix board, pleaded with Kirk to consider very significant downsizing soon in order to preserve capital and give us more time to let market conditions improve. Kirk, a true believer, was confident that we were going to turn the corner, but for Symphonix, the world had changed. That was not Kirk's fault, and there was little he could do about it.

In May of 2001 we began downsizing, and the totally implantable development was slowed down. It was painful to watch as good people had to be laid off. With our stock continuing to trade below two dollars, we were now facing de-listing from the NAS-DAQ exchange. Worse, both of these conditions combined made new financing options for Symphonix almost impossible.

Many believed that if Medicare decided to cover the Vibrant Soundbridge, it could save the company. A positive coverage determination would not only improve reimbursement for Medicare patients, but also encourage other health care insurers approve coverage of the Soundbridge.

I kept pointing out that we already had excellent coverage determinations by firms such as Aetna and many other insurers. Few outside our reimbursement department (staffed by only one person) knew that the reimbursement coverage patients were getting was already very good. We had a positive hit rate of around 60 percent among patients with insurance who submitted a claim, and the better and smarter we got about how to submit the forms, the faster that rate was improving. We had been approved for coverage for all four branches of the military, including military families and many retired military. Our rep for the West Coast region and I had recently helped support the implantation our first patient at the San Francisco VA. The VA is the single largest purchaser of hearing instruments in the world, and given all the hearing loss caused by military service, we could really do incredibly well with just the military. By my count, more than 12 million people in the U.S. had coverage for the Soundbridge. "We just need to hire more people to process the forms and get as many insurance forms submitted as possible," I said over and over.

We explored every option: distribution deals, strategic partnerships, cross-licensing deals, anything and everything we could think of. At the end of the day, the only things the other companies seemed interested in were the implantable microphone and totally implantable technology. The problem was that because the totally implantable technology was so new and novel, they had a hard time evaluating and understanding it. Symphonix was simply too far ahead of the curve.

In August 2002 the Medicare reimbursement decision on coverage of the Vibrant Soundbridge came down, and it was negative. To rub a little salt in the wounds, or maybe just to piss me off, they classified the Vibrant Soundbridge as a hearing aid, the very device I had worked my entire life to offer an alternative to. This was the final nail in the Symphonix coffin.[10]

---

10 I found out years later that the CMS decision was made by a board made up of three people, only one of whom voted for approval. The report was that the two who voted against it both had strong ties to the hearing aid industry. One was even a researcher who had not only an extensive network of relationships in the hearing aid industry but was also deeply involved with my main competitor. In other words, he had ties to the two primary groups with an incredibly strong interest in not seeing positive coverage happen for the Soundbridge. Talk about a conflict of interest! In my opinion, this person should have recused himself on this. I have no idea how such a board could be made up this way, but there was nothing we could do. It is a fact that some hearing aid industry leaders are against middle ear and alternative treatments despite everything that is the good about offering an alternative option to the majority of people who for whatever reason reject conventional aids. Others, including me, believe that middle ear implants could complement the hearing aid market and help increase amplification.

I also found out years later that the same individuals who had voted against the Vibrant Soundbridge had also defined what a hearing aid was from a Medicare perspective: They had determined that middle ear implants were "the same" as hearing aids. I was nonplussed. What? They were two totally different things. If the Soundbridge was so much like hearing aids, why did so many hearing aid companies have such a negative view of middle ear implants?

Even today this determination is maddening and just plain wrong on so many fronts. It is especially unbelievable to me, an inventor whose entire career has focused specifically on making a device for the hearing impaired that is *not* a hearing aid. At the end of the day, having two or three people decide to change the language so that your new invention was just the same old mousetrap was heartbreaking. I will never get over it.

Going, going, gone!

*"You do not merely want to be
considered just the best of the best.
You want to be considered the
only one who does what you do."*

Jerry Garcia

As odd as it may seem now, I was certain that I was actually watching Symphonix go through some growing pains. I believed that most of the negative stuff could be ignored and that we would work through it. I had to believe it. The alternative would be to go mad. The layoffs had been heartbreaking, but as the summer of 2002 wound down, I felt positive that we were on the right track. The new marketing guy had left Symphonix because he had decided not to move to California after all. No surprise there.

John Luna stepped up and took charge of the sales efforts. All through May, June, July and August, Jon and his team had made good progress. They were booking a lot of orders and were actually on target to either achieve or come close to achieving the annual sales goal.[11] He had also predicted that at the rate things were going, the third and fourth quarters could be even better than we thought. I had been traveling with John a lot, helping out as a spokesman, and I had seen the momentum first hand. August 2002 was a terrific month. I accompanied Jon and the sales team on visits to a host of sites and to many well-attended patient seminars all that summer. We were making headway and we thought we could see the light at the end of the tunnel. But then another round of board-mandated layoffs left us with only essential staff and put the TI development on hold.

---

11   A main issue was that even though we were filling up the book with orders, it was not the
same as actual sales orders being recognized. Booked sales always lead actual, and the
time from book to order was always too long, especially when we were waiting for health
insurance determinations. On the other hand, we rarely received an order without it
being in the book.

The great irony in the second round of layoffs was the timing: It coincided with the activation of the first Veterans Affairs patient implanted with the Soundbridge. I had attended both the surgery and the activation at the VA hospital in San Francisco. The Department of Veterans Affairs, as already mentioned, is the largest single purchaser of hearing instruments the entire world, and I knew breaking into the VA was absolutely huge.

In late August, John Luna and I went off on a two-week road show across the country, visiting our sites and focusing on the military hospitals, The Soundbridge had been approved for what we estimated to be more than six million active and former military personnel who would have full coverage for the VSB. We toured all the major facilities and made plans for getting the word out to the hearing impaired in these communities and putting the final pieces in place for the new military Soundbridge programs. The trip went so well and the sites were so supportive that we were elated, and the book was filling up with orders. Our last stop on the tour was the Walter Reed Army Medical Center in Washington. It was a special place, and I was eager to see a product that had been studied at the VA used to help our troops. Dr. Brian McKinnon was there, and the Walter Reed staff had arranged for Dr. Jon Spindel to present on the status of middle ear implants at the center. It was a great meeting. We were pumped up when we left, and the light at the end of the tunnel seemed to be burning brighter.

The other team members flew home from Baltimore, but my flight was out of Dulles Airport, on the other side of town. Dr. Spindel was heading back right past Dulles anyway, so I hitched a ride with him. We were about halfway to the airport when my cell phone rang.

"Geoff, Kirk here." It was actually a bit out of the ordinary for Kirk to call on my cell, especially late on Friday evening.

"Hey, Kirk. It went well at Walter Reed today. Extremely well."

"Yeah. Good. Hey well. We just had a board call." The board had started using conference calls to update the board members on Symphonix in the interims between the quarterly formal meetings.

"Oh?"

"Yeah, Geoff. Bad news: They voted to shut down the company."

"Say that again?" I thought my ears were playing tricks on me.

"I'm sorry. Symphonix is finished," Kirk replied.

The strangest sensation went over me. It was like all my neurons were turned off, like I was floating in total darkness and not on earth at all. There are no words to describe how I felt except surreal. I have no recollection of how the call with Kirk ended. Dr. Spindel tells me that all I could say was something to the effect of, "Oh my God! What am I going to do?" I can't remember. In fact, I have no memory of the flight across the U.S. back to California. I do remember feeling incredibly angry, upset, fearful, horrified and incredulous all at the same time, though. I remember the gut-wrenching feeling of conflicting emotions all pulling in different directions at the same time. I can recall the terror of the reality that my life's work was coming to what I believed was a premature end. It was a brutal way to end the story. I was too upset to cry. Or maybe I knew that if I started to cry, I might not be able to stop.

When I got back to California, I went to Kirk's house in Los Gatos, not far from where Harry had lived, to talk to him. Kirk did everything he could to make me feel better. I may not have always appreciated everything about Kirk's management style, but he was just about the nicest guy I have ever met, and he helped me work through the demise of Symphonix.

"But didn't you tell them about the VA, the military?" I remember asking him. "Did you tell them about all the orders we had in the pipeline? Did they understand the positive insurance hit rate we were getting? We have orders! A lot! Jon thinks we are going to come close or hit the sales numbers, and they are going up. We just need to get more insurance forms. We don't need CMS to make a positive call; we have enough at Aetna alone!"

"Geoff, it's over. The dream is over," Kirk said firmly but as nicely as he could.

And that was the bottom line. Inside, I was dying. I was watching my dreams disappear down the drain. I felt like I was on the dance floor without a partner when the music stopped and the lights went down.

On Monday morning I returned to the Symphonix headquarters. The plan was now to go to a skeleton crew and to try to sell the company's assets as a whole. It was really a dismal position to find ourselves in. Notices went out to all prospective buyers. We had been in talks with potential buyers and strategic partners many times during the Symphonix years, but these talks had never produced a solid offer. If we had had a crystal ball to show us that September 11 was going to happen and that the CMS determination would be negative, I guess we would have pushed harder for the best possible deal even sooner. But none of us had any way of knowing these things. The course Kirk had plotted for the good ship Symphonix had been based on our belief in our product, and we all thought we were on the right tack.

I had invented the technology in 1992, and now, after ten years of dedicating nearly all my waking hours to its success, I felt cheated. I am well aware that this may come across as sour grapes, but I feel that I never got a chance to really launch my product in my home country, the United States, for a full, normal business year. I understand that even if 9/11 had not occurred, Symphonix would probably still have faced significant challenges and might have gone under – perhaps sooner, but most likely much later. Statistics show that the odds are always stacked against any new venture, and I know that in all likelihood Symphonix would have still failed. But if 9/11 had not occurred when it did, our ship might have reached land at a different time or place. Maybe we would have had the time we needed to catch a good break. I can't help but feel that if I had had a normal chance, I could have accepted failing better. There is an angst in my heart that leaves me feeling cheated, betrayed and fearful of the future, and it will probably never completely go away.

To this very day I still feel that when it was my company's turn to take the stage, some jerk at the back of the room shouted "Fire!" and everyone rushed for the exits. That is a tough pill for me to swallow.

Symphonix was a good company. It was a fun place to work, and it made a good product that the world needed. It had great people, talented people. It was only just getting started, and the Sound-bridge was to be Symphonix's first product. There were other gems that we had not even explored yet. There we were: great people who had made great progress and were offering the first real alternative for the hearing impaired. Then just when it seemed like we were getting going ... Whoops, sorry! Game over.

Looking back, I think that having more physicians involved at the corporate level would have been a terrific help. We had a lot of U.S. physicians who were true believers and true champions for us: Dr. Leutje, Dr. Hough, Dr. Baker, Dr. Maw, and Dr. Roberson, to name only a few. But there were too many others who were too conservative. If I had been a surgeon, I might have had more success convincing people to embrace the technology even though it was a radical new concept. Several physicians told me that they would not implant any product until we had ten years of clinical experience. The conversations usually went something like this:

Physician: "I am just saying I want to see the ten year data. What will it be in ten years?"

GB: "Ten years? Are you saying that you never use any technology unless it's ten years old?"

Physician: "Oh, no! That is not what I mean."

GB: "Then can you tell me what would happen in the middle ear at year ten that would not happen within the first three months to a year?"

Physician: "I don't know. That is why I want to wait and see what that data says at ten years."

GB: "The VSB does not cause disease, and all the components are biocompatible. The middle ear response is almost always complete three months post surgery. If something were to happen, it would have to have to have a mechanism. What would the mechanism be? Cells do not grow arms and legs and move transducers around in a concerted effort to push and pull the FMT out of position."

Physician: "I don't know what could happen. I don't think we can know that until we have the data."

GB: "What data?"

Physician: "The ten year data."

GB: "That data showing that nothing happened?"

Physician: "Right, ideally."

I had quickly learned that continuing this type of conversation was generally pointless. Maybe if the Soundbridge had been invented by a surgeon, that would have helped win over the skeptics. Regardless of whether they needed it or not, too many surgeons wanted ten year data simply to feel better and more confident. On the one hand I get it, but on the other I know this is almost an impossible order for new technology. Looking back, I think that a surgeon inventor could have laid a lot of the worries to rest. I just always had the feeling that as a non-surgeon, I had to prove myself a lot more. I once overheard a surgeon say, "Hey! There's that kid with the can." That kind of thinking is not really helpful. But in a weird way, the ten-year-data types were right: It takes an awful lot of breakthrough technology in the medical device industry – sometimes ten or twenty years – for the adoption rates to rise significantly.

If more U.S. groups had been willing to really embrace this technology, the device might have been used to treat mixed and conductive hearing loss first in the U.S., where it was invented. When I started my career in the hearing sciences, the United States was a powerhouse for innovation in hearing treatment. Now it seems to me that Americans are content to sit back and watch as the Europeans innovate and many U.S. medical device companies do all their important clinical trials abroad. The latest and greatest technology is being exported and used in other countries first, and it follows that sooner or later, the innovations will move abroad as well. In fact, it has been suggested that some medical innovators are now moving abroad because they cannot work the way they would like to in the United States. I find this surprising and cannot believe that this is where the U.S. wants to go. It seems like the U.S. is just sitting idly by as leadership in key fields slowly dwindles away. What happened to embracing new things and "making it happen?" We cannot blame it all on oversight, regulators and attorneys. If it has come to a point where such things and such thinking stifles innovation, then is it not up to all of us to do something about it?

In a last-ditch effort raise money, Terry Griffin and I talked to the few remaining banks that would meet with us, but there were no takers. Terry had sent out letters to all the competitors and potential acquirers announcing the Symphonix fire sale. Jon Luna and I hatched a last-minute plan, if you could call it that: We thought that if we could raise enough money, we would be able to finance for some kind of "re-start" or to at least hold the company over until the markets improved. The fact that Symphonix was a publicly traded company eliminated other options, and the cost of other alternatives was very high. We went up and talked to Greg Onken at his offices at Bear Sterns. Greg was one of the key bankers for the Cowen team that had taken us public. He was probably squirming in his chair as we made a clumsy attempt to articulate what we thought we might be able to do, but we were desperate and wanted to find a way to save the company.

Greg listened politely and finally said, "You guys do not even know what you are asking for other than you know you need six to ten million. I just do not see it."

We explored every option that we or Greg could think of, but it became clear that none of them would work. And that was that.

As Greg walked us out of the building, he turned to me and said, "You know, Geoff, if you had quit and sold all your stock, you would probably be in a position now to buy back your mission in life. But you didn't, and that really sucks."

"You have no idea how crazy it makes me," I responded. "Whenever I think about it, I just want to jump out the window!" I joked.

"The good thing," Jon joked back, "is that Symphonix is only a one-story building, so we don't have to worry about that too much!"

Gallows humor again, only this time, it was for a dying company.

The Call

I made the most important phone call of my life in early September 2002. The call was to Ingeborg Hochmair, the CEO of MED-EL. You may recall that until the first time I met Ingeborg Hochmair, I had thought she was Erwin's brother, not his wife. MED-EL had been notified of the sale of Symphonix but, like the others, had not replied. We had just had the final layoff at Symphonix, and we had started the process of liquidating the firm's assets. We had not been able to find a buyer, so we were forced into garage sale mode. Things were worse for Symphonix than anyone had anticipated.

Inge and Erwin Hochmair and the rest of the MED-EL team had been to Symphonix headquarters a few months earlier to evaluate our implantable microphone technology, but nothing concrete had materialized. The calls Kirk and others had made to MED-EL had not yet been returned.

No one should ever have to watch workmen tossing engineering plans into dumpsters, cubicles being dismantled and carted off to be resold to the next startup, or tearful employees, all dedicated hard workers, leaving the building for the last time But in September 2002, that is exactly what I was doing. Some might say that living through such an event is a character-building experience. If that is true, then I must be Groucho Marx. It was a nightmare. In the last days of Symphonix there were events so surreal that I had to pinch myself to make sure I was not dreaming. Nobody can be prepared for such events.

I closed my office door and dialed the number for Ingeborg Hochmair, MED-EL's CEO. To my surprise, she answered on the first ring. It was quite late in the day in Austria, where her headquarters were located.

"Hallo?"

"Ingeborg Hochmair?" I asked.

"Yes, this is Ingeborg Hochmair. Is this Geoffrey Ball?"

"Yeah! I mean, yes!"

"Ah. Hallo, Geoffrey. How are you?"

"Look, Ingeborg, I am not sure that you understand the situation here at Symphonix. It is really, really bad. It is horrible. Did you read the paperwork for Symphonix that they sent to you?"

Inge admitted that she had not read all the details, so I brought her up to date on the situation.

"Geoffrey," Inge said, "I will read it first thing, as soon as I get to the office tomorrow, and I will call you back. It is going to be fine."

"I cannot tell you how important it is."

I hung up and walked back outside my office. To my horror, the cleanup crew had started tossing my research work and the TI and implantable microphone files, along with the prototypes and test systems, into the trash.

I ran up to them. "Stop this! Stop it! Stop it now!" I yelled.

I rushed back into my office, and suddenly, for the first time in weeks, I felt like I was in control again. I had an amazing sense of power, and something told me to follow my instincts. I picked up the phone and called Ingeborg again.

"Hallo! Geoffrey?"

"Inge! You have to listen to me really carefully. They are throwing my company in the trash. Right now. Everything. Do you understand? If you want the implantable microphone, if you want all my patents, you can have them all. If you believe in anything I have done over the last ten years, you cannot wait until tomorrow. You need to get on the next plane."

There was a long pause. Then Inge said, "Oh, Geoffrey. I had no idea that it was coming to that point."

"This is the end for me, but I need to try and save as much of this work as I can. It cannot all be thrown away. You need to call Kirk."

"I will get on the next plane I can and will see you there soon. And don't you worry too much."

I walked out into the main floor of Symphonix and shouted to Kirk and Terry, "We can stop this now! MED-EL is interested. The CEO is on the way."

We told the guys to knock off for the day and sent them all home. Thank God, I had at least stopped the madness for twenty-four hours.

I do not know how Ingeborg managed it, but the very next day she was in San Jose with her team. She had brought along Ali Mayr, Martin Kerber, Darcy Ochs, and Walter Fimml. Ingeborg broke the team into groups to assess the remaining assets of Symphonix and meet with Kirk and Terry. I met with Darcy and went through the intellectual property, the technology applications, plans for the TI and the future, the competitive update, what I thought was right and wrong about the business model, and so on. It was like doing a doctoral defense as Inge picked my brain clean for a full two days. She also worked with Kirk and Terry to secure the assets of the company and to get a deal done.

I showed the rest of the team the R & D labs, the TI testing lab, and all the facilities. I did not have to show Ali Mayr much, though. Ali was the head of manufacturing at MED-EL, and his task here was to establish whether he could transfer the production of the implant line to his facility in Innsbruck, Austria. Class III medical devices require massive documentation, and thanks to the incredible quality systems we used, it would theoretically be possible to replicate the line as long as the documentation and the quality system were maintained. Walter just had to make sure that our electronic data systems and electronic files were preserved.

At the end of the second day, the MED-EL team met in our conference room without us, and Inge listened to her team. Their reports must have been satisfactory. Inge came in to my office, closed the door and sat down.

"I am really impressed. I really admire your work, and I think it just needs more time. We will try this again. I want you to come to Innsbruck, with your wife."

"And work there? But I don't speak German!"

"We all know English anyway. So what do you think?"

"Sure! Yes! Absolutely. Well, I think so. Austria?! But there is one thing ..."

"Yes?"

"Do you think you and the team could come to my home for dinner tonight? It will be one of the last times since I guess we will be selling the house."

"Yes! I would love to meet Sabina."

So just like that, I had a new boss, I was selling my house, and I was moving to Innsbruck, Austria. This was far better than watching my life's work get tossed into the trash. What a day!

When I got home that evening, Sabina and I talked as usual.

"How did it go today?" she asked.

"Oh, it went real, real well!"

"Really, for once? Good! So what's going to happen?"

"Here is the plan. We sell the house, pack up all our stuff, and move to Innsbruck, Austria."

Long pause.

"Are you serious?"

"Yeah. Really. I think so."

"You're kidding."

"No, I am serious. I think."

"Well, OK. Let's try it. What do we have to lose?"

"Oh, just the house, the backyard that we love so much that we wanted to be buried in it, our friends ..."

So through our tears, we made a deal. We decided we would go to Austria and see how it went. We would not talk about whether we liked it or not for six months; we would just try to make it work.

"Is there anything else?" she asked.

"I have to fire up the barbecue," I told her. "The Austrians are coming for dinner."

Ingeborg and the team returned to Austria. Ali and Klaus Holzer came back to Symphonix a couple weeks later with a manufacturing team, and several of our former employees graciously agreed to teach the MED-EL staff how to build the products. After two weeks of manufacturing, we began packing all that was left of Symphonix into boxes. Crews then loaded them into the giant shipping containers lined up behind the building. We filled approximately 20 containers. The remaining items, such as desks, chairs and benches, were all sold off on the open market. We did not even have to advertise. Word got out fast.

In 2002, approximately a year after the Symphonix launch on 9/11 2001, I found myself attending the 2002 American Academy of

Otolaryngology meeting as a member of MED-EL. The world had certainly changed for me a lot in the last 12 months.

In December Inge (I had since learned that she prefers this shorter version of her name) had had Sabina and me fly over to Innsbruck for a few days. I gave presentations during the day and met with other key staffers at the MED-EL headquarters, while the MED-EL human resources staff showed Sabina around the town. Even by Innsbruck standards, it was very cold when we arrived, but the town was even more beautiful than we imagined. It is surrounded by Alpine peaks, and with five ski areas visible from the MED-EL headquarters, it did not take long for me to figure out that there were far worse places on the planet to wind up than here. I was impressed by the MED-EL staff and by Ali Mayr and Plamen Kamenoff, who were already hard at work making room for the Vibrant Soundbridge products on their manufacturing lines. I could not wait to get started.

It had been hard enough to take a private company public, but we were learning that it was even harder to dismantle a public company and to comply with all the regulations and SEC questions involved in doing so. For weeks and weeks Terry was always on the phone, either with the SEC or with our attorneys. Since we were selling the assets and not the company, the deal points were critical. The shareholders had to agree, as did the board of directors. I wanted to move to Austria as soon as I could. The house had sold the first day it was on the market, and I was ready to start the next phase of my life.

The few remaining employees, including Kirk, Terry and me, had to move into temporary offices to support the transfer. Inge had selected eight other former Symphonix employees to move over to MED-EL. I wished that she had taken more, but most of them had already found new jobs. Watching Terry battle with the SEC over seemingly minor deal points was infuriating, and it seemed like it would never end. Each time we would file, the SEC would respond with more questions. We would answer them, only to get more questions, and so on. As far as I could tell, the only people winning were the attorneys. After a few more rounds, it became clear that this was just going to go on and on and on. And it did. It was not until about five months later that the sale was officially approved.

Once the approval came through, the bond on the shipping containers was lifted, and the shipping company was finally allowed to deliver the equipment. Throughout this whole the process, I was sending Inge weekly reports, supporting the asset transfer, and maintaining the IP files as well as making sure that the conforming product remained controlled and that we were continuing to support our patients. My life seemed like an endless procession of boxes: packing them, labeling them, wrapping them up, and making sure no key items got lost. During this time, all the documents, files and records imprinted themselves on my brain, and I felt like a living, breathing index. My work life was all about boxes and labels and files, and I was soon doing the same things at home as we prepared for the move to Austria, the place with no kangaroos.

I had thought that starting a company had been hard work, but packing a company up and moving it overseas was not much different. Moving a company is all about making sure you do not lose anything. But moving a medical device company is also all about the equipment and the mountains of documentation that must be maintained and readily accessible. The record keeping requirements are immense, and the irony of packing everything up was that we knew we would have to unpack it all on the other side of the Atlantic. Linda Ferner and I sorted through hundreds of file cabinets and endless stacks of documents, logging and labeling everything and entering them into spreadsheets for tracking before packing them up.

When I left my Symphonix office for the last time, I loaded the last of my private mementos into my car (which was also for sale) and drove out to the Symphonix main building, where the new tenants were already getting settled in. I then drove over to the original Symphonix offices on Orchard Parkway. I pulled into the parking lot where Bob Katz and I used to play football, and all the memories came back. I wept for what had been, for what was now, and for what could have been. Then I drove to my parents' house back in Sunnyvale for a farewell dinner.

The next day, April 1, 2002, I left for Innsbruck. The plane took off from San Jose and flew over Silicon Valley. I looked down and saw the place I was raised, where I had my first jobs. As the Santa Cruz Mountains receded into the distance, I thought of the road ahead. This was not like leaving for college or going work in Colorado. This time I had some idea of what to expect. Sabina, who had stayed behind to sell our cars, pack the rest of our stuff to go into a shipping container documents and finalize the sale of the house, would be joining me in March.

My wife has been my rock through it all. In addition to being the awesome person that she is, Sabina is also European, a dual national who had escaped from Poland and followed her mother to the United States when she was a teenager. Moving back to Europe would actually put her closer to most of her relatives in Poland. We were trying to start a family but not having any luck, and we thought a break from work might be a good thing for her. We also knew that there were many more advanced fertility treatment options in Europe should we need to go that route.

Look out, Europe! Here we come!

Safe Landing and New Beginning

"Talk about your plenty, talk about your ills.
One man gathers what the others spill.
Ashes, ashes, all fall down."

Jerry Garcia

I arrived in Innsbruck, and Inge met me at the airport. We drove up to the Hochmair home in Axams, which is a village on a plateau just outside and overlooking Innsbruck. She and Erwin and I had a nice dinner. Inge then took me to my temporary apartment, which was located near the company and where I would be staying until we found something better. She also set me up with my new cell phone and put the SIM card in herself. I was impressed. She was truly a hands-on CEO.

Inge and her husband Erwin are legends in the field of hearing research and implants. In 1974, Ingeborg Desoyer had arrived at a cochlear implant design, but she needed an electronic signal processor and telemetry scheme. During her quest, she met Erwin and asked him to design the drive electronics. Inge needed a circuit, and Erwin designed it. Soon after, they got married. In 1977, they implanted the first hybrid multi-channel cochlear implant in Vienna.

When Erwin was hired to chair the physics department at the University of Innsbruck, they took along the cochlear implant. Inge, a keen scholar, also joined the faculty. Inge and Erwin later worked together in research at Stanford. They were involved in the early 3M cochlear implant. Together, they put their stamp on much of the key work that made hearing implants possible. Without their pioneering efforts, there would not have been the Soundbridge. In 1989, they founded the MED-EL company to commercialize their research into a family of hearing products.

Inge and I actually have a lot in common: We both love research and thrive on the trappings of academia, but most of all, we share a burning desire to build and create devices that will help society and the hearing impaired. Both of us had to become corporate in order to achieve this; to realize our dreams of taking technology from the lab and delivering it to the people who need it. We both had to leave academia and start our own companies.

Inge is the hardest-working person I have ever met. Bob Katz, who was legendary for burning the midnight oil, had previously held the previous title, but Inge is super-charged and dedicated beyond belief. Maybe she is also a cyborg running on ultra high power batteries! Whatever the case, what she has achieved in building MED-EL is something to behold: It is one of the leading companies in the field and certainly the most successful implantable device firm in Austria. Today, the company she built from the ground up has nearly one thousand employees and provides work for thousands more indirectly through distributors, researchers and clinics. Her cochlear implant product lines are used to treat severe and profound hearing loss in nearly a hundred countries, and MED-EL's implants now are the market leader in most of them. I have always thought that her crowning achievement as CEO of MED-EL came in 1991, when it was the first company to market an ear-level processor. Prior to this development, cochlear implant users had to wear battery backs on their belts or in a pocket to supply power for the implant electronics. MED-EL made a processor that could be worn behind the ear and held in position with an ear hook. This resulted in a tremendous improvement in the device's user friendliness and in the lives of cochlear implant users. MED-EL also led the field by adopting advanced sound coding strategies that produced remarkable improvements in the speech and sound perception of implant recipients.

MED-EL went on to pioneer combined electro-acoustical stimulation devices (EAS) as well as auditory brainstem implants (ABI). It was also the first outfit to drive the concept of preserving the remaining hearing structures as much as possible, even in profoundly deaf patients. Since acquiring the Vibrant Soundbridge and supporting the product through its sales and distribution network, MED-EL has become the number one middle ear implant manufacturer in the world, with a market share of over 95 percent.

When I arrived in Austria, my product line was on life support. I wish I could say that relaunching the Soundbridge was easy after we arrived in Innsbruck, but wasn't. Linda and I had to unpack all the boxes we had packed up in the States. I had brought with me on the airplane a full copy of the server that contained all the directories and documents. We got it up and running, and soon we were back in business. Linda was in charge of our service and repair department and also served as an invaluable resource for Symphonix topics. She was an ace at being able to find nearly anything. The transition would have been much more difficult without her excellent support, and I would have been lost without her.

Despite the bumps and turbulence that accompanied the Soundbridge's landing in Innsbruck, it has certainly been worth it. Mergers and acquisitions are always challenging to some degree. The acquisition of Symphonix's assets has enabled Inge and MED-EL to transform their product offerings into new hearing loss indication ranges and their firm into "the hearing implant company."

For me, Innsbruck has been a new beginning. Oddly, the advances in the Soundbridge research began shortly after my arrival. An example: I have seen hundreds of surgeries during the course of my work with hearing implants, but one of the most memorable was a surgery I attended in 2003 in the Clinique Causse in Bezier, France. Dr. Dumon installed the Vibrant Soundbridge into the middle ear in a patient who was suffering from a chronic conductive hearing loss as well as province-amplified sound stimulation to the ear. Rather than install the FMT onto its normal placement below the intact ossicular chain, Dr. Dumon installed the FMT onto the remaining long process of the diseased ear and then positioned prosthesis over the top of the FMT attachment and reconstructed the connection of the ear. In other words, he replaced the diseased ear bones and then used the FMT to impart additional vibration energy to the ear. It was the first time that the vibrant Soundbridge had been used to correct a mixed hearing loss. Word of this application and the fantastic results spread quickly, and soon other surgeons began using Dr. Dumon's technique.

In 2005, Dr. Colletti in Italy did the first placement of an FMT onto the round window of the ear using tissue to hold the unit in place. Sure enough, it worked! He did several other cases, and the use of the FMT to treat mixed and conductive loss soon gained a strong following. We did a clinical trial for the new indications and received approval in 2007. A new field of treatment called vibroplasty had been born. It is amazing to me that Dr. Colletti was able to develop the round window technique pretty much on his own and through his own determination. It was brilliant. There were plenty of contrary views, but he just forged ahead and made it happen. I reminded me again that even though there were so many good reasons why such a concept could not and would not work, they were outweighed by the fact *that it did work.* That made all the difference.

In 2007, we were startled to learn that the Vibrant Soundbridge was being implanted in a significant number of children who had no other option for hearing loss treatment. This was truly amazing. We organized the first International Pediatric Meeting in Frankfurt in 2007. Thanks to the efforts of and results obtained by this group, the Vibrant Soundbridge was approved for use in pediatric indications. In 2009, we launched the new Amadé audio processor, which had much more output and range than the previous model. And 2010 saw the approval of the first advanced designs of FMT couplers that will facilitate further adoption for reconstructive otology applications. Achieving all this has all taken a lot of work by our dedicated teams, and it has all led to consistent and steady growth. Today, every hour somewhere in the world, one of my implants is being installed. Today there have been thousands of round window placements and installations of the FMT to treat conductive and mixed hearing loss. In fact, a majority of our implants are now applied in mixed and conductive cases or in cases where all other treatment options cannot be used for medical reasons. Thank God I managed to save the Soundbridge from the dumpster.

It amazes me today to think how close the world came to losing really good technology. Everyone who hears it today is amazed by the clarity. People who switch from hearing aids to a direct drive experience a real improvement in their quality of life, as evidenced by their smiles of relief and exclamations of joy. For patients who have had mixed hearing loss and have often been functionally deaf for years, the Soundbridge restores hearing and brings tears of happiness that they can hear again. That holds true for me and for my competition in the hearing implant arena.

I wish I could communicate just how awesome a treatment option direct drive really is. If you could hear what I hear now and compare it to what I heard with hearing aids, then you would understand the difference. Imagine you're listening to a ball game on a small transistor radio. You can follow it even if the reception is fuzzy and the speaker isn't good, but that is not the kind of sound you want to hear all the time. You want clarity, with no fuzzy sounds or whistling.

Hearing aids can provide some help, but you get tired of having a foreign object in your ear all the time. Even experts are often hard to convince because most of them have never, ever worn hearing aids. I know that most could not and would not tolerate the high gain and output levels that the hearing impaired need. For me, the most frustrating thing of all is that I think that the hearing field still hasn't acknowledged that having options is a very good thing.

One thing that pioneers in the field of vibroplasty have recognized is the importance of giving the hearing impaired real alternatives that work for them. Thousands and thousands of people are already benefiting from my technology now, and that number will grow to tens of thousands who will have direct drive type implants done each year. This is still just a drop in the bucket considering how many people need them, but we are making good headway!

Small Things, Big Issues

"I am among those who think that science has great beauty. A scientist in his laboratory is not only a technician; he is also a child placed before natural phenomena which impress him like a fairy tale."

Marie Curie

Don Lucas Senior, one of my original venture capital contacts and one of the most successful investors in Silicon Valley, once made a comment that has stuck with me: "We like small. It has been good for us." I think that this is a really potent way to view the world. The person who makes the next big breakthrough is often the one who figures out how to make something small: a smaller battery, a smaller machine, a smaller chip design, and so on. "Smaller, cheaper, faster, better" is a tried and true axiom that is the mantra for Silicon Valley success. But I like Don's more basic concept better; fact, I think it is probably the most memorable thing anyone ever has said to me.

Getting developed research concepts and developments from the labs to the point where they can benefit society typically involves crossing the death valley of funding. Some ideas are simply too big for the coffers of a university or grant funding arrangement because there are just too many zeros at the ends of the numbers in the budget proposal. That is when venture capitalists can step in and help many startup concepts that, if given a shot, might go all the way. Then there are all those researchers with really good ideas that get lost in the shuffle because they may not be interesting enough for the VC's and could not be funded within the available research funding schemes. Researchers themselves are also often incapable of presenting their ideas in a way that communicates effectively to non-experts what their value and potential are. In some cases it may not be possible to fully appreciate the value of the concepts or even what the breakthroughs truly are without further investment. We never know where the next big thing is going to come from, and it is incredibly difficult to predict which researchers and ideas have the best chances. Investors are not interested in funding concepts that will only produce interesting publications. Ironically, the best minds to evaluate such matters are not typically sitting in offices reviewing grants or investment opportunities all day. So what happens? Well, it pretty much follows that the labs and programs with the best publication track records and the best output history are the ones that get the lion's share of funding and investment. The deck is stacked against new, untested, brilliant yet unknown researchers with fantastic ideas, any of which could be the next new thing – especially if they happen to be interesting people who like to eat pizza for lunch in the lab.

Economists know that there are only a few levers that governments and policy makers can pull in an effort to keep and create jobs and to maintain and hopefully secure future economic growth. These are investment in R&D, the acquisition of new technology, development of natural resources, and energy production (and/or increases in energy efficiency). As I write these words, the State of California has just gone through its worst recession and economic crisis since 1929. Unemployment officially stands at around ten percent, but if you include the underemployed and the thousands upon thousands of people who have fallen off the statistics and are no longer counted, the figure is much higher. I have no doubt that many of them are interesting people who are no longer in the labs where they ought to be. Research budgets at California universities are also feeling the pinch in a major way. But here is the pickle: It is at precisely such times that it is most important to invest in R&D. That is the smartest solution because it stimulates immediate spending, boosts the economy by putting more cash into circulation when it is most needed, and provides the potential for long-term economic and jobs growth.

In my view one of the most successful research projects in history is the creation of the University of California system. This system churned out the best and most cutting edge of any macrosystematic research approach in modern times. The output has been U.C. Berkeley, Lawrence Livermore Labs, and nine additional major campuses that have led West Coast research for the past sixty years. Now this macro research project is in funding jeopardy. True, the institutions have their own issues. They must find a way to achieve a reduction in the research overhead rates. There must be mechanisms in place to increase the rate of tax credits for all basic, applied, and formal research and development programs. There must be a meaningful effort to encourage and expedite the technology transfer from lab to business and industry and reduce the bureaucratic hurdles. Researchers must be helped with the concept of patenting key developments before they are published and shared, which puts patentable concepts into the public domain. Maintaining real intellectual property rights through patents and proprietary developments is too often at odds with the thinking and actions of academia. Solutions for many of these issues exist. California is not alone in tackling the research funding issue, and many states and governments worldwide are finding themselves in similar situations.

In my opinion, Austria and other countries like it would be wise to invest a higher percentage of their GDP in advanced research and startup companies. They could and should find ways to encourage young entrepreneurs to start new companies faster. The bureaucratic hurdles to starting up new entrepreneurial organizations should be as low and as few as possible. MED-EL's purchase of the assets of Symphonix and its moving me and the production line to Austria has been a success that has resulted in positive revenue returns and significantly contributed to job creation, which will hopefully continue for years into the future. This could be repeated in other industries as well. Any country or state that pushes investments in R & D today – assuming they are well managed and have a coordinated strategy – will find itself enjoying a healthy economy five to ten years in the future.

One key issue is improving the approval and distribution process of research money by changing the current priorities. It is a trap to repeatedly grant funding only to mature and successful heavyweight research programs. Younger labs and researchers that lack a proven track record should receive an equal amount of research funding. In a perfect world, all researchers would get more investment funding. This is not going to happen as there will always be competition no matter how much or little money is available, but it makes sense to fund younger programs and labs as they are most likely to go out and start new companies. Figuring out which ones is the tricky part.

Another component of research investments that must be addressed and encouraged is that a majority of funding should go to directed research; in other words, research with a directed focus. Labs and programs should have clear mission statements and goals posted for all to see; for example, "Our lab is studying how to build a new fuel-efficient cooking oven and hopes to develop the concept of a more efficient oven that can be utilized in a majority of second and third world countries to improve fuel efficiency by 50 % and thereby reduce greenhouse emissions and fuel requirements by 50 %." Researchers, even perhaps truly basic researchers, must be forced to at least conceptualize how their work can translate into societal benefit or new economic growth and products. It may be fully appropriate for a lab to study the flight patterns of the mustached fruit bat; however, such projects with no clear output that could benefit society or result in a new economic impact should have a lower funding priority than the cooking stove. Some funded topics are what I call "hobby and crafts science," which should be funded privately or not at all. Sorry to the crafts people.

I believe that healthy research funding schemes should take a jack-of-all-trades approach. From a macroeconomic perspective, research can often be swept up in current fads of the day. At one point in the 1980's, HIV research became the largest single research expenditure area for the NIH, for obvious reasons. It is easy to argue that this was a good strategy at the time: after all, lives were at stake. However, without trivializing the need for or importance of HIV research or any such area, there is a cost of putting too many eggs into one basket. People are also dying of malaria, tuberculosis and resistant staph infection. Denying funding to other programs in order to grow one area that has a sense of urgency and is high on the political agenda at the time is a dangerous concept. In fact, it may actually delay the development of a cure by minimizing or losing valuable but unpredictable crosspollination from different fields. A breakthrough in HIV could come from a breakthrough in malaria treatment or a stem cell program or even a drug delivery project. One just never knows. Do not misunderstand me: I am not saying it was wrong to make HIV a priority. I just think we just need to consider the ramifications of inadvertently unfunding something that could have made a contribution to the priority topic. Looking back at the breakthroughs, it is truly remarkable and often surprising to see how the connections from one idea to another were translated from one discipline to the next, and to evaluate where the inputs for breakthroughs came from. A minor improvement or new idea in one field can be and often is a major key that unlocks a door to a different area in a second field. Most of these connections are impossible to predict. We do know, however, that unless we encourage and foster a multi-disciplinary research approach from a funding allocation standpoint, there is less chance of crosspollination and connections across differing fields, and experience has shown that we never know in advance where these will be.

In a perfect world, there would be more than enough money to fund all key research areas and projects, and we would not have to limit or not fund the "hobby" areas. We need to fund young researchers who have new and challenging and often unproven concepts and ideas. We must also adopt a multidisciplinary approach to funding and increase funding for key political and strategic topics of the day but at the same time perform the difficult balancing task of not grossly underfunding other areas. We must find, employ and grow our great scientific talent and interesting researchers. At the same time, we must help them translate their concepts into measurable goals, encourage the development of intellectual property, and facilitate technology transfer. These are easy concepts to on paper, but it will take some heavy and well-paid brainpower to make them work in the real world. In the words of Don Lucas Sr., we need to create the next new generation of "big guys," especially in the new technology areas. If we don't do it, others will.

Remember the sign that said, "If we are not here by ten, then we will be here by noon. If we are not in by two, then we will definitely be here tomorrow." The lab that had this sign on the door meant it as a joke, and it would seem that way to many, but in fact it was true. There were many, many days when there was no discernable activity in that lab. It would come to life for a few hours; then nothing for a week or two. So the sign was correct in a sense, except that the lab was often a hubbub of activity between the hours of five in the afternoon and three or four in the morning. On Saturdays and Sundays, when nobody else was on campus, the lights in that lab burned as the researchers worked. In fact, the staff of that lab put in a lot more hours than the standard 40 per week; those hours just didn't happen to be from nine to five. The person in charge lived over on the coast in Capitola, and it was easier to commute to the lab later in the evenings and on weekends. The point is that the lab was getting it done.

The other point is that intellectual contributors and researchers do not have to work nine to five to be productive. This is a source of constant consternation for some bean counters and non-innovative types who fail to realize that innovative people's brains do not turn on at 9 a.m. and shut off at 5 p.m. Most creative people don't punch a clock, and many of us are just about always working. Some of my best innovative ideas came to me when I was on vacation in Hawaii. One time after a day of swimming and hiking with Sabina and the boys, I sat on the hotel balcony after they had all gone to sleep and penned four invention disclosures. Two of these are now issued patents, and one is still pending. I doubt that accountants close their books at three in the morning while sitting on the balcony of their vacation hotel.

I am for interesting people. I am for governments and institutions increasing their investment research and development and even more for it when times are tough financially. I am for multidisciplinary thinking and for forcing crosspollination between different fields. I am for making positive changes that will guarantee inventors a fair return on their inventions. I am for recognizing and supporting intellectual contributions to organizations and against the bureaucratic and narrow thinking that inhibits the contributors' ability to maximize them.

Against the Odds?

A lot has been written about the qualities great inventors have that set them apart. Many believe they were just born with a creative gift. I cannot speak for the others, but for me it has really come down to hard work. I feel like I always had to work harder than the next person. I had to struggle to get my B's in school, while others seemed to work less to get their A's. Rarely has anything come easy for me. I think the fact that I had to work so much harder just to get the basics of a subject may in some weird way have made it possible for me to go on to the next level. Luck and timing certainly played a role as well. There have been exactly seven times when I left the lab at night knowing that I had just come to truly understand something in a way that nobody else ever understood it before. The first time that happened, I didn't really know what to think and was unsure how to come to terms with it. But as time passed and I was more and more sure that I was right, I grew more confident. The next time it happened, I handled it better, and the time after that I was able to fully appreciate it. There is nothing like the feeling of knowing you are the first to discover something new or of solving a problem in a way that has never been done before. Do this a few times, and it really boosts your confidence.

What inventors and innovators do is actually quite simple: We take a blank sheet of paper and put things on it. Period. It's having an idea for something and trusting yourself and being enthusiastic enough about the idea to write it down and follow through with it. If I go to the marketing department and ask them to put together a new surgical manual such as the one we needed for the round window surgical technique, it will be a tremendously difficult task for them. However, if I take them pages with the basic outline, some basic steps, and a few crude images that illustrate the surgical steps, they have something to work with and can start asking the right questions. After that, it is relatively easy for them to describe and illustrate my ideas, and the finished document will be much different and much better than what I had started with initially. The hard part is the blank paper: Many people find it difficult to take the first steps into new and uncharted territory, get something down on paper, and figure out a good way to start.

Being first takes a certain amount of boldness and fearlessness. Being hearing impaired is a terrific quality that I share with the greatest inventor of all time, Thomas Edison. Being severely hearing impaired and being shy and/or easily embarrassed are really almost mutually exclusive. We hearing-impaired people often misunderstand words and are used to the strange looks we get when we appear to be stumbling with our thoughts or occasionally have odd behavior and conversations. We learn that dwelling on such matters is an exercise in futility, so we push on the best we can. So we are not afraid of getting the odd glance, of saying the wrong thing or off-putting from time to time, or even of being completely wrong. We just do it, knowing that we will eventually get it right. And if not, so what? No one else has yet either. From these experiences we also know that inventions sometimes come about by accident: We're looking for one thing but find another, and this new thing turns out to be even better than the one we were originally looking for.

The best innovators, in my view, are also really good at explaining their discoveries to others. Take Einstein, who used a greatly simplified model of what happens when trains are moving past one another to explain his theory of relativity, one of the most advanced concepts ever. Trains! I have probably delivered a hundred or more lectures on my FMT and how it works. Even though my little transducer is quite simple compared to the theory of relativity, I doubt that more than a dozen people truly understand it.

I truly wish I had Einstein's ability to simplify a topic. I sometimes think that if I had been able to explain the operation of the FMT in a better, more convincing way, more physicians might have adopted it faster. My only hope is that by recognizing the importance of trying to explain complex matters in the simplest terms, I will be able to get some of it across.

The best communicator of complex topics I ever heard was Joe Costello, who had a real a gift for it. I once heard him speak for an hour straight about complex software platforms, and he made everything crystal clear. Dr. Rodney Perkins has the same talent: He can make a mundane topic seem truly new and magical or a complex topic and seem straightforward and simple. I attended one talk Dr. Perkins gave on a topic that I find ludicrous, and I sat there amazed as the audience bought it hook, line, and sinker. At the end of the presentation I turned to a colleague and said, "You know, I don't believe in it one bit, but after seeing that I must admit that I want to!" "Yeah, so do I. I mean, what a great presentation!" Being a great explainer naturally leads to becoming a great salesperson, and to be successful in the art of inventing, you really have to sell your ideas and even yourself if need be. You have to do better than you possibly can.

We live in an era of hyper specialization. I think such unidirectional thinking and specialization is a trap for the inventive mind. It is a good thing that the art of inventing is a skill that can be taught, and maybe we should have a specialization in that as well. The leading innovations and those that have the biggest rewards are those that came from solving the toughest problems. The key is to avoid the beaten paths. Too many people think they can open up the next hottest restaurant in town, make the next great gadget or gimmick, or outsell all the other t-shirt companies, but most new restaurants are gone in less than two years (almost all by year five), and there are very few pet rocks. Those who select a difficult and challenging area, often one that is incredibly difficult to explain and perhaps even harder to understand, have chosen to go where the future is. Success rarely comes from picking fruit off the low-hanging branches unless the tree is in a place where nobody else has thought to look.

As an inventor I am biased on the topic of encouraging and rewarding innovation. Too often, inventors are shortchanged, and they often lack the resources to even file key patents. Should they get stock or a royalty, they often see the values of their shares, if they got them in the first place, diluted down to nothing or almost nothing. In order to reward true inventors and encourage innovation, we must make sure that inventors receive their just reward. At a minimum, inventors should receive a one percent royalty on the net sales of their inventions. If an invention is sold, then inventors should receive a minimum payment equal to at least five percent of the sale price up front. Should a technology firm go public, then the inventors should be required to sell ten percent of their stock on the opening and allowed to sell up to ten percent of their initial stock holdings per quarter regardless of events and share price. Lastly, inventors should have the option of placing 5 percent of their stock into an independent inventor's stock pool that is independently run. I admit implementing these ideas will take some work and that there are many unanswered questions. What about institutions such as universities that pay for the research? What about situations where there are multiple inventors and multiple patents? What if an inventor is paid for an innovation and the patent is later invalidated? What about sales in international markets? There are certainly a lot of issues, but I think they are manageable even though we may not find a perfect solution. The fact of the matter is that if we make sure that the inventors and innovators are appropriately rewarded, it can only benefit institutions as a whole and improve the larger economic picture. The goal should be to ensure inventors a fair share of the returns on their intellectual contributions and encourage more innovation. At present, too many inventors are shortchanged, and most get little or nothing for their contributions.

Such a program would undoubtedly make multimillionaires of some inventors who otherwise would not be rich, but most would realize a fair and modest contribution to their incomes. Universities might cry foul, protesting that this is what they pay salaries for. The truth, however, is that the rate of invention disclosures for universities and patent filings is often much lower than it should be. Too many research institutes have weak programs that encourage researchers and labs to file the appropriate invention disclosures and then file provisional applications before publishing results. Many labs are not even aware that if they publish the next new thing without taking care of the intellectual property filings and documentation beforehand, they can lose their rights to the invention forever.

They say that startup people work harder in two years than most work in a lifetime That may be true, but I am not sure what it means because I have usually either been or been involved with the founder of new concerns. The fact is that startups do take a lot of time and often do require a lot of sweat equity. In the early days of a startup things are great: Everyone is on board a hundred and ten percent, communication is maximized, goals are super clear, and there is a lot of attention and visibility from executive management since they all share the same office. New businesses always start out with the loftiest and most idealistic of aspirations, and it is really good stuff. There is nothing like the feeling you get from new startup: It is like an epic elixir.

A lot has been written about the business of startups, and Biodesign recently published a book that describes in great detail everything medical device startups go through. One small matter that is hinted at but largely missing from this text is the fact that true startups, with true breakthrough concepts, often take many years, but they are undertakings with both huge rewards and huge downsides. Most startups are not a walk in the park; most do not make it; and the consequences and effects on an individual's health and well-being can be enormous and lasting. The strains on marriages, family, and social networks cannot be overstated, and the risk of burning out is real. Non-disclosure and financial laws and agreements often leave the torch-bearers with few outlets to voice concerns, worries and other issues. It is a tough row to hoe, and the highs and low lows are extreme. Creating your own company, taking it public, watching it take its first baby steps, and then suddenly watching it get crushed despite your efforts to protect it is no fun. Sometimes there is a fair market reason for why this happens; sometimes there is not. Sometimes it is just bad luck. The Biodesign book does not talk about how good luck and good timing can benefit an inventor, probably because those are two things we have little or no control over.

Inventing, I believe, can be taught, though some certainly seem to be more readily predisposed to the skill than others. Taking an invention all the way from a concept to a full-on product is a daunting task. Looking back, I wish that I could have invested an extra $50,000 to build even better transducers and a working prototype of a much higher level. Having the best prototypes and something for others to hold on to physically is a great help and one that I think would have greatly increased the value and perception of me and my concept in the early stages. I also would have hired an expert graphics person at the beginning to help create really good presentations and documents and the corresponding images. They say a picture is worth a thousand words, and great graphics are an invaluable help in illustrating your concept.

A Bridge to the Future

"In this bright future you can't forget your past."

Bob Marley

Today my Soundbridge is implanted multiple times each and every day and in is available in over 50 countries. I have been blessed with success in terms of helping the hearing impaired. The Soundbridge has been used to treat almost all the major hearing loss indications including sensory, neural, mixed, and conductive hearing loss as well as, in a few cases, even specific forms of tinnitus. Otologists have also used it for treatment where reconstruction of the ear failed or was not possible and for treatment of chronic malformations of the ear. The couplers that were approved in early 2010 have ushered in a new era in otologic reconstruction, where the FMT works in concert with reconstructive otology to restore the conductive path of hearing and to provide additional vibrational signal. It goes without saying that it is truly gratifying to see the world's leading otologists and researchers working to find new ways to use my invention to help the hearing impaired. Hundreds if not thousands of people have worked on the Vibrant Soundbridge over the years to make this possible. Such results and such success never rest in the hands of one person alone.

The next implant stage is called the Bonebridge. A couple of years ago, Sebastian Foidl and Alexei Iltchenkoo, two of the leading sales team members in Innsbruck, described an implant design they wanted for their customers. They were surprised when I replied, "Really? I have an idea for that." We reworked the concept and eventually funded and hired a new team to design the implant.

The Bonebridge implant utilizes a transducer that is mounted via screws to the mastoid region of the skull. An electronic signal is delivered to the implant via an externally worn audio processor similar to the one used in the Vibrant Soundbridge. The signal is sent across the skin to the Bonebridge implant, which demodulates the signal and sends an audio signal to the transducer, causing it to vibrate. The vibrations are sent to the mastoid region of the skull, and the resultant vibrations are interpreted through bone conduction by the inner ear as sound. The beauty of this implant scheme is that it obviates the need for a percutaneous transmission scheme and the resultant open wound that other bone-anchored implant solutions require. It eliminates the need for percutaneous bone conduction implants. This solves the primary issues with bone conduction hearing treatments, which is that the open wound around the screw is subject to infection or being knocked out of position. The surgery for the Bonebridge installation takes between 45 minutes and an hour. The implant's new transducer design is a novel concept that makes it safe for MRI as well as all other types of imaging technology.

On July 7, 2011, the first Bonebridge was implanted by Dr. Georg Sprinzl at the Innsbruck clinic. It was great to see this done in Innsbruck because all the employees could go and watch the first surgery of the device. It was also really good for the Innsbruck community as that is where MED-EL is headquartered. Innsbruck is becoming a significant landmark, to say the very least, in the field of hearing technology, and I think this is very cool. The implant went in beautifully. At the activation four weeks later, the results were phenomenal and far exceeded our expectations. They were much, much better than even the first VSB results. In a word, they were perfect. The other patients implanted also had remarkable results, so we were off to a great start. It was personally gratifying for me to repeat our former successes with a new implant and prove to myself and perhaps others the first was not a fluke. I reckon that with the Bonebridge plus the ongoing success of the Soundbridge, we will continue to hire more people to help build and support these products. The Bonebridge itself could create a lot of work, and work means jobs. A majority of these jobs will be in Innsbruck, and that is good to see.

The Bonebridge will fulfill my goal to develop an implant system for all the major forms and types of hearing loss. The Bonebridge offers patients a new option for treatment in cases where medical conditions rule out other solutions. It is a superior treatment option and an alternative to existing therapies.

My next goal is to improve the use of our implants by improving human factors and features for patients and to improve the diagnostic and monitoring options for our centers that utilize our implants. We are also always improving our audio processor products to include the latest and greatest features and signal processing. Utilizing the same implant platform, we can improve the performance by upgrading the audio processor. This, in my view, is the greatest advantage of partially implantable solutions. And before I retire, I want to build at least two more implants. As far as I know, nobody has ever done three, but I have always thought my number should be at least four. It looks like I have enough to do at MED-EL to keep me busy for a long time, and I hope I can grow the business units I work on into little technology powerhouses.

Golfing, the Austrian Way

"Golf is a good walk spoiled."

Mark Twain

Cherry Chase Golf Course was located on a strip of land off of Bernardo Drive near El Camion Real on the West side of Sunnyvale. When I was a kid, a group of us would regularly scrounge up some clubs and hop on down for a round of golf. For kids under age 12, the cost was $2.25 for full round of 18 holes. However, we learned that if it was a slow day and if the cool golf rangers were on duty, we could cut from the 17th back to 2nd hole and play another round. We would also head up to the Deep Cliff course in Cupertino. We liked it better than Cherry Chase, but the fee there was a whopping $4.50 for under 12's and $8.50 if you were over 12 but had a student I.D. card. Golfing was just something that I loved, and we had just as much fun wading through the ponds and streams for lost balls as we did playing. During summers I would often find myself back in Massachusetts to stay with Grandma and Grandpa. My Uncle Butch let my cousin David and me hit balls all around his property and took us down to the driving range. We spent our days and late evenings there going through buckets of balls. Hitting golf balls was and still is my favorite thing to do. Though my scores do not reflect it, I have played a surprising amount of golf at a surprising number of courses throughout Europe and the U.S.

When I arrived in Austria, one of the first friends I made was Alois Griesser, who is one of our sales managers. Alois is a keen golfer, and when he learned that I fancied myself a bit of a player, he invited me to play at his club, located up in the idyllic Alpine village of Seefeld. I parked my car, pulled out my golf bag, and headed to the clubhouse, where Alois was waiting for me. One thing I must say about Austria is boy oh boy do they love bureaucracy! Alois had to explain to the course managers that I was an American and that I had a handicap index of 13.5, but that I had left my card back in the United States. It was a bit of a stretch, yet mostly true. Then he had to stretch the truth a bit further and explain to them that

I was a member of a club. In the U.S., getting a handicap is really no problem, but in Austria the rules are incredibly strict. First you must pay to be a member of a club, and the cheapest annual club membership fee is around $500. Then you must play in official tournaments, and only official scores from sanctioned events can be entered into the handicap computer. Then, whenever you play, you also have to pay green fees, though it is usually cheaper to pay the additional 400 to 1,000 euros for a season of unlimited play. But Alois convinced them to let it slide, and they let me use the range and play a round.

On our way out to the range, I stopped and looked around and was absolutely stunned. The course was packed. There were instructors running around helping students and were on all three of the putting greens, which had chalk lines and circles drawn all over them. Austrians were lined up and waiting at every single practice pitch, and there was a queue for the range, which was already over capacity. Everyone was practicing: sand shots, pitch shots, putts, fringe putts – you name it. On the range, people were not simply blasting balls down the pitch as is common in the U.S.; they were all aiming for neatly positioned and accurately marked distance targets and flag sticks. Everyone was practicing in neat, orderly groups. I stood there and thought to myself, *Geez, it's like someone gave them the book on how to learn to play golf and they are following it and doing all the drills. Don't they know that nobody actually does that? But when in Rome ...*

I decided to just do everything Alois did. He pulled out a pitching wedge and pitched balls, so I did too. He practiced putting for an hour, and so did I. He hit sand shots, so I hit some too. When we had finally finished the pre-game workout, we headed off to tee number one and got in line. I was amazed at how closely the Austrians followed the etiquette guidelines. Two of Alois' friends joined us to make a foursome. Alois teed off and pulled the ball slightly to the right. I went next and hooked my shot way right way off into a meadow of waist-deep grass. I called for a lost ball and hit a provisional shot, sure I would never find the first one.

As we were walking down the fairway to hit our second shots, the most amazing thing happened: All three Austrians waded into the waist-high grass and organized a search party for my lost first shot. I stood there, stunned.

"What are you guys doing?" I hollered.

"Vee look fur de ball!"

"What? I called the ball lost!"

What on earth were they doing? I wanted to play golf, not waste time looking for a ball. But again, when in Rome ... I headed over and started to help look for my lost ball. Sure enough, Alois found it, and I played out back into the fairway. I had never seen anything like it.

On the next hole, one of the other members of our group pulled the ball into the rough beside the railroad tracks that ran through the center of the course. Again, off we went in search party mode. They had an organized system: Single file. Slash, step, look. Slash, step look. Found that ball too. Next hole, another golfer shanked one right. New search party. Single file. Slash, step, look. Slash, step look. Next hole, same thing. By the end of the day, we had had eight searches but not lost a single ball. I had never seen so much attention paid to finding bad shots. It all made sense later when I found out that decent standard golf balls cost four times more in Austria than they do in the U.S., and that the really good ones are even more expensive.

Alois got me hooked on golf. I was able to arrange a real international handicap card via an Irish club, and I paid for a club membership in Austria that included unlimited play for the remainder of the year. Alois and I could often be found out on the course before work, after work and on weekends. Each time, I practiced pitches, putts, and sand shots, and I used all my clubs on the range to nail targets. I took group lessons. I took individual lessons. I changed my grip. In short, I threw out my U.S. golf game and habits and switched to the hyper-organized Austrian system. I even learned how to find those expensive golf balls in the high grass.

You know what happened? My golf game improved beyond measure. In two years I had an honest 8.5 handicap. I made annual holiday trips to Ireland (to my Irish course) with my wife and was regularly shooting in the low-mid 80's and a few times even in the 70's. One day, if it had not been for two horrifying triple bogeys (one on a par three, to add insult to injury) I would have had a scratch round.

I stopped playing golf in June of 2006, when my wife gave birth to our twin sons, Travis and Trevor. But what I had learned was that these Austrians and their approach were not bad, not bad at all. The Austrian way, though it may not always be what we are used to, works.

The golf in Austria was new to me, and so were the haircuts. The first time I needed a trim, I went to the nearest barber shop I could find. When it was my turn, they sat me down in the chair and asked me what I wanted. In my finest broken German I said, "Haar Razor, bitte." The next thing I knew, the barber was putting hot towels all over my face, and I was not sure what to think. He removed the towels and lathered up my face. Then he produced a straight razor and gave me the closest shave of my life. After he was done, one of the assistants who could speak English came over and said, "He wants to know if that is OK."

"Uh, yeah," I replied. "Do you think he could do the hair on my head now?"

"Oh! You wanted a hair cut! Oh. Sorry."

So the barber put me back in the chair and gave me the shortest hair cut I had ever had. To my horror, the service included using a miniature flame thrower to burn off all the extra hairs that he could not get with his razors and scissors, but I survived.

One of the things that probably surprised me most about this part of the world is the attitude toward nudity. I didn't really know what to expect, but I was born and raised in America, where there is zero tolerance of exposing one's private areas. In the meantime I can tell you that it's just the opposite here. When my wife and I went to the pool, we were stunned when the Austrians changed their suits right there in front of everyone, without even attempting to hide behind a towel. It seemed to us that the older a person was and the less attractive his or her body was, the more likely this was to occur. It was clearly no big deal to them, and nobody else took notice. When my wife and I go to the doctor here in Austria, it is quite common for them to walk into the examining room and have you remove your clothes with the door wide open, in full view of the waiting area. The first time this happened to me I was shocked; now I just roll with it.

Once, while we were doing construction, I had a testing lab that had been temporarily set up in the gowning areas for our clean room. I was shocked when a group of attractive female workers from our clean room came in, stripped down, and changed back into their street clothes right there in front of me, leaving little if anything to the imagination. If that happened in the U.S., there would be lawsuits, by golly! As it was, I just sat there with my mouth hanging open, thanking my lucky stars and feeling like a slimebag at the same time. Clearly, I was not in the U.S. Saunas, most of them co-ed, are quite popular here. Wearing bathing suits is *verboten*, and the mandatory towels are to sit on. I had never been to a sauna, so how could I know this? Well, one night as I was driving home, the windows of the sports center were lit up, and I could clearly see (from the road!) all the sauna guests lying around naked inside. I mean, they had not even closed the blinds! In the U.S. there would not even be windows. In Austria, it is quite common to walk into a men's room and to find a woman happily cleaning away right next to men using the facilities. That would never happen in the U.S. either. I am happy to report that I have now learned to relieve myself in front of a woman who is a total stranger and think nothing of it. But you know, I think their attitude toward this stuff, though different from what I grew up with, is probably much healthier. After all, a body is just a body, naked or clothed; and nudity, believe it or not, does not always mean sex. It is just a different way of looking at things, and it did take some getting used to.

We have a bit of an expat community here in Innsbruck. One day I heard an expat say, "Well, the good news is I have now learned enough German that I am no longer embarrassed when I go to the grocery store." This really hit home. My German is horrible, and when I am speaking to someone who knows little English, I often have to do a lot of pointing and gesturing to get my point across. Having grown up hearing impaired, this is something I'd done often in the past, and it had never occurred to me to be *embarrassed*. I had never thought of it that way before. Now, however, after so many years of living among native speakers of German, my poor attempts at speaking it are still nowhere near the level they should be. I feel bad rather than embarrassed, though, because I know it must be hard on my listeners to hear me mangle their native language. They almost always revert to English once I start speaking, and that of course makes it more difficult for me to learn their language.

For me another interesting aspect of living in the Alps is the extreme athletes that we have. In fact, one of winners of the Race Across America is the guy who fixes my skis each year. Within a thirty minute drive of Innsbruck, there are approximately thirty ski areas, so the person sitting next to you at work might be one of the world's best extreme skiers. I would say that there are probably at least ten of the world's top mountain alpinists at MED-EL. There are also extraordinary snow boarders, mountain bikers (including a person who actually wrote a mountain biking tour book for Tirol), marathon runners, and BMX riders. It is quite extraordinary. When someone from MED-EL invites you to the mountains, you had better know what you are getting yourself into.

Sabina's and my approach to living in Europe has pretty much been to just watch what the Austrians do and do the same thing. At times it makes little sense, yet it almost always works out. We try to focus on the fact that there are more similarities than differences. We try to focus on the positives (and there are many) and ignore the negatives as much as we can.

People sometimes ask me what I miss most now that I have lived in Austria for so long. Well, the first thing I miss is Round Table Pizza. When we lived in Sunnyvale, I actually had a t-shirt that my wife bought me that said, "Body by Round Table." I was definitely packing on extra pounds thanks to more than my share of pizza. I also miss really good Mexican food, but I have to admit that I would probably be quite a porker by now if I had kept on eating the way I was. A lot of the food in Axams, the village in which we live, is farm fresh and organic. It takes a bit of getting used to, but now it suits us fine. It also took us a while to get used to the fact that almost all the stores in Austria close by 6 p.m. and are never open on Sunday or holidays. This can be quite a problem as there seem be a lot of holidays. They are big on recycling here, and throwing your trash into the correct, color-coded bin is a hassle at first. We also had to learn to live without a kitchen garbage disposal, which is apparently considered too wasteful.

Whenever I go to a store back in the United States, I cannot get over the mind-boggling number of products consumers have to choose from. Take for example the toothpaste section: There must be hundreds of brands and varieties: gel, paste, white, red, whitening, gel with whitening, toothpaste with tartar control, and on and on. Americans have the best teeth in the world, but do they really need so many choices? The selection is much more limited in Austria, so if you come to here, you might want to bring your favorite brand of toothpaste. I am even more amazed when I see the cat and dog food sections in U.S. supermarkets: They take up an entire aisle of shelves displaying hundreds of pet foods in different flavors, sizes, and concoctions. Are American cats and dogs really so finicky? Austrian supermarkets only sell a few brands of pet food in either dry or canned form, and the cats and dogs here do just fine.

Nobody ever gets my sense of humor here in Austria, but my wife says that most people in the U.S. never got me either. I miss going to Santa Cruz and playing golf at Pastiempo with my buddy Rick Adams. I miss our neighbors, Janus & Lee, the Ogerrinos, and the rest of the folks who live on Black Road. I miss the funkiness of the Santa Cruz Mountains and the way the sun sets behind them. I miss Frontier Village and the hippies from my youth. The restaurant I miss most of all is actually the long-gone Farrell's in Sunnyvale, and I am sorry that I will never have a chance to take my kids there. I miss the old downtown Sunnyvale of my youth. I miss the patent library and the staff, the VA and Stanford, and of course all the people who worked with me on the Symphonix project. I miss the feeling of believing that everything was possible in Sunnyvale, California, where last night's dream could be today's reality and where the guy sitting next to you at Clarke's Hamburger Stand could be the billionaire who pioneered the innovation of the hard disk.[12] There is a good chance that I will feel the same way about Innsbruck someday.

I found out via Facebook that one of my old roommates from college is now a successful local politician and just won re-election. This guy was, well ... let's just say he never struck any of us as being the sharpest tool in the shed. In fact, I do not think he ever actually earned a degree. His success just reminded me that I will probably never get a chance to run for mayor of Sunnyvale or even serve on the city council. I am missing out on chances to try my hand at participating in government, something that I had always secretly thought I would get to do some day.

Austria is so darn pretty that it hurts your eyes. From our kitchen window we have views that rival Yosemite Park in California. Whenever visitors come, they gaze at the Alps with an expression of utter amazement on their faces. "You can keep on blinking," I usually tell them, "but when you open your eyes, it will still be there."

One of our visitors from the U.S. said, "It is like you live in a giant Disneyland." It's true. It is quite a place, with amazing sights: everything from pastoral valleys to jagged, snow-capped peaks that seem to pierce the sky. Vienna, Austria, has to be the most underrated tourist destination in Europe. People from the U.S. who have been to Europe will typically tick off the cities they have visited, and the list usually includes London, Paris, Munich, Rome, Venice, and Amsterdam but rarely Vienna. The Austrian capital is an amazing and delightful city. Everywhere you turn, there is a palace, a monument, or a coffee house. Incredible buildings reflect everything from the glory of the monarchy to the talent of modern designers. Vienna is an architectural extravaganza interspersed with parks full of statures and promenades, and carriage roads. In fact Inge and I took a ride in one of the city's famous horse-drawn carriages in on the day the Symphonix transfer was finalized.

The towns of Innsbruck and Salzburg also have a lot to offer. Innsbruck is a fine example of an Alpine town. Known for its skiing in winter and its epic hiking the rest of the year, it is a true gem in

---

12   This actually did happen.

any season. Salzburg, the home of Mozart, is a stellar place that can more than hold its own. Visitors can have a fine time visiting the nearby pristine lakes, seeing the real *Sound of Music* sites, or taking an incredible salt mine tour. An evening at a nice Mozart concert up at the castle overlooking the town is tough to beat. I assure you I am not being paid by the Austrian tourism people, but let me tell you, this is an amazing place to visit. Austria sometimes gets an ill-deserved and unjustified view because of its past, but the new generation has learned from those mistakes and moved ahead in a very positive direction. In some of the more remote Alpine valleys and villages of the Alps, time seems to have stood still, yet this country is also a great place to run a high-tech company. Austria is awesome!

Since the arrival of our identical twins and later their brother Tristan, Sabina and I have come to the conclusion that Austria is a terrific place to raise a family. The three boys are quite a handful and were all skiing diamond runs by the time they were four. My wife says that there is "a one in a million chance" of us having more kids, so for now I'll take that to mean that the option is still on the table! Trevor and Travis are now at the age where they are getting to be really good little swimmers and football players, so if I ever want to coach their swim or football teams someday, I'll have to start getting really serious about learning German. They took to ski team lessons this past season, and the instructor was happy when he realized that my sons were not monolingual English speakers like I am. He pointed to them and called out to me, "Yah, dey are Tyrol. Gut! Super!"

We used the proceeds from the sale of our home in California to build a house at the bottom of the toughest run of the Axamer Lizum ski area. The Axams villagers have been very accepting of us even though we are not Tyroleans. I strongly suspect that even those who regard us with a bit of a curiosity are thinking that we might be OK despite not being locals. We are grateful for this, and we love living in Axams. The views and surrounding mountains are inspiring, to say the least. Factor in the ski area practically in our back yard and rumors of a golf course being built nearby, and our quality of life could not get much better. Sure, we still have the occasional problem with clueless neighbors, but all neighborhoods everywhere have them, and I think they exist just to remind the rest of us just how good we are. We are doing quite well indeed at the moment. Just fine.

Lately I have been running a lot, training for marathons. I usually run late at night with a little headlamp on my hat so that I can make my way along the mountain trails in the dark. I often run up to the base of the Axamer Lizum, and sometimes I even go up over the top and down into the adjacent valley. Alone at night, running in the mountains, usually with no cars anywhere and no one else around, I have found lots of time to reflect on the past and the events that led me to Austria. In the peace and quiet of my runs, I have found a bit of clarity about the past. There are many tales that I have not told and many that are best left that way, but I have come to believe that in my story there might be something that others might need to hear.

Technology is an Adventure

"I never see what has been done;
I only see what remains to be done."

Mare Curie

Ingeborg Hochmair read an advance copy of my book and really liked it except for the title. She said, "You know, it should be called something like *Sound Success.*" I thought that was a pretty clever title and considered it until I realized that this story is clearly not a success story because in fact I never really achieved what I set out to do. Today, although tens of thousands of hearing implants have been implanted worldwide, we still have a long, long way to go before we get the best technology to everyone who needs it. It gets better every year, and every day more and more people who need hearing implants are getting them, but we still have a lot of work ahead of us before we satisfy the need in a majority of the countries When we have done that, then I think we can call it a success. It also occurred to me that my work and life are not really a success. Perhaps in some ways I have done well for myself, my family and others. But all in all, it is a mixed bag. Again, I used to think that that my quest for success was to develop the perfect hearing implant, be it a VSB or a Bonebridge or something else. I now think it is to develop a complete family of implants, and a couple are of them are still missing.

As I walked around the City of Sunnyvale, I took pictures that I thought I could use to show where all my technology came from, including a few shots of the library that held the patents and of the old garage. I noticed that the city of Sunnyvale is again in the midst of completely redoing its downtown area. It certainly cannot turn out as bad as it did last time, when they bulldozed the best parts of the original downtown area and put up what had to be one of the most ill-conceived shopping malls of all time. It appears they are in the process of making downtown Sunnyvale even harder to find than it was before, and that is quite a tall order! I doubt that our downtown will ever be finished.

The shops and restaurants on Murphy Street are still there, but they are struggling in what seems to be a perpetual construction zone. The Town and Country shops are now largely shuttered and gone. I can only imagine how the people of Innsbruck would react if someone suggested bulldozing the Old Town, the historic downtown section of the city. In my dear hometown of Sunnyvale I have now seen this happen twice.

The Sunnyvale patent library has been shuttered, and the helpful folks on its staff have either retired or been sent back to the main library. Its resources were no longer needed after the U.S. patent and international patent libraries were put into digital format and made easily searchable. Rather than ask the helpful experts at the library desk face to face, I can now do my searches from my desktop PC, including custom searches.

On New Years' Day 2010, I walked over to Serra Park with my three young sons. The park's sequoia and redwood trees are huge, and some of the trees I used to climb now tower over a hundred feet high. The good old Serra Park boat is still there, but trial lawyers and safety officers have conspired to remove the rooftops we used to jump across. The steep slide has been removed, along with the climbing net. Even the floating plank bridge has been removed for safety reasons, though I cannot imagine how anyone could have gotten hurt on that. The park was fine before, and I struggle to find the good intentions in this overly safe design.

My sons rode their Big Wheels on the park's well-maintained paths and bridges under its amazing canopy of trees. What was a freshly planted new park when I was a young lad is now surprisingly beautiful in a new and more mature way. My three Austrian sons were outnumbered by kids of Latin, Asian, Indian, and Middle Eastern descent, who will no doubt enjoy some of the same benefits and advantages I had growing up there. My three sons will grow up in a vastly different world. Instead of Serra Park, my sons have the Alps as their playground. They speak English with a British accent (we are not sure how it happened, but one of them actually sounds like a young Winston Churchill when he speaks) as well as German.

There is not a Californian dialect among them. My brother Chris says, "Travis and Trevor sound like they learned English from a German who learned English from an Englishman. Nobody else sounds like them." My sons are not American at all. They eat the crust off the bread first, which is totally the opposite of what American boys do, and they eat their pizza backwards, from the outside in. They love *Zwiebelrostbraten* (flank steak cooked in onion sauce, with sautéed onions) which no American kid would go near. They eat *Gulasch, Sauerkraut, Spaetzle,* and heavy, dark bread-all foods that red-blooded American boys would turn their noses up at. In fact, I have seen my son Travis watching TV and casually chomping away on an onion.

I am proud to have gone from being diagnosed with hearing loss in the parking lot of Serra Elementary School to working with the best and brightest leaders in the field of hearing science and medicine. It has been quite a journey. As I write this, I am now forty-six years old. My devices have completed four clinical trials in the United States and Europe; and there is currently one active clinical trial for new indications in the United States. I have produced a grand total of 23 medical devices (including AP's and surgical instruments) and three class-three implant stages. My devices have been used to treat all the major hearing loss categories with the exception of profound hearing loss, which is covered by cochlear implants. I have worked for five startup companies either as an early stage employee or a founder. I now have over eighty U.S. and international patents either issued or pending. Many thousands of patients have been implanted with technology that I invented.

I love working and living in Austria and hope to stay in my present role for many years to come, but the future of business is always uncertain. Working for Ingeborg is a joy, and I have told her that I am willing to stay with the company and in Austria for the rest of my career. Some days I even can see myself retiring here because the skiing is so good. My first priority is to take care of my wife and my family. It is great to have had the chance to help the hearing impaired and to have made a small contribution to making the world a better place. It is terrific that I have a position where I can still work to achieve my life's dream of having an implantable solution or surgical correction for all types of hearing loss. It is also awesome to know that I am a leader in my field and that there is a real possibility that I will go into my lab and discover something new or make something better. I get a chance to make it happen each and every day. In addition to working in the field of hearing implants, I still have an intense interest in neural repair and neural recovery, which has always been a fascinating area for me and one that I have not taken as far as I would like to. Another topic I love is the next generation or next level of microsurgery and the development of devices, techniques and machine-assisted instruments for it. I miss California and Sunnyvale from time to time, but I am more than satisfied in Austria and thankful for the wonderful people here.

By this point, it should be obvious that I am bullish on technology. In my lifetime so far, I have witnessed the garage spirit of Silicon Valley spread throughout the world. Today it is not only the garages of Silicon Valley where future entrepreneurs are toiling away on the next new thing. The value of clever thinking and brilliant ideas can never be overstated.

When I was a kid growing up, one of my childhood dreams was to have my own private movie theater where I could show any movie I wanted. It would have headphones that would allow me to turn the sound up super loud so I could hear it and not bother anybody. But this was an impossible fantasy. Today my sons can watch any movie they want as loudly as they want without bothering anyone, and they can do it in the car while we are driving to Venice. That is incredible to me. Innovation can make the seemingly impossible real.

I watched Apple Computer[13] grow from one building to two, to its present size today, where it takes up most of the space in

---

13   I swear that I can distinctly recall purchasing parts from Steve Jobs at Haltek before he became the famous Apple co-founder. When I checked the facts, I found out that he may not have actually worked at Haltek (which was the best surplus electronics store ever). However, there can be no doubt that I saw both Steve Jobs and Steve Wozniak at Haltek: like me, they were regulars there. The sales rep who sold me a computer for the lab was Steve Wozniak's brother, and I think I still have his business card. I had the same high

the city of Cupertino. I have also seen companies achieve stellar success and then implode. I have completely missed great opportunities that were right in front of me. I have had some success, and I have had colossal failure. I have been at the top of the field and leading the way for others, and I have been at the bottom of the heap. I would not trade it for anything. It is a great feeling to know that the device I dreamed up in the garage and financed with credit cards turned into something that is helping so many today and will help so many more in the future. Inventing is what gives me an indescribable feeling of satisfaction. Inventing is hard work, but developing a technology is even harder.

Technology is also confounding. It seems counterintuitive that when economic times are tough and there is little funding available, that is precisely when it is most important for economies to invest in more research. It seems like it should be the other way around, but it is not.

The people that offer the greatest hope are often the ones we least suspect. It is hard to believe that a couple of guys I used to see down at Haltek electronics surplus shop founded Apple, but they did. It seems crazy that I ran across the guys that started Yahoo at Stanford or that the smartest guy I ever met swam across the Golden Gate just because it was there. Some might find it just as improbable that a hearing- impaired kid would go on to invent an implant to cure his own hearing loss. Unlikely people are often the true innovators. In fact, real deal people seldom have a lot of academic degrees, easy-on-the-eye looks, the latest clothes, or the ability to explain themselves or their ideas well.

The single greatest challenge to innovation and invention today is something I fear is coming: the age of ultra-regulation. In the old days, the regulatory and bureaucratic workforce did most of their work using typewriters, pad and paper, and reference books. In today's world they all have computers that allow them to cut and paste tables and lists and create text that they can instantly

---

school electronics teacher as both the Steves, and I'm quite sure I saw Steve Wozniak when he dropped by to see Mr. McCollum on more than one occasion. Let's just chalk it all up to brief encounters with the truly famous.

share with others. References, standards and directives can all be called up instantly via the internet and used to create more thorough and larger documents at rapid speed. They have shown an uncanny ability to develop documents, standards and directives that too often conflict with one another. If I were to start Symphonix today, I would have to raise twice as much money as I did in order to comply with the even higher level of regulatory, quality and compliance measures in place. It is mind-boggling, and just thinking about makes my head hurt. To be fair, folks have been complaining about regulations since the original maritime requirements for shipping were put into place more than one hundred years ago. I am pro regulation, but I also am keenly aware that ultra-regulation, if embraced, could develop into an out-of-control Goliath that will be hard to put down.

I have already seen the first attempts at what I call "retroactive regulation" – applying new rules to products that are already in the field and working fine. Those products, however, would have to be taken off the market if they did not comply with the new regulations. I have seen hundreds of perfectly readable and good documents shredded (more costs, more landfill) simply because a regulator had changed the look of a symbol (that few people actually understood anyway) by replacing it with a new and improved symbol in a better font. It is tough. Medical devices are one of the most highly regulated products in the world. Stringent regulations prolong the time it takes us to get new products to market now, and if more regulations are added, new treatment options might already be obsolete by the time they become available. As a society, we cannot insist on having the latest and greatest that science and medicine has to offer and at the same time demand that it involve zero risk. That is not possible. A majority of clinical trials and medical developments are now being done outside of the United States for regulatory, legal and cost reasons. The physicians and researchers in the countries where this work is being done will be the ones using the latest and greatest technology, the next generation of products and treatments. It almost goes without saying that the people who are actively using the latest and greatest technology and treatments will also be the ones who eventually develop the next new thing. I think overregulation is a tremendous loss, and other countries would be wise to take notice. It is a not a good idea to regulate your innovation potential to a point where the innovators head elsewhere. Not a good idea at all.[14]

Medical device innovation and clinical work is happening, but it has moved to new places, and I predict that those are the places where the next breakthroughs will occur. You just cannot be a researcher and do everything with a computer model. At some point you have to actually do it. If you have to move to develop your idea, then that is what you do. Technology is an adventure, and you never know where you might wind up.

Technology development is also unpredictable and constantly changing. In 1996, my good friend Dr. Alex Huber said to me, "I think that if you could make a totally implantable device, that would be the Holy Grail." At the time, I thought Alex was right. But I now believe that the real Holy Grail is not one particular device. The perfect device in fact does not exist. What we really need is a perfect family of devices that can be chosen according to the individual patient's needs and used to address most kinds of hearing loss in a majority of the hearing impaired. We need options, and the more, the better.

At present, there are many new implant designs speeding down the development pipeline. There is much to be excited about. Today Inge has product lines that offer treatment options for most types of hearing loss. Her competitors have seen the value of this and now have followed suit by expanding their lines as well. At the time of the Symphonix acquisition, Inge was certainly taking a huge risk. In hindsight, it was a good strategic move. She was able to get all of our valuable research and manufacturing equipment as well as the Symphonix patent portfolio I had been working hard to build up, plus the hidden gems that it contained. The Soundbridge and Vibrant teams have also had a positive impact on the sales of the other product lines and have created a lot of visibility and positive direction in the field as a whole. I can trace all of these blessings

---

14   By the way, I find it a bit ironic that I am sitting in an office in Innsbruck, Austria, as I write this.

back to the chances and the upbringing I received from my family and the good citizens of Sunnyvale, California.

Technology development is like asking out the prettiest girl in school to go to the dance: You do not know what she will say until you are bold enough to ask. You never know what might happen. And you'd better be ready to dance all night.

The End

Acknowledgements

There is no letter *i* in the word 'team.' Dr. Goode approved the appropriate rights to the FMT to be assigned to me. I also need to express my endless gratitude to Ugo Fisch for his help with the input on the basic design concept; for his work on the lead, size and development of the surgical method for the VORP; and for his participation in the original SAB meetings. In addition to Ugo Fisch the PI of the EU VSB, clinical trial key participants include Cor Cremers, Thomas Lenarz, Benno Weber, Gregorio Babighian, Alain Uziel, David Proops, Alec F. O'Connor, Robert Charchon, Jan Helms, and Bernard Fraysse. Anders Tjellstrom published the results of our first *Acute Trial of the Vibrant Soundbridge* in 1997 and was the first to publish the observation that the VSB could "also be used to treat conductive hearing loss." The first patient was implanted by Ugo Fisch in 1996. The first known use of the VSB to clinically treat conductive and mixed loss was by Thibaud Dumon in France. Vittorio Colletti pioneered the use of the FMT in alternative locations on the RW beginning in 2005.

In the U.S., Dr. Hough was the principal investigator for the VSB clinical trials, and Dr. Stan Baker, Dr. Dormer and Dr. Gan helped tremendously with the development of our original surgical product, as did all the other members of their team. Other surgeons who contributed to SAB work and clinical trials work included (but are not limited to) Charlie Luetje, Derald Brackman, Thomas Balkany, Jennifer Maw, David Kelsall, Douglas Backous, Richard Miyamoto, Simon Parisier, and Alexander Arts. U.S. audiologists who helped with our clinical trial work included Deborah Arthur, Christine Menapace, Pamela Mathews, Darcy Benson, Theresa Clarke, Charles Berlin, and many others. The attachment clip project was completed by Chris Julian with the help of the SAB input. The implant attachment magnet concept for the VORP was licensed from University of Oklahoma; the original size for the FMT (same as it is today) was arrived at with Ugo Fisch and others and in T.Bone studies that Stan Baker and I conducted. The surgery was developed again with the SAB members in the E.U. and the U.S., and the original implant telemetry scheme was based on the work of Erwin and Ingeborg Hochmair, which they use for cochlear implants. Hans Camenzind was my original "angel" investor, followed by B.J. Cassin, Peter McNerney and Karen Bozie. Ron Antipa helped me write the original business plans and arrange the funding for Symphonix, and to him, I am eternally grateful.

On the Symphonix design team we had Bob Katz, Craig Mar, Dan Wallace, Chris Julian, Tim Dietz, Eric Jaeger, Duane Tumlinson, Frank Fellenz, all on the implant side. On the audio processor development side there was Bruce Arthur, Jim Culp, John Salsbury, Steve Trebotich, Wyn Robertson and several other engineers. Manufacture of the tiny FMT's was developed by Pat Rimroth, Ahn Troung and Sue Clarke. Many of these people are listed on the patents, where they had made appropriate contributions resulting in issued claims. Bruce Maxfield and I developed the original detailed mathematics that describe how FMT's work. Special thanks to Peter Hertzman, Alf Merriweather, Beth Anne McDonald, Jeff Rydin, Mike Arendt, the Symphonix sales and clinical support staff, and the many other key support personnel from the Symphonix era. Today the VSB is supported by our R & D staff, including Peter Lampbacher, Marcus Shmidt, Klaus Holzer, Ali Mayr, Markus Nagl, Michael Santek, Klaus Triendl, Bernd Gerhardter and many others on the RA, QA, and clinical sides. And of course Ingeborg Hochmair, my CEO, who saved the VSB and has been the greatest! I would also like to thank all the people who helped on the "save the VSB project" by moving the operating assets from San Jose, California, to our new home in Austria, especially Alexander Mayr, Linda Ferner, Martin Kerber, Walter Fimml, Klaus Holzer and the MED-EL transfer team.

Then of course there are the many others that have helped me out personally, including Joe Roberson, Klaus Boeheim, Wolfgang Baumgartner, Alex Huber, Norbert Dillier, Timothy Wild, Thomas Lenarz, Jon Spindel, Michel Beliaff, Bill Perry, Joachim Mueller and Harry Robbins. Special thanks also go to Jan Helms for his willingness to spend extra time with me over the years. Invaluable all! I thank the many researchers that have contributed original work (too many to list again) and applaud the many people that have earned higher academic PhD's and other degrees for original work on the VSB, FMT and related topics. Thanks to the entire Japanese team at Ehime for working with me all these years. Again, I am grateful to Dr. Goode, who imprinted his view of hearing and of all things otology, engineering, medical, philosophical, design and invention-wise upon me and my paltry inferior brain capacity. He is a great teacher and mentor, and I thank him so much for believing in and taking a chance on me. And sorry for the days when the Goode maxim "When the surf is good, the lab ain't doing what it should!" was sometimes correct.

As for me ... I'm not yet finished, I assure you.

Cheers,

Geoff

Literature on hearing and the VIBRANT SOUNDBRIDGE®
(at press time)

Böheim, K (ed) (2010). *Active Middle Ear Implants.* [Advances in Oto-Rhino-Laryngology, Vol. 69] Basel: Karger.

Beltrame M, Martini A, Prosser S, Giarbini N, Streiberger C (2009). Coupling the Vibrant Soundbridge to Cochlea Round Window: Auditory Results in Patients With Mixed Hearing Loss. *Otology & Neurotology* 30(2) (Feb 2009): 194–201.

Colletti V, Carner M, Colletti L (2009). TORP vs round window implant for hearing restoration of patients with extensive ossicular chain defect. *ActaOto-Laryngologica* 129(4) (Apr 2009): 1–4.

Frenzel H, Hanke F, Beltrame M, Steffen A, Schönweiler R, Wollenberg B (2009). Application of the Vibrant Soundbridge to Unilateral Osseous Atresia Cases. *Laryngoscope* 119(1) (Jan 2009): 67–74.

Linder T, Schlegel C, DeMin N, Van der Westhuizen S (2009). Active Middle Ear Implants in Patients Undergoing Subtotal Petrosectomy: New Application for the Vibrant Soundbridge Device and Its Implication for Lateral Cranium Base Surgery. *Otology & Neurotology* 30(1) (Jan 2009): 41–7.

Hüttenbrink K, Zahnert T, Bornitz M, Beutner D (2008). TORP-Vibroplasty: A New Alternative for the Chronically Disabled Middle Ear. *Otology & Neurotology* 29(7) (Oct 2008): 965–971.

Mosnier I, Sterkers O, Bouccara D, et al. (2008). Benefit of the Vibrant Soundbridge Device in Patients Implanted For 5 to 8 Years. *Ear & Hearing* 29(2) (Apr 2008): 281–284.

Truy E, Philibert B, Vesson JF, Labassi S, Collet L (2008). Vibrant Soundbridge Versus Conventional Hearing Aid in Sensorineural High-Frequency Hearing Loss: A Prospective Study. *Otology & Neurotology* 29(5) (Aug 2008): 684–687.

Arauz SL, Campo Mercandino E, Campo E, Arauz SA (2007). Vibrant Soundbridge – Ubicación en Ventana oval utilizando prótesis ad-hoc. *Otolaringológica* XXIX: 10–14.

Böheim K, Nahler M, Schlögel M (2007). Rehabilitation der Hochtoninnenohrschwerhörigkeit: Einsatz eines aktiven Mittelohrimplantats. *HNO* 55(9): 690–695.

Dumon T (2007). Vibrant Soundbridge Middle Ear Implant in Otosclerosis. In: Arnold W, Häusler R (eds.) *Otosclerosis and Stapes Surgery.* [Advances in Oto-Rhino-Laryngology, Vol. 65] Basel: Karger: 320–322.

Venail F, Lavieille, JP, Meller R, Deveze A, Tardivet L, Magnan J (2007). New Perspectives for Middle Ear Implants: First Results in Otosclerosis With Mixed Hearing Loss. *Laryngoscope* 117(3) (Mar 2007): 552–555.

Wollenberg B, Beltrame M, Schönweiler R, Gehrking E, Nitsch S, Steffen A, Frenzel H (2007). Integration des aktiven Mittelohrimplantates in die plastische Ohrmuschelrekonstruktion. *HNO* 55(5): 349–356.

Colletti V, Soli S, Carner M, Colletti L (2006). Treatment of mixed hearing losses via implantation of a vibratory transducer on the round window. *International Journal of Audiology* 45(19): 600–608.

Foyt D, Carfrae M (2006). Minimal Access Surgery for the Symphonix/MED-EL Vibrant Soundbridge Middle Ear Hearing Implant. *Otology & Neurotology* 27(2) (Feb 2006): 167–171.

Huber A, Ball G, Veraguth D, Dillier N, Bodmer D, Sequeira D (2006). A New Implantable Middle Ear Hearing Device for Mixed Hearing Loss: A Feasibility Study in Human TemporalBones. *Otology & Neurotology* 27(8) (Dec 2006): 1104–1109.

Kiefer J, Arnold W, Staudenmaier R (2006). Round Window stimulation with an implantable hearing aid (Soundbridge®) combined with autogenous reconstruction of the auricle – A new approach. *ORL* 68(6): 378–385.

Truy E, Eshraghi A, Balkany T, Telishi F, Van De Water T, Lavieille J-P (2006). Vibrant Soundbridge Surgery: Evaluation of Transcanal Surgical Approaches. *Otology & Neurotology* 27(6) (Sept 2006): 887–895.

Kochkin S (2005). MarkeTrak VII: Hearing Loss Population Tops 31 Million. *The Hearing Review* 12(7) (July 2005): 16–29.

Needham AJ, Jiang D, Bibas A, Jeronimidis G, O'Conner AF (2005). The Effects of Mass Loading the Ossicles with a Floating Mass Transducer on Middle Ear Transfer Function. *Otology & Neurotology* 26(2) (Mar 2005): 218–224.

Saliba I, Calmels MN, Wanna G, Iversenc G, James C, Deguine O, Fraysse B (2005). Binaurality in Middle Ear Implant Recipients Using Contralateral Digital Hearing Aids. *Otology & Neurotology* 26(4) (Jul 2005): 680–685.

Todt I, Seidl RO, Ernst A (2005). Hearing benefit of patients after Vibrant Soundbridge implantation. *ORL J OtorhinolaryngolRelat Spec* 67(4): 203–206.

Jiang D, Bibas A, O'Conner AF (2004). Minimally invasive approach and fixation of cochlear and middle ear implants. *ClinicalOtolaryngology Allied Science* 29(6) (Dec 2004): 618–620.

Langevin S (2004). Surdité neurosensorielle: Les implants d'oreille moyenne. *Cahier Biomédical* 165 (Avril 2004): 25–30.

Snik AF, CremersC (2004). Audiometric evaluation of an attempt to optimize the fixation of the transducer of a middle ear implant to the ossicular chain with bone cement. *Clinical Otolaryngology Allied Science* 29(1) (Feb 2004): 5–9.

Snik AF, Noten J, Cremers C (2004). Gain and Maximum Output of Two Electromagnetic Middle Ear Implants: Are Real Ear Measurements Helpful? *Journal – American Academy of Audiology* 15(3) (Mar 2004): 249–257.

Todt I, Seidl RO, Mutze S, Ernst A (2004). MRI Scanning and Incus Fixation in Vibrant Soundbridge Implantation. *Otology & Neurotology* 25(6) (Nov 2004): 969–972.

Vincent C, Fraysse B, Lavieille JP, Truy E, Sterkers O Vaneecloo FM (2004). A longitudinal study on postoperative hearing thresholds with the Vibrant Soundbridge device. *European Archives of Oto-Rhino-Laryngology* 261(9): 493–496.

Sterkers O, Bouccara D, Labassi S, Bébéar JP, Dubreuil C, Frachet B, Fraysse B, Lavieille JP, Magnan J, Martin C, Truy E, Uziel A, Vaneecloo FM (2003). A middle ear implant, the Symphonix Vibrant Soundbridge: Retrospective study of the first 125 patients implanted in France. *Otology & Neurotology* 24(3) (May 2003): 427–436.

Uziel A, Mondain M, Hagen P, Dejean F and Doucet G (2003). Rehabilitation for high frequency sensori-neural hearing impairment in adults with the Symphonix Vibrant Soundbridge: A comparative study. *Otology & Neurology* 24(5) (Sept 2003): 775–783.

Dubreuil C (2002). Limites d'indication entre l'implant d'oreille moyenne Vibrant Soundbridge ymphonix et l'implant cochléaire. A propos d'un cas. *Journal Français d'Oto-Rhino-Laryngologie* 51(4): 159–161.

Garin P, Thill MP, Gérard JM, Galle C, Gersdorff M (2002/03). Speech discrimination in background noise with the Vibrant Soundbridge middle ear implant, *ORL Nova* 2002/03, 12(3): 109–118.

Junker R, Gross M, Todt I, Ernst A (2002). Functional Gain of already implanted hearing devices in patients with sensorineural hearing loss of varied origin and extent: Berlin experience. *Otology & Neurotology*, 23: 452–456, 2002.

Luetje CM, Brackman D, Balkany TJ, Maw J, Baker RS, Kelsall D, Backous D, Miyamoto R, Pariser S, Arts A (2002). Phase III clinical trial results with the Vibrant® Soundbridge implantable middle ear hearing device: A prospective controlled multi-centre-study. *Otolaryngology – Head and Neck Surgery* 126(2) (Feb 2002): 97–107.

Thill MP, Gérard JM, Garin P, Offeciers E (2002). Belgian experience with the Vibrant Soundbridge prosthesis. *ACTA Belges d'ORL* 56(4): 375–378

Todt S, Gross E (2002). Comparison of different Vibrant Soundbridge speech processors with conventional hearing aids. *Otology & Neurotology* 23(5) (Sept 2002): 669–63.

Winter M, Weber BP, Lenarz T (2002). Measurement method for the assessment of transmission probe of implantable hearing aids. *Biomed Tech (Berl)* 47 Suppl 1 Pt 2: 726–727.

Ashburn-Reed S (2001). The first FDA approved middle ear implant: The Vibrant Soundbridge. *The Hearing Journal* 54(8) (Aug 2001): 47–48.

Biesinger B (2001). Die Revolution in der Hörgerätetechnologie. *DSB Report* 2: 14–18.

Chasin M, Spindel J (2001). Middle ear implants: A new technology. *The Hearing Journal* 54(8) (Aug 2001): 33–48.

Dieler R, Dazert S, Shehata-Dieler WE, Helms J (2001). Evaluierung der funktionellen Ergebnisse mit dem aktiven Mittelohrimplantat "Vibrant Soundbridge". *HNO Informationen* 25(2): 75.

Ernst A (2001). Implantierbare Hörsysteme. *HNO Aktuell* 9(1).

Fisch U, Cremers CW, Lenarz T, Weber B, Babighian G, Uziel AS, Proops DW, O'Connor AF, Charachon R, Helms J, Fraysse B (2001). Clinical experience with the Vibrant Soundbridge implant device. Results from the EN540 Clinical Trial in Europe. *Otology & Neurotology* 22 (6) (Nov 2001): 962–972.

Fraysse B, Lavieille JP, Schmerber S, Enée V, Truy E, Vincent C, Vaneecloo FM, Sterkers O (2001). A Multicenter Study of the Vibrant Soundbridge Middle Ear Implant: Early Clinical Results and Experience. *Otology & Neurotology* 22(6) (Nov 2001): 952–961.

Irving RM, Proops DW (2001). Middle ear implantable hearing devices. *ENT News* 10(2): 35.

Lenarz T, Weber BP, Issing PR, Gnadeberg D, Ambjornsen K, Mack KF, Winter M (2001). Vibrant Soundbridge System: Ein neuartiges Hörimplantat für Innenohrschwerhörigkeit. Teil 2: Audiologische Ergebnisse. *Laryngo-Rhino-Otologie* 80: 370–380.

Snik AF, Cremers CW (2001). The Vibrant semi-implantable hearing device with digital sound processing: effective gain and speech perception. *Archives of Otolaryngology Head and Neck Surgery* 127(12) (Dec 2001): 1433–1437.

Snik AF, Mylanus EA, Cremers CW, et al. (2001). Multicenter audiometric results with the Vibrant Soundbridge, a semi-implantable hearing device for sensorineural hearing impairment. *Otolaryngologic Clinics of North America* 34(2) (Apr 2001): 373–388.

Babighian G, Mazzoli M (2000). Prothèse implantable d'oreille moyenne. Résultats cliniques. *Les Cahiers d'O.R.L.*, XXXIV(8): 322–330.

Dazert S, Shehata-Dieler WE, Dieler R, Helms J (2000). Das Mittelohrimplantat "Vibrant Soundbridge" zur Hörrehabilitation bei sensorischer Schwerhörigkeit: Klinik, Indikation und erste Ergebnisse. *Laryngo-Rhino-Otology* 79(8) (Aug 2000): 459–464.

Snik AF, Cremers WR (2000). The effect on the "floating mass transducer" in the middle ear on hearing sensitivity. *The American Journal of Otology* 21(1): 42–48.

Boucarra D (1999). Nouvelle modalité de réhabilitation de l'audition: Prothèse Vibant Soundbridge Symphonix. *La Lettre d'oto-rhino-laryngologie et de chirurgie cervico-faciale* 241 (Mars 1999): 29–30.

Cremers CW, Snik AF (1999). De Vibrant Soundbridge, een semi-implanteerbaar hoortoestel voor perceptieslechthorendheid. *Ned Tijdschr KNO-Heelkunde* 5 (Oct 1999): 158–161.

Hüttenbrink KB (1999). Current status and critical reflections on implantable hearing aids. *American Journal of Otology* 20(4) (July 1999): 409–415.

Richards A, Gleeson M (1999). Clinical review, Recent advances. Otolaryngology. *British Medical Journal* 319: 1110–1113.

Snik AF, Cremers CW (1999). First audiometric results with the Vibrant Soundbridge, implantable device for sensorineural hearing loss. *Audiology* 38(6) (Nov-Dec 1999): 335–338.

Lenarz T, Weber BP, Mack KF, Battmer RD, Gnadeberg D (1998). Vibrant Soundbridge System: Ein neuartiges Hörimplantat für Innenohrschwerhörigkeit. Teil 1: Funktionsweise und klinische Erfahrung. *Laryngo-Rhino-Otologie* 77(5): 247–255.

Snik AF, Mylanus EA, Cremers CW (1998). Implantable Hearing devices for sensorineural hearing loss: A review of the audiometric data. *Clinical Otolaryngology Allied Science*, 23(5) (Oct 1998): 414–419.

Zenner HP (1998). Elektronische Hörimplantate zur operativen Behandlung. *Deutsches Ärzteblatt* 1998(4).

Ball GR, Huber A (1997). Scanning Laser Doppler Vibrometry of the middle ear ossicles. *The Ear Nose and Throat Journal* 76(4) (Apr 1997): 213–222.

Gan RZ, Ball GR, Dietz TG, Dormer KJ (1997). Implantable hearing device performance measured by laser Doppler interferometry. *The Ear Nose and Throat Journal* 76(5): 297–309.

Tjellstrom A, Luetje CM, Hough V, Arthur B Hertzmann P, Katz B, Wallace P (1997). Acute human trial of the Floating Mass Transducer. *The Ear Nose and Throat Journal* 76(4) (April 1997): 204–206.

Goode R L, Ball G, Nishihara S, Nakamura K (1996). Laser Doppler Vibrometer (LDV). *Otology & Neurotology* 17(6): 813–822.

Villchur E (1974). Simulation of the effect of recruitment on loudness relationships in speech. *Journal of the Acoustical Society of America* 56(5): 1601–1611.

Villchur E (1973). Signal processing to improve speech intelligibility in perceptive deafness. *Journal of the Acoustical Society of America* 53(6): 1646–1657.

United States Patents Issued to Geoffrey Ball

(as of January 2010)

7,322,930 & 7,322,930 Implantable microphone having sensitivity and
          frequency response
6,676,592 Dual coil floating mass transducers
6,626,822 Implantable microphone having improved sensitivity
          and frequency response
6,475,134 Dual coil floating mass transducers
6,217,508 Ultrasonic hearing system
6,190,305 Implantable and external hearing systems having
          a floating mass transducer
6,139,488 Biasing device for implantable hearing devices
6,093,144 Implantable microphone having improved sensitivity
          and frequency response
6,024,717 Apparatus and method for sonically enhanced drug delivery
5,949,895 Disposable audio processor for use with implanted
          hearing devices
5,913,815 Bone conducting floating mass transducers
5,897,486 Dual coil floating mass transducers
5,859,916 Two stage implantable microphone
5,857,958 Implantable and external hearing systems having
          a floating mass transducer
5,800,336 Advanced designs of floating mass transducers
5,795,287 Tinnitus masker for direct drive hearing devices
5,624,376 Implantable and external hearing systems having
          a floating mass transducer
5,554,096 Implantable electromagnetic hearing transducer
5,456,654 Implantable magnetic hearing aid transducer

All United States Patents for the FMT have been issued to Geoffrey Ball
(www.uspto.gov)

Further information on MED-EL, cochlear implants and middle ear implants
can be found at www.medel.com. Country-specific websites are available.